WAITING for CHARLIE

Jan Menell, retired community midwife, lives in a small village near Cambridge with her two dogs, two miniature donkeys and fifty plus chickens. She has had a menagerie of animals, gifted or found, in need of homing and tolerated by her late husband. Two sons and four grandchildren live nearby. Jan has been a parish and district councillor for over forty years since moving to the village and still teaches for the federation of antenatal teachers.

Also by

JAN MENELL

A Playbus called Buffy - Book One

A Playbus called Buffy - Book Two

WAITING for CHARLIE

JAN MENELL

publishing

Published in Hardback , Paperback and eBook
in Great Britain in 2016 by Milton Publishing

1

A CIP catalogue record for this book is available from the
British Library.

Hardback ISBN: 978-0-9955565-1-5
Paperbook: 978-0-9955565-0-8
eBook: 978-0-9955565-2-2

Text set using 10pt Olsen Light

Milton Publishing
23 Bowker Close, London Road
Newport, Essex CB11 3BQ

www.miltonpublishing.co.uk

Dedicated to my dear friend, Walter Webb, now deceased,
and my many Mums.

Thanks to my editor, Janice Hurst for her constant
encouragement, Carol Goodchild for charming cover
illustration, loyal friend Roz Saggers for proof reading
and encouraging input from Rosanna Ley,
the Finca el Cerillo writers group and
my late husband, Anthony Menell, for his forbearance.

MAKING BABIES

MISCARRIAGE/ SPONTANEOUS ABORTION

Both terms are used to describe the spontaneous termination of a pregnancy before the 24th week, the loss of a foetus before it is able to survive.

To lose a baby in the early weeks of pregnancy can be quite shocking. I say 'baby' because that is how most women refer to a confirmed pregnancy. To them it is exciting to realise that they are going to have a baby; no one normally would feel the urge to tell anyone that, oh 'joy of joys' they were going to have a foetus. Would they?

I will dwell on the planned and wanted pregnancy, the baby to be.

The confirmation of pregnancy with a positive test can send a woman on an emotional roller coaster. The world looks different, feels different, and is different. A sense of inner happiness consumes her, together with an often-overwhelming desire to tell every one, including the postman. This smugness in the knowledge that you've made the grade and are up there in the exciting world of mothers and babies, is hugely satisfying. Suddenly shops seem only to sell baby goods, television and radio presenters talk about parents and mothers and babies, all the time. No paper or magazine gets beyond the first few pages without reference or photos of beaming babies, proud and happy couples, and nappies. Bliss is an inner secret to puff you up with joy, as is a caring solicitous partner who enfolds you in cotton wool and becomes more hands off than on. The world is full of smiles. You proudly make the announcement to your nearest and dearest; they, along with you and your partner are 'over the moon'. The reaction of potential grandparents is equal to your own.

Imagine then the distress and concern if pains come and go where your baby lies hidden from view. You may bleed a little.

Initially you have a mixed reaction of fear and disbelief. You are frightened, your heart pounds and suddenly you are aware that you could be losing your precious baby. An unemotionally attached doctor or midwife may answer the nervous phone call for help. The advice is nearly always the same - sit tight, do little, and await events, let nature take its course for you are probably having a miscarriage. In the obstetric world a miscarriage is not anything more than an unfortunate occurrence. It is a matter of concern of course to the sensitive practitioner, and there will be a reaction in clinical terms; the examination, the scan, and the follow up.

What about you?

If, in the event that you do lose the baby, guilt may enter your world. You ran, you walked, you tripped over a cat, you lifted a bucket, you put up wallpaper, you ate cheese, you drank wine and you had intercourse. You will blame yourself for all these things. The phone calls to waiting grandparents, brothers and sisters, will be a tearful affair. Sorry you say, sorry that we've lost the baby; sorry you aren't going to be a granny, an uncle or an aunt. So why the apology? Why the guilt? You certainly never intended to harm your baby. Often it is the thoughtless question that adds pain to your whirring brain of emotion. Well meant comment really does touch a nerve. Yes, you did walk up the hill when the car broke down. So, you really were to blame? No, of course not.

You will grieve. Your partner will feel the guilt too, especially if intercourse is mentioned. Of course you will get pregnant again the world announces. It does not help at this moment; you wanted the baby you lost. The sight of babies and pushchairs and happy parents are hurtful now, bitterness and some resentment will overwhelm you.

Does it help to hear statistics? Generally, I think not. Nothing is going to get you back in to that happy world. It can help a little to realise that it is not uncommon. It will help to meet and talk to others that have suffered a miscarriage, empathy is easier to absorb. Once the miscarriage is confirmed the medical profession will offer advice. They are trying to be as helpful as possible and it may be conflicting.

The advice will be along these lines:
Try again as soon as you feel you want to. Leave trying to get pregnant for a couple of months. Wait until you have had another period. Get fit and healthy, rest, exercise, eat well, no alcohol, no smoking, take Folic acid tablets, avoid sheep at lambing time and attend pre pregnancy sessions.

I spoke to many couples after a threat of miscarriage, or actual miscarriage. Words were never adequate for the sadness that enveloped them. Many had not for one moment contemplated the possibility of losing their baby; such thoughts never entered their mind. Many knew about miscarriage of course, it happened to other people as most tragedies do.

Suffice to say that there is wisdom in all the advice meted out by doctors, midwives and well-meaning friends. Only you will really be the best judge of when you are ready to try again to make a baby. Try, you will, and eventually I hope that blissful state of hope and expectation will once more enter your soul. You will be fertile again by the time you restart your periods.

It may be easier to come to terms with this emotionally devastating loss when you realise that nothing you did caused you to lose this baby. You can also take comfort in the knowledge that this is not considered an abnormal event and that you actually were pregnant, an achievement in itself.

Your partner has experienced guilt, fear, disappointment and failure too, though his main concern will be to protect you from further harm. Together your relationship will be strengthened by this sad experience. It is to be hoped that you will hold a new baby in the future, and that it will not harm either of you to grieve for the baby you have just lost. That little one was not meant to be.

Research continues in to the causes of miscarriage. Genetic faults and a failure of the baby to implant in the womb securely are possibilities. Contributory factors of multiple pregnancy, age, illness, smoking, extreme stress and anxiety are recognised. The renowned Professor Regan pioneers much of this work with her studies into recurrent miscarriage.

The emotional trauma experienced by couples when they have a miscarriage is much more appreciated by the medical profession now. Women themselves feel more able to discuss these issues and though no single cause is likely to be found, thoughtful preparation for pregnancy is one way that all women can contribute to their own health and well being.

Janet Menell has been a qualified nurse and midwife since the early 1960s. She retired from community midwifery in 2002, having practised in the same area since 1974.

WAITING
for
CHARLIE

PROLOGUE

Maggie Edwards, a midwife in a large London maternity hospital, was idly cleaning equipment in the sluice room and reflecting happily on the fact that she herself was pregnant. She and her boyfriend, Robert, shared a flat in the Shepherds Bush area and had lived together for a year. The pregnancy was unplanned but despite their unmarried status both were excited and agreed that having a baby was a dream they shared. With Robert's promotion imminent in Sutton's Scenario, the Interior Design Company he worked for, and the company's decision to move out of London, they would soon be setting up home together in the countryside.

Maggie was thankful that her mother, Elizabeth, critical of their unmarried status, had received the news of the pregnancy without further comment. It was a love of babies that had set her daughter on the path to midwifery and she considered Maggie's pregnancy an inevitable consequence. Following the recent death of Maggie's father, Elizabeth was looking forward to her 'granny' role and felt that Maggie's career could only be enhanced by the practical reality of birth.

CHAPTER 1

BRIEF LIVES

"It's not unusual my dear, you're a midwife who should know about these things," the doctor smiled, helping her off the couch. "You're young, plenty of time for more babies," he added, rapidly recording the brief examination and allowing her a moment to dress. "Mistakes are easily made, as you've discovered, so don't be too hasty and let things settle down. Come back and see me if they don't." Opening the door he patted her retreating back. "Send the next patient in."

Maggie Edwards, the midwife but no longer a mother to be, clung to Robert, her boyfriend, as they left the clinic. She felt unable to speak and was trembling uncontrollably as tears ran unchecked. They sat in numbed silence in the car park, overcome with sadness.

"Oh, Maggie, I really don't know what to say. I was shocked when you told me you were pregnant, my fault I know, but I never dreamt this might happen. I've even got used to the idea of being a father, even if it......" Robert held her tight, finding it hard to control his own emotions.

"I'll be okay, Rob, it's all over and the doctor said there's nothing more to lose. I'll try and get some sleep and you can get back to the office. Could you phone the ward later and tell Sister I'm going off sick for a few days? I'll make something up when I get back."

"I know the clinic was busy but that doctor seemed a bit heartless if you ask me. I suppose they have to deal with things like this all the time."

"Oh, Rob, it wasn't a 'thing' or a 'mistake', it was a baby, our baby."

"I know, I'm sorry, you know what I meant."

"It happened so suddenly in the end. I thought I'd got indigestion and those fish and chips we had last night hadn't agreed with me. I ignored the stomach pains this morning and then it all started when I was in that corner shop. I just made it to their toilet."

"I feel so bad about you being on your own then. Come on, you're shaking and I'm shivering, let's get back home."

"You weren't to know, silly, I never thought for a moment that I would miscarry. Thank goodness those two women were there and understood what was happening. The ambulance crew were so kind; one of them told me his wife had lost their first baby at about the same time."

Robert helped Maggie slowly climb the four flights of stairs to the flat they shared with two students. He made a pot of tea, filled a hot water bottle and settled her in to bed.

"This tea's a bit strong."

"It'll do you good. I wish you'd have something to eat though. I don't think the others will be back till late so hopefully you'll get some sleep. I've got some calls to make first."

Reluctant to leave he lay beside her before using the telephone and returning to his office in Shepherds Bush. Maggie dozed fitfully; overwhelmed by the despair and the desolation she knew they both felt. Yes, she would probably get pregnant easily again, but the thrill of preparing for this first baby and its future, albeit unplanned, had consumed Maggie's every waking thought. Robert had been equally excited and supportive from the beginning. Now that new life had been lost – down a public toilet.

Within a fortnight Maggie was back on duty at the hospital and a month later it was her turn for night duty. She was alone in the nursery when one of the babies woke. Picking him up she gently cupped the small head in her outstretched hands. Benjamin, just three days old, focused deep blue eyes on her face and stared, fixedly. Barely a minute passed before she felt the tiny thrusting drumbeats of his feet pressed against her, and observed his changing mood. Maggie had fought hard to overcome the grief she had felt and still yearned for her own baby. She loved her job, and other people's babies, but the emptiness within her was a distraction when holding them and a feeling she found increasingly difficult to cope with.

The small face puckered and seven pounds of pink fury demanded immediate attention.

"All right, all right," soothed Maggie, lifting him to her shoulder and patting his back. "Don't cry little one. Come on, we'll find your mum."

With his head nestled against her neck, the baby's mouth searched in vain for sustenance as she tiptoed past the other cots lined up in serried ranks, just as Sister Myrtle, night sister, liked them. Baby boys pinioned under blue cellular blankets one side, girls under pink ones, swaddled and immobilised. Heads covered like miniature Virgin Mary's, with barely a movement of limbs, pouting lips occasionally suckling imaginary teats. She walked quickly down the corridor and gently pushed open the door to Ward D.

"Benjamin's getting hungry, Emily," Maggie whispered, as Emily struggled to a sitting position and stretched out her arms.

"Thanks, did he sleep much?" she yawned.

"Yes, he's been an angel for the last three hours."

Emily needed little help with her third baby so Maggie left them to it and hurried back to the nursery. Some babies were beginning to stir and it would only be a matter of minutes before they were all awake; a nursery of hungry babies in full throttle demanding instant attention could be an alarming experience to the uninitiated. Sister Myrtle, wedded to hospital rules, would arrive to supervise the feeds. She insisted on keeping most babies in the nursery at night which discouraged new and more reluctant mothers from feeding them themselves but enabled Sister Myrtle to gain firm control over her staff and 'patients'.

In the milk kitchen Susie, the nursery nurse, lined up bottles of formula. Maggie cleared the surface and wiped away the scattered milk powder. They were ready for inspection when Sister Myrtle bustled in.

"Now, let's get on with it shall we?" Sister Myrtle checked the row of bottles, tipping one up to test the milk flow and temperature. "You take the boys tonight, Edwards," she said before turning to Susie. "Nurse, you take the girls and see if you can get them settled down quickly, I've noticed you have a dreadful tendency to dawdle. I'll check on the women, there's no need to wake any of them unnecessarily." Her starched apron flapped noisily against her legs as she bustled out. "Oh, and by the way," she paused at the nursery door, "I'll be coming back to supervise any slow feeders."

"Poor wee mites," said Susie, sniffing loudly. "That woman's as cold as a fish." She bent over and picked up the first baby girl in her row. The baby whimpered as Susie hugged her, "They need cuddle time. She doesn't know how to handle them like we do."

"Take no notice," Maggie said, picking up the noisiest baby boy whose tiny fists had escaped the tight wrappings, "these little ones are very lucky to have you looking after them."

Despite her own longing Maggie cherished the spare moments they had to cuddle them; the crying never fazed her and she felt she had a natural ability to calm even the most raucous: a precious time for her to reflect on what could be. "I'll really miss feed times, Susie. I'm back on the labour ward in a couple of weeks."

"Lucky you," Susie said. "Think of me stuck here with that dragon."

Soon all the babies had guzzled their feeds. Maggie was thoughtful as she watched baby Simon drain the last drop, his features relaxed and contented. Gently she removed the teat. "Well done, little one. Goodness me, that's all of two ounces." She placed a napkin over her shoulder and patted his back; a loud satisfying burp and a mouthful of milky curds followed.

This could be me and mine this time next year, Maggie thought as she took another nappy off the pile and changed and wrapped the sleepy baby, placing him sausage-like in his crib, relishing the sudden surge of memories, recalling their recent passionate weekend. All things were possible and as they had failed to take precautions again she would know soon enough.

Following her earlier miscarriage Maggie had returned home to her mother in the Lake District for a week's break with

Robert's blessing, and an overwhelming need to be mothered herself. She had been surprised and reassured to learn that her mother, Elizabeth, had also lost a first baby in the early weeks of pregnancy and understood her distress; a pregnancy that had never been spoken of, a sibling that Maggie, and her sister Eleanor, had never before been told about. However, her mother did not hide her disapproval of Maggie's unmarried state and sought constant reassurance that she would be 'more careful in future'; advice that both Elizabeth's daughters seemed reluctant to obey.

CHAPTER 2

BIRTH, 1970's STYLE

Maggie walked hurriedly down the corridor of the Labour Suite in the Carlton Maternity Unit. The lusty cry of a new born baby filtered through the door of a side ward. She smiled at a small family group huddled together, their faces awash with thankful tears and happy smiles, waiting for a glimpse of their latest family member.

The ward maid, Annie, busy mopping the corridor, manoeuvred her bucket in Maggie's direction,

"Morning, Maggie, nice to see you back here. You'd better look smartish; Room Two's won't be long coming. I'm always right you know, she'll be getting them urges any minute."

Maggie grinned, "If you say so, Annie."

Jo, a colleague from their training days greeted her. "Oh, good, I'm so glad it's you, I thought nobody was ever coming. You're welcome to take over." She lowered her voice, "Listen, last night after scrubbing up for a section for twins I had two of the new admissions, a breech, then one had forceps, and guess what, that new Registrar went off sick. Sister Ramsey had me running around all night." Jo's chatter stopped suddenly. "Sorry, Maggie,

I just needed a good moan." She turned to pat the arm of the young woman lying on the high narrow bed before raising her voice, "Just going to have another listen in, Sally" she said, watch in hand, pressing her ear against the small trumpet indenting the swollen abdomen. "That's fine, baby's doing really well. My friend Maggie's with us now, love."

Sally, dozed on, motionless as Jo continued her list of woes.

"I'm ready for my bed but she's almost fully dilated and ready to push. I'll stay with you now." Jo yawned. "Here, turn round, I'll give you a hand with that gown, half the ties are missing. I'd better get my notes written up too."

Scrubbed up, gowned and masked, Maggie checked her equipment. "Sister Ramsey was a bit slow handing over, Jo. One of the new housemen needed her attention."

"Don't they always," said Jo, patting the young mother's outstretched leg. "I'd like to get Sally on her side for the delivery if we can. She had a jab at five and has really cracked on, haven't you, love?" There was little response. "I'll see if they have a boy or a girl, and then I'm off. She didn't want any gas; as usual the injection's knocked her for six."

Maggie cast her eyes at the empty armchair. "Is anyone with her?"

"Yes, Mark, her husband, he's gone out for another smoke. Just what I could do with," said Jo reaching up to readjust the overhead beam of light. "That's better, now you can see what you're doing." She peered at the chair. "I can't say I agree with all this. Poor chap, some of them would far rather not be involved. We make them feel guilty if they don't join in. I know you're a fan of all that natural birthing stuff that Dr.Grantly Dick-Read was encouraging."

Maggie chose to ignore the comment; she had become a keen convert to his teachings. She was also aware that some midwives were sceptical and considered the National Childbirth Trust, an organisation she had recently joined, as only suited to middle class mothers.

Sally, slumped against the propped pillows, eyes closed, tight copper curls glued sweatily to her glistening forehead, bent knees idly lolling, suddenly lunged forward, "I want to push, I want to pu---sh," she yelled, grabbing at Maggie's sleeve, her eyes widening with fear. "Where's Mark? Where is he?"

"He's coming. Look, hold here, Sally, and listen to what we say," ordered Maggie.

Mark crept back in to the room.

"Tell them to leave me alone." Sally pushed Maggie away and flopped backwards, sapped of energy. "Where've you been? Don't leave me," she cried.

Jo placed a cool wet flannel on the young girl's forehead. "You're almost there, love. You're lucky to have Mark with you."

Mark stroked her arm. "Hear that, Sal? Baby's nearly here."

Forty minutes later and nearing total exhaustion from her valiant efforts Sally rose from the damp pillows for the birth. Maggie controlled her with louder, more encouraging commands. "Stop pushing now, dear, just pant, pant, pant.. Another little push, good, pant, clever girl, keep it going, keep it going, PANT. Brilliant, well done," and finally. "Your baby's here!" chorused the two gleeful midwives.

Maggie stood back as Mark gazed in awe and disbelief at the baby's head, nestled between Sally's open thighs.

"Is it out?" Sally pulled at Mark's outstretched arm. "I can't do any more, please, I can't do any more."

Jo mopped her face; "The worst's over, love, you've been quite quick for a first. Just one more push and it'll all be over."

With one final effort, and barely a murmur, the baby was born. Maggie found it difficult to hide her emotions at the sight of this little human being, safely delivered, damp and glistening, the startled reflex of tiny hands like starfish clawing at the air. The cry filled the room with its intensity and reassured her that all was well.

"It's a girl!"

The baby sprawled, protesting as sterile towels mopped her dry. Maggie considered how the bright lights and first human touch would be a shock to her, invading her senses as she was finally separated from her mother. Jo wrapped her and placed her in Marks arms. Tears sprinkled the tiny face of his daughter as he kissed the small head of thick dark hair and held her in an awkward embrace.

"Did I do all right? Sally asked, alert now. "It wasn't that bad after all," she said, smiling at Mark. "Sorry if I made a din."

"You were wonderful, Sally," he murmured. "I'm so proud of you."

"Just look at that mop of hair," said Maggie. "It's an old wives tale but did you have a lot of indigestion during your pregnancy?"

"Not much, my Dad's got thick black hair."

"Runs in the family then. I'll leave you to it now," Jo murmured. Maggie saw the relief etched on her face. Exhausted she may have been but Jo, like many of her colleagues, felt duty bound to stay until the delivery was complete.

An hour later the baby, named Holly, checked, weighed and bathed lay securely swaddled in more pink cellular blankets. Maggie wheeled her trolley down the corridor to the sluice room, struggling to suppress her own feelings of envy. She reminded herself that all she had to do was get through the next few weeks without mishap. If a pregnancy test proved positive the timing would be perfect. She wondered if she dare hope this time.

Back home that evening Maggie was piling spaghetti on Robert's plate. "By the end of my shift we'd had three baby Hollys," Maggie said. "Mind you, it's not unusual at Christmas. At least this year no one had a Jesus, or Gabriel. The breech baby was named Joseph though."

"Thanks, that's enough. There's a week to go until Christmas Day, Maggie. There'll be hundreds of little Hollys. Any Ivys I wonder? Pass the Parmesan, darling."

Maggie peered out of the window at the rush hour traffic, streaming past in an endless file down Grafton Street. She and Robert had shared the flat for less than a year but Maggie had begun to loathe the dirt and grime, the ceaseless smell of exhaust fumes amid the constant noise. She felt sapped of energy after each shift returning to the dismal surroundings.

"That was good," he said, pushing the plate away. "By the way, I've picked up some details of a cottage not far from our company's new offices in Waldersby. It's in a small village."

"Really?" Maggie turned in surprise. "That's exciting, Rob. Tell me more."

"The village is called Little Fordham, it's about nine miles from Cambridge. The cottage needs a lot doing to it, some old girl lived there all her life, she died three years ago and it's been empty ever since. I've talked to the bank manager and I can afford to make an offer. Unfortunately, they can't let us have the keys to look around it for some reason." Robert's firm was moving to Waldersby and his promotion and new position would start in the spring. "If you're not on duty next Friday we'll drive down there and have a look around, the outside anyway?"

Maggie sat herself on Robert's knee and wrapped her arms around him. "It sounds just right, a fresh start and real fresh air." She pulled the bowl of fruit across the table. "It could be fantastic. A country idyll and making love in a haystack. Sorry, no pudding, it'll have to be a banana, darling."

She had sounded flippant but was genuinely excited by the idea; daring to hope that maybe the countryside and its tranquillity would be the perfect setting for them to raise the family she craved.

Three weeks later Maggie woke as cramping pains aroused her. Shivering and cold she made her way sleepily to the bathroom unable to stem the flow of a warm trickle of blood which oozed through her protective fingers. Livid red streaks seeped on to the grubby pink bathroom carpet. The loss was rapid and complete. She had kept the pregnancy a secret from everyone, including Robert, hopeful that this time it would last, fearful of sharing the news too soon. Her tears ran unhindered as distressed and trembling, she eased herself back under the blankets. She would tell Robert later, it seemed pointless to wake him now.

"Here, drink your tea, Maggie. I thought they'd never answer the phone, there's only one doctor on duty. He says you're to sit tight for the next twenty four hours." Gently Robert dabbed at her tear stained cheeks. "Darling, why didn't you tell me?" he murmured, tenderly placing his hand on her abdomen.

"Rob, we're never going to keep a baby, it's so unfair. There's nothing anyone can do."

"'Course we will," he said, choking back his own tears.

"You do want children don't you, just as much as me?"

"Look, Maggie, you know I'd like nothing better than some little sod waking me up early in the morning." He drew her closer. "I'm sorry, I didn't mean to joke. I'm really sorry, but we will have a baby, you'll see. Now I know why you've been rejecting me. I thought you were just too tired to make love these days. "

"I thought if we took care and no one knew it would give me a better chance."

Robert flinched, "I'm not just anyone, Maggie," he said, gently caressing her, "We'll never give up, I promise. Maybe your mother is right and we need to make an honest woman of you first."

Maggie spent the following week tussling with a mixture of emotions. She felt her heart would break, overwhelmed by feelings of guilt. What had she done wrong? What had she eaten? Was it the odd glass of wine she'd drunk? Had she lifted something too heavy? Should she have stayed away from work? Should they have avoided sex altogether? Irrational thoughts preyed on her mind. Despite being a midwife and having medical knowledge she couldn't prevent feeling as she did. In her dreams she had held their baby once more, never 'a foetus'.

CHAPTER 3

A NEIGHBOURLY ENCOUNTER

Maggie, surrounded by a pile of ironing felt the need to talk to Robert. She had been reluctant to keep reliving her failure to stay pregnant and had shied away from any discussion. Two weeks had passed and now she felt anxious to return to work and more ready to face the future.

"Rob, I'll go and see the consultant at the hospital if it happens again. I know now that it's not unusual to have one miscarriage but two's a bit less common. I've read up a lot about it," she said, putting down the iron to sit on his lap.

"We'll go together whenever you like," he said. "Didn't the doctor suggest it to you anyway?"

Maggie hugged him, "Yes, I'd be happier if we went together. I love you very much I hope you realise," she murmured, feeling safe and reassured. "I know you were upset that I didn't tell you and you want to make an honest woman out of me if only to please my mother. I don't want to see anyone yet though and I promise I won't hurt you like that ever again." She stood up, "I must get my uniform ready. I've decided to investigate a few alternative remedies that might do me some good, hypnotherapy or something before we try again. I'll also be very careful with my diet, lots of fruit and veg, no more alcohol and get really fit first. I've put on far too much weight lately."

"If you say so. It's not really the getting pregnant that's our problem though is it, darling? We'll canter round Clapham common every night if it helps to keep you fit."

"That doctor called this morning, the one we saw the first time, he was really helpful and had more time to talk. I don't need any further investigations thank goodness. He mentioned the idea of being stitched up inside, I'd hate that, but I realise I don't stay pregnant long enough for that to happen anyway. One day, Robert Groves, I'm going to have our baby and it's going to be the most beautiful baby ever," she said, bending to kiss him.

"You will, Maggie Edwards. I love you too and one day I'll be a very proud dad, you'll see." He stood up and she knew from the look on his face how hard she'd made it for him to console her and felt a lump in her throat. "I think it's time we went to see that cottage again, don't you? It's still up for sale," he said. "If you like it I think we should put in an offer."

"Let's go soon, Rob, I'm curious to see it inside even though it's probably a wreck and full of creepy crawlies. Now then you can't love me as much as I love you," she said, teasing him away gently. "I must finish this lot for work tomorrow. Could we travel down to the village on Saturday? Can you get the keys this time?"

He nodded, "Yes, they'll be under a flower pot."

"That's wonderful," she chuckled, picking up her uniform, "By the way, if Mum rings promise you won't tell her about me having another miscarriage, I avoided telling her I was pregnant."

"I won't. Haven't you spoken to Eleanor yet either?"

"No, why on earth should I?"

"Okay, darling, she's your sister after all. "

"Sorry, I didn't mean to snap. It's just that, well you know, Eleanor's got her own problems now she's on her own again and back living with Mum. She seems to change boyfriends every three months. If I tell her, she'll tell Mum, and then we'll have her wanting to rush down here. Frankly I can't face too much wailing and worrying from my family at the moment. Mum will only start lecturing me, even though she tries hard not to. She'd probably say it's our own fault for 'living in sin'."

"Something we must think about, Maggie, no more sin, just sex! Come on, leave that lot, I think we need an early night!"

—m—

It was bright and sunny as Maggie picked her way along the rutted cart track, sheltered between hedges of hawthorn in budding green. Two months had passed since their decision to buy the cottage in Little Fordham.

Nut Tree Cottage faced down the lane, the thatch roof was sound but the rooms were all in need of redecorating, layers of old wall paper clung damply to the lathe and plaster giving it a musty smell that pervaded the cottage. Mice and rats had enjoyed the empty building for three years and their evidence was everywhere. The overgrown garden wrapped itself around the cottage and a small stagnant pond was filled with the rotting leaves of a magnolia tree.

"You the one taken over Nut Tree Cottage?"

Startled, she turned to see an elderly man leaning over a rusting iron gate. Behind him a brick path led to a whitewashed cottage, its windows sparkling in the early spring sunlight.

"Yes. Lucky aren't we? We've fallen in love with it, and the village."

"Townies, eh, from London? Saw the vans."

Maggie wasn't sure she liked being labelled a Townie.

"It was my cousin's place. She's been gone three years," he said, adjusting his flat tweed cap. "Name's Charlie Watt."

He pulled the cap on and off a couple of times giving his bare head a good scratch. A pipe clenched between his teeth moved constantly from side to side, the contents added to and pressed down with the flat end of a penknife.

"I'm Maggie Edwards, it's lovely to meet you, I hope your cousin would have approved of us, Mr Watt," she said holding out her hand.

"Dressed a bit too well for living here, if you don't mind me saying," Charlie looked down at her feet, "them's silly shoes for muddy lanes."

Maggie grinned, sweeping her hair round her ears, "I'm a jeans and welly girl really. I've been exploring the village. Robert dropped me off."

Charlie looked puzzled.

"Robert's my other half." she explained. "He's started a new job and gone to a meeting in Waldersby. D'you mind me calling you, Charlie, or would you prefer Mr Watt? "

"Charlie'll do. That's what most people know me as. It'll be good to have the place lived in."

Maggie made to move. "We've got loads to unpack, Charlie, I'd better get on with it as I promised Rob I'd clear some space."

"You come inside with me young lady, I've got a little drop of something'll do you a power of good."

Maggie's eyes widened, "It's a bit early in the day for me, Charlie, if it's alcoholic. I wouldn't say no to a cup of tea though, if it's no trouble?"

"Now come on in, it'll do no harm. A small glass of my home brew seeing as you're to be my new neighbours." He opened the gate. "Got to make you welcome now you're here."

"Just a tiny drop then, but tea would suit me better, really."

Maggie bent under the archway and followed him up the brick path. If only Robert had stayed she wouldn't have been in this predicament. Bowing low she yelped as her head collided with a wooden beam just inside the cottage door.

"Oh dear, you're not the first, I should've warned you," Charlie said pulling a chair towards her. "Now sit you down, this'll cure it."

Maggie rubbed her smarting forehead as she watched Charlie unscrew the top of a murky bottle and pour a small tumbler of deep ruby-coloured liquid. Despite the gloom the room was warm and cosy.

"This is much better for you than tea. Sloe gin, m'dear, make it all myself," he said placing more grubby tumblers on the plastic tablecloth.

"Gin!"

"Made with berries and lots of sugar. I'll teach you how when you're settled."

"I've heard of elderflower wine."

"You'd better have a drop of the carrot whisky too, 'fore you go. Used to be the wife's favourite."

"You're kidding me, Charlie. Carrot whisky?"

As he spoke Charlie took a faded photograph from the mantelpiece above the range, and laid it on the table.

Maggie studied the picture of a plump smiling woman with kindly eyes, "She was a pretty woman, Charlie." Both their faces reminded Maggie of ripe apples.

"Terrible disease. The cancer took her in the finish." He blew his nose loudly into a large yellow handkerchief.

"I'm so sorry, Charlie, you must miss her so. I'm a nurse and a midwife; delivering babies is my first love," Maggie said as he topped up her glass. "I'm hoping to get a job round here if I can." She was enjoying herself now; the cosy cottage and the immediate trust she felt in the old man filled her with a sense of belonging she had not known in London. Townie she may be but she could soon adapt to country life, she felt a happiness and contentment for the first time in months.

Charlie told her all about his wife, Mary and the care she'd received from the district nurse and home help, until her death in the cottage the year before. He spoke briefly of their son with whom he had little contact since he had moved up North to marry and find work.

Maggie listened sympathetically before endeavouring to leave. "Forgive me, Charlie, but I really must go now."

"It'll be grand to have a bit of company," he said pressing another glass into her hand. "I don't mind new folk, but some in the village don't like changes. You'll be all right though; they like to have a nurse or doctor about the place. Useful in a village, like the vicar." He paused, then added, "P'raps better not mention if you're not married though, I'll keep it to myself."

Maggie barely heard him. A clock chimed on the mantelpiece and she realised she had been in his cottage for more than an hour. Just missing another beam, and clutching at the table, she walked unsteadily out of the front door, her glazed eyes bidding two Charlie Watts farewell.

She zigzagged and stumbled her way past the potholes, tripped on the flagstone path and fell through the heavy oak door of Nut Tree Cottage. Thick cobwebs clung to the mouldering plaster and festooned the windows, adding to the dark and damp interior as she sank into oblivion on a pile of coats.

"Good God, Maggie, what have you been drinking? You reek of alcohol." Robert was bent over her, shaking her awake.

"Please don't shout, I hurt," she said, easing herself up and shielding her eyes. "What's the time?"

"Half past four, they let me go early. Where the hell have you been to get in this state? "

"Sssh, I met our neighbour, Sharlie. I'm so happy here, Rob, you'll love him."

Maggie described Charlie and his homemade distillery, as Robert prepared some black coffee.

"When do I get to meet this old boy? He sounds a great find." Robert said, his voice tinged with relief. "He gave you far too much, darling. I've never known you to get in this state! It must be pretty strong stuff even if it is home made."

"I like it when you look shoo sshmart, darling," she slurred. "Quite the Townie!" she giggled, pointing to his new suit.

"Come on, sober up now, drink this. Oops, hello, is this him coming?"

Maggie's heart sank as she tottered unsteadily to the kitchen window, "Oh, help, he must have seen you drive past, Rob. Yes, here comes, Charlie!"

They watched Charlie approach. He walked with a rolling gait, resting every few steps on his homemade walking stick. He wore an open-necked shirt, baggy fawn corduroy trousers held up with yellow braces, and a leather belt to support his large stomach.

"Mr Watt, I presume?" Robert said, pulling open the heavy front door.

"That's my name. Your young lady stopped by earlier and I

wanted to meet you too, seeing as how you've bought my cousin's place."

Charlie pulled a bottle of sloe gin out of his trouser pocket, as Robert settled him into the one armchair surrounded by several large unpacked cardboard boxes.

"Oh no, no more for me thanks, Charlie," said Maggie, trying to regain her composure.

For the next two hours Charlie regaled them with the story of his cousin, the history of their cottage, his wife's illness, how to grow good carrots for whisky and pick the best sloes for gin and about the village and the people of Little Fordham.

Maggie's head was pounding and she was beginning to feel unwell. Barely able to stay awake any longer she politely excused herself. Robert, also feeling a little light headed, helped Charlie out of his chair and offered to accompany their new neighbour back up the darkened lane as Maggie retreated up the staircase. Waves of nausea urged her to lie down. Ten minutes later she heard Robert return and guessed he would be peering hopefully round the kitchen for something to eat.

"Sorry, I'm in bed. 'Night darling," she called, "Try and get something at the pub on the green, you might even meet more of our neighbours."

The front door slammed.

CHAPTER 4

BOTTOMS UP

Work on Nut Tree cottage began, watched and enjoyed by Charlie Watt. He stood sentry in the lane and chatted to the workmen, delivery men and decorators, issuing his own instructions. Life had returned to his surroundings and Charlie felt happier and less lonely. Lights from the cottage comforted him at night and his new neighbours driving past and waving to him increased his contentment.

Maggie called in frequently to keep him up to date with the improvements they were making. Charlie supplied her with vegetables and fresh eggs. He taught Robert to garden, helped him clean out the old greenhouse and found some locals to sort out the pond. Charlie's renewed interest in his own vegetable patch provided extra produce for the village shop.

"You know, darling, I really love Charlie," Maggie said, "I feel I never want to leave this place, or him."

"Me neither, I've a great liking for the old boy. Pity his son doesn't visit him but we can't interfere in his family affairs," said Robert, as they strolled back down the lane after a meal at the Dog and Duck Pub on the village green. "Now we're straight, you'll be able to start your ante-natal classes soon won't you?"

"Yes, I've already had two enquiries. I can get six couples in the sitting room I think."

"That's fine, I can stay in my office upstairs when they come. By the way, my boss, Frank Sutton, has asked us to dine out with him and his wife in Waldersby at that new hotel in the Market Square. I suggested next Saturday?"

"That'll be interesting. I'm so glad you get on well with him."

"I might have to do a bit of travelling now. We've cornered a big market in soft furnishings here and Frank wants to get in to the Swedish market. He's keen on their designs."

"Perhaps you can take me with you if you go?"

"You'd be very bored; it'll involve a lot of meetings. I think Frank wants us to go over there fairly soon and use the excuse to get away from his wife. His secretary says they're always arguing and he keeps telling me never to get married! Let's hope they don't argue at the dinner next week."

"That would be embarrassing. Anyway, I was only teasing, I've no wish to go on any business trip. Did I tell you that I'm meeting one of the local midwives next Thursday; she's going give me the low down about the area and the maternity unit in Cambridge."

"Good, you'll find that helpful."

"We met at the NCT refresher day in London last week."

"Somehow we both seem to have fallen on our feet here don't we," Robert said, hugging her and opening the front door. "Come on in, Maggie Edwards, I'll put the coffee on and you see if there's anything good on TV."

With the completion of work on Nut Tree Cottage, Charlie Watt took pleasure in the novelty of chatting to some of the couples attending Maggie's sessions when they parked in the lane, or stopped to say 'hello' as they walked past his gate.

It had taken three months to get the cottage habitable, the kitchen and its new Aga became Maggie's favourite place, providing constant and welcoming warmth. The size of the sitting room proved to be perfect for her classes, and it had not taken long for each course to be fully booked. Robert, enjoying his work with Frank Sutton and helping him expand the company, benefited by obtaining much of their furnishings at special rates. Their decision to move to the country proved to have been the right one, just as they had hoped.

—⁂—

It was late summer when Angela Morrison, one of Maggie's 'women' who lived at the bottom of the hill near the entrance to Little Fordham, had been going over some of the instructions for coping in labour that Maggie had given her. The baby was due in two weeks and she had a lot to prepare for. She started by rocking unsteadily on her knees in the middle of the double bed, practising positions she could use for the early stages.

Angela and Gordon Morrison had moved in to the village at much the same time as Maggie and Robert and lived in a large converted barn, called 'Nelsons'. Delighted to discover that she was pregnant, Angela had been the first to enrol for Maggie's NCT classes. Both couples had formed a close friendship, united as 'Townies' in the eyes of Charlie Watt.

"I've got to get this right or you'll never get out of here," Angela muttered to her large pregnant bump slung hammock-like beneath her as she huffed and puffed, "That's the first stage, mustn't think of pain, they're only contractions, so Maggie would have us believe," she continued, struggling into a sitting position.

"Baby, let's pretend you're really coming."

Smudge, her large tabby cat, chose that moment to leap on the bed.

"Sm-u-u-u-u-dge, you beast." Angela pushed the cat to the floor. Her enthusiasm was waning as she sat on the side of the bed and decided to give up on the role-play and have a comforting bath instead.

Doing her best to wrap Gordon's soft white bathrobe around her she straddled the wooden toilet seat, tied her hair back, and waited for the bath to fill. The smell of lavender filled the air. It looked inviting as she undressed and lowered herself beneath the foam. The shiny dome of her abdomen rose above the bubbles. At least I've still got an 'inny' she mused, touching her navel and feeling the baby lurch inside her. She smiled as she watched distorted shapes cruise beneath her skin. Could that be a knee or a bottom? Angela revelled in the comforting warmth for a full ten minutes before clambering out with difficulty, remembering with a slight twinge of conscience that Maggie had warned her not to bath alone. She grabbed a towel and waddled across the bathroom floor, almost skidding on the black and white floor tiles. As she patted herself dry, she heard the faintest 'pop'. Warm liquid seeped between her clamped thighs and knees to form a glistening puddle and soak her slippers. Scurrying into the bedroom she grabbed the phone.

"Maggie, please can you come? My waters have just gone! Can you get hold of the midwife?"

Maggie busy cleaning, put the Hoover away and left a brief note for Robert before contacting the hospital. She could be gone several hours. She drove quickly down the hill and gave Angela a reassuring hug before switching to professional mode.

"Can't leave you alone for a minute. Come on, let's have a look and listen," she said, guiding Angela gently to lie on the largest settee in the sitting room.

"I'm so glad you're here, I leak every time I move."

It was unusual to see Angela slightly dishevelled, a sharp contrast to the immaculate appearance she portrayed as her husband, Gordon's, personal secretary.

"I've spoken to Sister on the labour ward. She knows I'll be with you and was quite happy about it." Maggie assured her. "Everything's fine here, baby's doing well. Your midwife is held up in the clinic, so I'll give her another call and let her know what you're up to."

Maggie was delighted at the thought of being at the birth of her friend's first baby. She enjoyed her classes but loved being allowed to attend the labours of couples she had got to know well; this was a special privilege. "Come on, I'll make you some tea for a change."

The kitchen was warm despite its size and the lofty beams that once housed a grain store. Angela rocked gently and leant heavily on the Aga rail. Smudge purred, rubbing back and forth against her legs.

"You'll be the first in the group to deliver. Don't forget to breathe properly through every contraction, just concentrate, you can do it." Maggie massaged Angela's back, "And don't forget your obstetric focal point," she laughed. "Remember; stare at something, at anything. It will help, really it will."

"I'm scared Maggie, the pains started as soon as I put the phone down, they're so much stronger now."

"Contractions, remember? Come on, eyes fixed, do the breathing as soon as one starts. You're in charge."

Angela mastered her self control and allowed Maggie to

monitor her labour as they waited for the midwife to call and Gordon to arrive; the contractions were short and sharp. Between them Maggie tried to distract her. She gazed round the kitchen, "This colour scheme's worked out so well, hasn't it? Wish I'd chosen it, not brave enough I'm afraid." Maggie loved the bright red poppies on the blinds and red worktops.

"Yes." Angela gripped the rail. "That one was so painful, Maggie. Smudge, stop it please." Smudge casually wrapped himself around her legs again, purring loudly.

"Your breathing's just perfect, you're doing so well. I'll let Smudge out as Gordon won't be long and then we'll be on our way. Red's brilliant, especially for the Aga." Maggie opened the kitchen door and shooing Smudge outside whispered, "I'm afraid your nose is about to be put out of joint, Smudgy."

"Will I get sent home again if I'm not that far on?" Angela pushed the tea away. "I thought these weren't supposed to hurt so much at the beginning?"

"A pity your waters have gone early, but it happens. I think you'll be quick when labour's established. Try and eat something, you'll need the energy." Maggie pushed some biscuits towards her, "I'll be reminding you what to do and they'll definitely keep you in."

"Can't eat a thing. I'll be sick. I'm not sure I want Gordon with me now, I'd rather be with a bunch of strangers if I'm going to yell my head off."

"You won't, and even if you do nobody minds. He won't I'm sure."

Maggie heard the sound of Gordon grinding the car to a halt on the gravel drive and just managed to jump sideways as he rushed in.

"There's bags of time, they're both fine, Gordon," she said. "Angela's coping really well and I've just spoken to her midwife."

"Sorry darling, I had a client I couldn't get rid off. I'll put the bag in the car and then let's get going, can we?"

Angela remained calm, whilst Maggie attempted to reassure him. "We really don't need to rush, nothing's going to happen for hours. Drink that tea and then we'll make a move."

Gordon's agitation was not helping and got worse each time Angela had another contraction, so Maggie settled her in the car seated on a pile of warm towels and finally allowed Gordon to regain some control when she gently closed the car door and handed him the keys.

"I'm right behind you, now please don't drive too fast," she urged.

Gordon, wanting only to transfer his wife to the safe confines of the hospital was already revving the engine. As the small convoy of cars made its way towards Cambridge, Maggie's visit and hasty exit were closely observed and word quickly spread in Little Fordham that the new baby was about to be born.

—⁓—

The next morning Charlie Watt and his friend, Edna Newbold, were enjoying a regular gossip in the village shop. Edna, and her niece, Jennifer, had taken over the shop when it had been threatened with closure.

"Nice to 'ave another little'un in the village," said Charlie, who was sitting at the counter while Edna plastered his corned-beef sandwich with mustard. The two 'village elders' had been friends since school days and Charlie was Edna's most regular customer.

"That young woman's a bit stuck up, if you ask me," said Edna, "and he's too handsome by half."

"She'll change, they always do." said Charlie. "A few nights with a baby feeding and crying and she'll be a lot different, you'll see."

"How come you know so much, Charlie Watt?" Edna said, eyebrows raised. "Long time since your boy was that age."

"I know all about babies from my young friend, Maggie, next door. She's got another lot in her classes," he said scooping up more mustard. "I reckon her Robert's getting a bit fed up."

"Why's that, then?"

"He doesn't like her draping ladies all over their new sitting room carpet, 'case they leak!" he chuckled as the doorbell jangled.

"Can I join you?" Maggie entered the shop, beaming. "Angela had a boy. He's called James and he weighed over eight pounds. She did really well."

"So we already 'eard," sniffed Edna. "Hope she drops her la-di-dah ways now."

"Oh, Edna, what a thing to say. Angela's lovely, she's not at all stuck up if that's what you mean. Is it because she always has to look smart for her job? You know, she's her husband's secretary?"

"Well, she won't be looking smart for long when that baby starts sicking up all over."

Maggie smiled, accustomed now to Edna's sharp tongue. "Who told you both anyway? She only had baby James last night, for heaven's sake. It was so special for me to be with them."

"News travels round 'ere. You'd better take your ham now as the shop's closed this afternoon."

Maggie, still elated, gave Charlie a warm hug. Edna's waspish comments were best ignored.

"Okay, Edna," she said, turning to go, "I'll see you later Charlie.

I could do with some of your sloe gin. Can we have a little celebration when Robert gets home?"

"That girl would be better off having her own baby if you ask me," muttered Edna as the door closed.

Ten days later Gordon and Angela arrived back at 'Nelsons' with their baby. The early days in the hospital had been such a rollercoaster of emotions. Angela found that she couldn't stop crying. Every time she looked at baby James she wept, when Gordon came to visit her she wept. She was so overwhelmed at the sight of other babies in their cots that she retreated to the bathroom, and sobbed on their mother's shoulders. Then, despite their happiness, they all wept.

"The blues dear, just the blues," the midwives had said, comforting them. "Funny things hormones, affects some more than others."

Gordon placed the carrycot gingerly in the middle of their sitting room, praying the baby wouldn't start crying. "Hope this lasts, he's slept like a top since we left the hospital," he said, gazing proudly at his new son.

"Well, don't wake him then darling, put the kettle on." Angela smiled, "Oh dear, I'm going to cry again. I never thought I'd feel like this about our baby, did you?"

Gordon gently clasped his arms round her. "Frankly 'Mummy', I feel scared bloody stiff, but I know what you mean. Chokes me up somehow, especially when the midwives called me Daddy!"

Baby James let out a sudden cry.

"Help, is he hungry?"

"Pick him up. I fed him just before we left," Angela eased herself into an armchair. "Tell you what, see if he needs his nappy changed, darling."

"Who, me?"

"Yes, of course you. I'll make a pot of tea when you've finished, I get so thirsty."

Gordon looked at the now screaming James. He could deal with his bank manager and property developers, difficult clients fell under his charm, but he knew nothing about changing a baby. James was red in the face and his small arms flailed like a windmill. Clutching him tightly Gordon took him upstairs to the nursery where Angela had lovingly decorated the walls with characters from Winnie the Pooh. They had been given some instructions at the hospital, and Maggie had mentioned nappy changing in the classes. He also recalled that the doll she used to demonstrate with always remained silent and unmoving. Gordon lay James down on a plastic surface. Slowly he unwrapped him and lifted up the baby's gown to discover the nappy had descended to his knees. A runny yellow goo had oozed out, pasted itself all over the inside of James's legs and was now being smeared over Gordon's best jacket by small pounding feet. Gordon tried to control the tiny limbs. He had no idea in what order to do things next; no instructions were pinned to his son. Gingerly removing the loaded nappy with his fingertips, he dropped it on the floor, and dabbed at the tiny buttocks with a fistful of cotton wool. Just as suddenly as the yelling had started, it stopped. The baby stared unwaveringly at the face of his father, his tiny penis erect. With uncanny accuracy, a sudden stream of urine hit Gordon in the centre of his right eye and dripped down his face onto his jacket. Gordon was now unable to see properly and both his hands were coated with what appeared to be human mustard. Long wisps of cotton wool clung like a beard to the baby's skin. Soundlessly the baby delivered the coup de grace, as the remaining contents of his bowel oozed out and slithered along the slippery surface to run silently over the edge, and drop like small bomb blasts onto Gordon's shoes. The baby turned his head sideways, and threw up milky curds. The regurgitated milk clung like glue to the fine down of hair, filled his tiny ear and seeped into the folds of his neck. Gordon thought he might faint.

"Having problems, Daddy?" Angela stood smiling knowingly in the doorway. "He did that to me yesterday," she moved to pick up the nappy, "I've poured your tea darling, shall I finish off here?"

Gordon fled.

CHAPTER 5

UNTIMELY DEATH

He stood in front of the cracked shaving mirror and trimmed the tiny bunches of ginger hair protruding from his nostrils. Rubbing the shaving brush hard on the square remnant of Imperial Leather soap; the label remaining to the last, he lathered his chin, stropped his cutthroat razor, and set about his Sunday shave. Charlie Watt always arrived in church with a sprinkling of small plasters adorning his jaw line.

"Edna don't like beards," Charlie had once informed the vicar, and what his friend Edna said, went.

He picked up the clean shirt Edna always delivered on Saturday, and fretted with discomfort. Buttons strained with his increasing girth. The Sunday suit was getting tighter too, and the sleeves seemed shorter. Stepping into his shiny black shoes, polished and spat upon like army boots, he had trouble doing up the laces.

It was at times like this that Charlie missed his wife, Mary. They had been married nearly fifty years. Sweethearts at school, where they had occupied adjoining desks, giggling at their own naughtiness, and helping each other through the awkward gangliness of teenage youth. He recalled their first fumbling kiss behind the bike shed when she went bright pink and burst into tears. They were just fourteen. Other boys had fancied her for the black curls, rosy cheeks and doll-like appearance, but she only ever had eyes for Charlie, and he for her.

It seemed natural for them to marry eventually. Mary gave birth to their son William, known as young Will, when she was twenty years old, and in the bed that Charlie still slept in.

Maggie Edwards reminded Charlie of Mary; she had the same humour, the same friendly dark eyes and abundant curls. She was just what Little Fordham needed, even though she was still considered a newcomer.

With a final comb through the wispy remains of his hair he picked up his stick and best cap, and set off for church. As he walked down the path he glanced at his vegetable patch.

"I'll weed you lot later," he said. "Nice carrots coming on, they'll make a tasty drop of whisky."

He ambled up the lane and turned right towards the Green. He heard Doreen Creasey tolling the single church bell. She yanked the rope so hard he wondered she didn't take off like Mary Poppins. One day he thought, she'll pull the bell out of the tower.

The distant roar of a motorbike coming up the hill stopped him in his tracks. Traffic often approached the village too fast, and there was a sharp bend just before the Green. He turned and waved his stick as the bike drew nearer. The bike was almost level and he could see the grinning youth, two fingers of his right hand gesturing at Charlie.

At the same moment a horse and rider rounded the bend, trotting towards them from the opposite direction. The motorbike, its driver mocking Charlie, was going too fast to avoid them and the horse reared up to protect itself as the bike slammed into it. Charlie heard a sickening scream as the rider was thrown into the air and landed heavily on the grass verge. The horse collapsed and smashed its head on the tarmac, writhing with terror. Its hind legs lashed out aimlessly as blood pumped from a deep wound. The young boy had been thrown off as the bike embedded itself in the hedge, and ricocheted against the oak tree on the far side of the bend; he lay grotesquely sprawled in the ditch.

The sound of the church bell mixed with the whirring of the bike's rear wheel and the last gurgling rattle from the dying horse. A steady flow of blood pooled around the shining chestnut body, the neck arched, the gaping jaw opened in a silent scream.

Charlie felt paralysed, unable to propel his shaking legs, his breath came in short gasps and his heart lurched oddly. The young rider stirred and moaned as he recognised Doreen Creasey's daughter, Kate, often described by Edna as wayward for not attending church.

"Don't move girl, don't move. I'll get help," he mouthed through dry lips. "You stay still now."

Relieved to see that she was alive he forced his legs to move forward and stumbled back towards the lane.

"Tolling the bloody bell and her daughter's dying," he cursed, frantically picking his way through the uneven ruts. "Maggie, I must get Maggie."

Maggie cradled the injured girl's head in her arms. Kate was fully conscious and apparently not as badly injured as Charlie had feared. The ambulance and police were on their way. Maggie had heard the screams; Charlie met her running towards him up the lane.

"Oh thank God you're all right, Charlie. What a terrifying noise, I didn't know what to think, so I rang the police station anyway."

Distressed to find the boy in the ditch lifeless and beyond her help she concentrated on Kate who was deeply shocked and appeared to have fractured her left leg and dislocated a shoulder. Maggie talked soothingly to her as they waited for the ambulance and gently tried to conceal the sight of the stricken horse with her jumper and Charlie's best jacket, as Kate sobbed uncontrollably.

The church bell had fallen silent and a small crowd was now gathered on the verge, summoned by the terrifying sounds of the collision. Doreen Creasey appeared; her face ashen as she saw her daughter and ran to comfort her. She knelt beside Maggie and the two women held Kate's hands tightly as the vicar moved among the onlookers.

"That Richards boy was always trouble, look where it got him." Edna's comments cut through the shocked silence.

The ambulance and two police cars arrived. The villagers remained watching, stunned onlookers of the tragedy. The local hunt was summoned to deal with Kate's horse.

Maggie left Charlie in his cottage with Edna to go home and get some sleep; she was exhausted herself, having been called out twice the night before. One baby had had feeding difficulties and just as soon as she got in to bed she had been called out to a home delivery. All had gone well, a capable mother had delivered her third baby with ease, but the broken nights tired Maggie. She had managed to get a temporary job on the district and had been covering the occasional shift in the hospital. It was taking her a while to get used to night duty again. One birth and now, she mused, a death. Maggie could not imagine the distress a mother would feel to lose a child so tragically. Trouble the young boy may have been but he didn't deserve to die so young.

"Poor old, Creasey," said Charlie." She'll be praying for her girl."

Edna handed Charlie another carrot whisky whilst doing her best to comfort him after he had made a statement for the police.

"If I hadn't waved my stick that lad might still be with us." Charlie repeated.

"He had it coming."

"You mustn't say that, Edna. I took his attention away from the road." Large tears rolled down Charlie's cheek. "I caused that accident. I'm to blame for that boy's death you know."

"Now, you listen to me, Charlie Watt. We've been saying for months that this village needed a speed limit. They career through here like they're on a blooming race track. It was bound to happen one day. You heard what PC O'Sheridan had to say. That lad's been cautioned several times. He was a bad lot, you mark my words."

"Too young to die all the same. You can be a hard woman, Edna."

"I'm not hard, Charlie. I've got more common sense than some," she said turning to put the kettle on, "I'll make us a strong cup of tea, you've had too much of that whisky."

Charlie was sometimes grateful for her bossy ways. Edna kept him in order when he got maudlin, and she was right about the boy being a bad lot. The Richards boy had been caught stealing from the shop several times, and he and his older brother had done a lot of damage with an airgun, taking pot shots at greenhouses and the ducks on the village pond.

"Shouldn't have died, even so." Charlie felt calmer as he and Edna sat either side of the warm range. "I've been thinking about what you just said, about the speeding. It's a terrible thing to say but that lad's death might get us a proper speed limit." He was silent for a moment. "We'll get young Maggie to have a go at the parish council when this is all over. They need a bit of stirring up."

The next morning Edna surveyed the shelves of Little Fordham Stores and tightened her floral apron strings. She had been responsible for re-opening the shop after its closure shortly after her husband, Bert had dropped dead in the middle of the churchyard.

Every Thursday Edna had cleaned the church brass and Bert, who worked on the nearby farm, tended the cemetery. They would enjoy a thermos of tea and a tongue sandwich, Bert's favourite, when their work was finished. Edna had just filled his mug when Bert had complained of the pain in his chest. Before he had finished sucking the peppermint she always kept for 'wind', he was gone. Bert was laid to rest next to his Uncle Archibald.

The shop had once been the hub of village life in Little Fordham until the original owner had moved away. It was on the north side of the village green with a good view across to the Dog and Duck pub. Edna liked the fact that she could see and hear most of what went on.

The village hall and play area were to the left, separated by a row of pink washed thatched cottages. Several red brick cottages adjoined the pub. In the centre of the green was the large duck pond overhung by an ancient oak tree. In the evenings couples sat on the seat beneath the tree and in the day the young and the elderly sat and over fed the ducks. The Jack Russell terrier from the pub had fun chasing them as they waddled, too plump to fly any distance.

Edna, having finally taken over the lease of the shop two months after Bert's death, moved from their farm cottage to the flat above it. She recalled the state of it, how everything on the shelves in the shop had been left tired and bleached by the sun, with magazines curling at the edges. Ageing packs of solidified sugar and flour sat on the grimy shelves. Dried out bluebottles lay amongst the tins of fruit, labels so sun bleached that the peaches looked the same as pears. With the help of her niece, Jennifer, she soon had the shop thriving again. Notices were distributed round the village to attract new customers telling them that orders would be delivered. Jennifer opened the post office counter every morning. Fresh bread and daily papers duly arrived and Charlie now kept her well supplied with fruit, vegetables, and eggs.

It was a Tuesday and quiet in the shop. Jennifer had gone to the cash and carry. Most villagers at home and not working elsewhere had gone to Waldersby for market day. Edna checked all the shelves. She didn't want the local inspector finding any faults. She straightened the cards for all occasions in their display case and, with half an hour to go before closing, she decided to sit on the bench outside in the early autumn sunshine, and read the current copy of People's Friend.

Edna finished a short story and found her gaze wandering over to Doreen Creasey's cottage where Kate, her injured daughter was often to be seen sitting by the window. Doreen waved from her front door and walked across the green to speak to Edna.

"Getting on all right is she?" Edna enquired.

"Very depressed," Doreen sighed. "I don't know what to do really. Kate'll never get over losing that horse."

"I said at the time that the Richards boy was a bad lot."

"I know you did but I can't speak ill of the dead, whatever they've done."

"Seen anything of the family?" Edna asked, "I don't want them near my shop I can tell you, all rotten." She felt for a handkerchief in the apron pocket and blew her nose loudly. "Splashed out on the funeral, never seen wreaths like it. Ridiculous if you ask me."

"The vicar said a lot of people came down from London," Doreen said, hoping for more information.

"They would, wouldn't they, all bloody crooks. Wide boys you see, "Edna said.

"I feel sorry for his mother, Edna."

"I don't. He nearly killed Charlie and your daughter, let alone the horse, poor animal. I suppose she hasn't been near to apologise for him."

"Oh Edna, you're too forthright at times. That young neighbour of Charlie's said she'd visit her. She called on us twice. Charlie's lucky to have her next door and we'll always be grateful for what she did."

Edna's mouth tightened, "Apple of Charlie's eye. Thinks the sun shines out of her backside."

"What a thing to say!" Doreen turned away to give a reassuring wave to her daughter. "Kate's out of plaster now, trying to concentrate on college work. Trouble is, she gets depressed and says she wishes she'd been killed." Her own eyes filled with tears. "The doctor says it'll be months before she's over the shock."

The two women sat in silence before discussing the flower rota for the church. The church bell chimed and Edna went and turned the shop sign to Closed.

"Cheerio, I'll call by sometime," Edna said, before leaving. She cut across the green to the road and rounded the bend before Charlie's lane; it was time for tea and a good gossip with him, a regular arrangement she had on Tuesdays.

She didn't notice the two men sitting in the car parked near the Dog and Duck.

CHAPTER **6**

GIRL TALK

"Can you meet me in town? You said you had to come in? I need to talk, so meet me at that place by the Arts centre, Maggie. I really need your advice."

Maggie threw the wet clothes back into the basket. Pity – it was windy and she loved the smell of washing dried in the fresh air, it would just have to wait. What could possibly make Angela so worried? The two women, closer friends after the birth of Angela's son, James, held no secrets.

"You've been ages," Angela said brusquely as Maggie hurried in to the small café.

"Sorry, sorry, I couldn't park anywhere, we don't all have our husband's office near by, you know."

"Two coffees?" Angela asked, peering at the menu. "Fancy anything else?"

Maggie smiled at the hovering waitress, "No, it's a bit too early for lunch."

The girl moved away as Maggie leaned forward. "So tell me, what's the problem?"

"Problem?"

"Well, something's up; you don't usually give me twenty minutes' notice to meet you. Has the nanny left?"

"No, no, thank goodness. No, I've charmed her into a three-day week; she's really good with James. He adores her." She glanced round the crowded room. "Maggie, would you know if your husband was having an affair?"

"What? Robert you mean? He's not my husband!" Maggie almost shrieked.

"Ssh, you heard me, not yours, silly. Husband, boyfriend, partner, whoever. What are the signs?"

Maggie looked thoughtful, "Well, that's a relief. How about unusual lipstick all over the teacups, strange underwear in the bed, changing his aftershave, that sort of thing?"

"Seriously, you know what I'm saying."

"No, I don't know what you're saying, you tell me what you mean. Are you referring to Gordon?"

Angela glanced at the couple at the next table before leaning closer, "Of course it's Gordon. I think he might be having an affair," she whispered. Tears threatened to spill on to her cashmere scarf. "I can't be certain, it's just the way he's acting at the moment. He keeps staying behind at the office, or going to London to meet business colleagues then he was away for two nights last week. I'm supposed to be his secretary, for heaven's sake. I see all his post so there should be some reference to a meeting, shouldn't there? I mean, surely I would need to know what work he had to stay behind for? He says it's work that came in on the days I wasn't in. Even the temp seemed puzzled by the London trip."

"So you're not certain then, just getting suspicious. He doesn't regularly meet any other women does he? He only has eyes for you normally. I'm sure there's a simple explanation."

"That's where you're wrong."

"Wrong?"

"I think I know who the other woman could be, Maggie. You know the couple who bought the other barn? She was a model for one of the top agencies, quite stunning. Her husband travels a lot; something to do with art you know, sells fine prints for a London gallery. Gordon always thought his job sounded a bit dubious."

"Can't say I know them. Edna did some cleaning for them once, didn't she? Gossiped about them a bit to Charlie."

"Well, Gordon helped them with the move and everything. She apparently asked him to bid for some lots at a house auction."

"So?"

"Well, I think something's going on between them."

"Come on, Angela. I'm sure Gordon wouldn't do anything so silly; he thinks the world of you and James. If anything he's probably just flattered by the attention of a pretty woman, making him feel he's wonderful. Just a momentary infatuation; he'll get over it. It's the sort of thing you read about you know, she flatters him and makes him feel good. D'you want me to tackle him, or get Robert to speak to him maybe?"

"No. Don't say a word. Look, I'm sorry to rush but I've got to get back to see a client. Thanks for coming, Maggie, you're such a good friend. I just felt I had to talk to you this morning, I couldn't sleep last night, it's horrid being so suspicious and I have to work late tonight. I still feel I need to check on things this week but we can catch up on this at the weekend."

"That's okay; I've got shopping to do anyway." Maggie ordered another coffee and lingered to ponder on what Angela had told her. Gordon was charming, she could see what an attractive man he was the first time they'd met. Angela was a pretty wife, and a loving mother but Gordon obviously found fatherhood difficult, loving James very much but leaving day to day care of him to his wife and often complaining about James restricting their lives somewhat. But would he stray so easily? Perhaps an innocent chat to Edna would reveal a little more about the ex-model, and her dubious art- dealing husband.

Maggie and Angela had previously arranged the following weekend away as part of Maggie's fitness programme. Robert had treated them and was going to Dublin on business, enjoying his recent promotion. Frank Sutton, the self- made boss of Sutton's Scenario, had quickly seen the potential in Robert, nurtured him for management and promoted him rapidly after the move from London. Now Robert was the youngest director of the company, just short of his thirtieth birthday. Gordon was to be at a conference too, and the nanny had been only too happy when asked to look after James. The drive to the health spa near Norwich gave Angela a chance to chat to Maggie again.

"D'you think I could have imagined it? It seems so strange to have these doubts." Angela put the route map down. "Slow down, Maggie, let's get there in one piece."

"Gordon told Robert he'd got a lot of work on," said Maggie. "And don't be a back seat driver!"

"Sorry. I know, he's got a lot going on at the moment that's why I've decided to do four days a week in the office. The nanny's living in now; she's such a sweet girl. Gordon's been as nice as pie to me for the last two days, buttering me up and giving me extra spending money for this trip. D'you think he realises I suspect something?" she said, delving into her handbag. "Want a mint?"

"That's possible. No thanks. My, that felt good," Maggie said overtaking at speed. "I really love this Mini; my old Renault was so slow. Robert calls it my new baby!"

"That's a bit tactless."

"I know, he doesn't think sometimes, it's still screwing me up."

"We're nearly there, another two miles," Angela said, folding the map. "Let's enjoy ourselves and forget Little Fordham for twenty-four hours."

The spa had the grandeur of a fading stately home. Their bedroom overlooked sweeping lawns and well-ordered flowerbeds. Embossed chintz covers, padded headboard and window drapes were patterned in roses. A potpourri of petals scented the air. Luxurious fluffy pink and green towels reflected the theme of roses.

"Can we have lunch first, I'm starving," said Maggie.

They ate hungrily whilst surveying their opulent surroundings and fellow guests, relaxed in fluffy white bathrobes and mules.

"We need a swim then we can have a snooze," Angela said, "this is beginning to take my mind off home nicely."

Maggie, couldn't help reflecting that she herself resembled a seal slithering off an ice floe, comparing her body against Angela's trim figure, as they joined a group of women in the pool.

"Move in a circle to the left please ladies," yelled a sporty young man, urging them to jog, jump, sway and exercise in the water. His enthusiasm never waned as he produced weights, boards, and balls for more aqua play. An hour later Maggie and Angela crawled out of the pool exhausted and collapsed on the sun loungers.

The following morning, refreshed after a long sleep, Maggie

and Angela enjoyed a healthy breakfast and discussed again the possibility of Gordon's affair.

"I'm sure you're wrong about him, Angela. He's such a bloody good looking guy I expect that woman's just trying it on."

"I do hope you're right, Gordon's changed a lot since James was born, after all he's still just a baby. Gordon gets very impatient with him, says he hasn't got time to play and is always coming up with some excuse to go out. We never have family outings like other new parents."

"Some Dads cope better when their children are a bit older though, perhaps he'll enjoy him more then? You mustn't blame yourself."

"I don't know, it's really upsetting."

"Let's not spoil this break, it's just what you needed just now. We'll see if he and Robert can have a chat about all this when we get back as they get on so well?"

"No, Maggie, he mustn't know I've been talking about him and our private affairs, he'd only get angry. It's a matter for us to solve if we can."

Later that day, pampered and relaxed, Angela joined a keen group for a brisk walk as Maggie decided on a final soothing massage. By the time Angela returned Maggie had had more sleep and was ready for their journey back to Little Fordham.

"Thanks for the treat, Rob. This looks gorgeous," Maggie said surveying the table, flickering candles and a favourite meal ready and waiting. The trouble with unwinding is that now I feel totally exhausted. So much for getting fit, I really must try and lose more weight though. I looked awful next to Angela; she's got all her figure back. I'm definitely going out jogging more and starting a proper diet next week."

"Maggie," Robert refilled her wine glass," Charlie was chatting to me this morning, it seems that Gordon's been seen by Edna, having it off, as they say, with the lovely Leanne."

"Oh, no."

"Didn't you say she suspected something was going on?"

"Yes, but obviously she hoped it wasn't."

"Well, it's all round the village now, you know what Edna's like."

—⁂—

A week after their visit to the spa Maggie decided she try and visit Jacky Richards, the mother of the boy that had been killed, and who appeared to be shunned by the rest of the villagers.

Maggie's heart lurched as the large half-breed dog stopped inches short of her leg; the chains attached to it straining as if they might break. A platinum blonde head peered round the grimy curtains. Several moments passed before the door opened. The house was one of four pre- war council houses in the narrow lane that had once housed men who worked the old gravel pit. The pit was a favourite haunt for village children with its matting of thick undergrowth and secret camps.

"D'you want something?"

"Hello, I'm Maggie Edwards. I live in the village."

"You're the nurse. What d'you want?"

"Forgive me for calling, but I need your help." Maggie smiled. "You couldn't let me in could you?" Maggie had guessed that Jacky Richards wouldn't welcome her with open arms.

"'Spose so, if you must. Don't mind him he won't hurt you," said Jacky, tossing a smouldering cigarette butt with expert aim and just missing the dog. "You'll have to excuse the mess, my Len's on nights down the factory. The boys don't seem to see it."

"I haven't come to inspect your house, Mrs Richards," Maggie said, keeping a good distance between herself and the dog as she nipped through the open door. "I wanted to see how you were, after the accident and everything." Maggie sat down carefully next to a large tabby cat curled up on a grey pile of ironing.

Jacky Richards lent against the sink, an assortment of gold and silver bracelets jangled as she lit another cigarette. Heavy make-up couldn't conceal her weariness. Several weeks had passed since the fatal road accident at the top of the hill. Maggie had been persuaded by Charlie to get up a petition about speeding to present to the parish council and the whole village seemed eager to sign up.

Cigarette smoke billowed across the room. Jacky Richards had a fit of coughing and flapped at the air with a grimy tea towel. "D'you smoke?"

"No, thanks"

"S'pose not, you being a nurse. I've tried to give up but I find it helps a bit," she said.

"I'm a midwife though my nurse training comes in useful at times."

"The vicar told me you were involved."

"I'm so sorry, Mrs Richards, there was nothing I could do for your son," Maggie hesitated as the cat sidled on to her lap, "I should have come before. I've been visiting the young girl, Kate, who was injured. She blames herself for the accident."

"My son was a tearaway."

Maggie noticed her flinch at her own words as she lit another cigarette. "I'm not blaming anyone. He was a show off and probably didn't see her or the horse coming. The old man says he was going too fast and to be honest with you I believe him." She looked away. Maggie saw the sparkle of unshed tears in her eyes. "I still loved him for all his bad ways, got himself in with a crowd in Waldersby, right little devils, all of them." She tapped the ash into the sink. "I hope the girl's doing all right?"

"She's out of plaster. You know, I just wondered whether it would be possible for you to visit her some time? Forgive me if you think I'm interfering, but I'm sure it would help you both and she wants to talk to you."

"Don't suppose her mother wants me near the place. My eldest heard some locals in the pub saying my son was a bad lot. Nearly started a fight."

"How many children have you?"

"Two more lads, they've all been headstrong but they're settling down now. Jimmy the oldest is twenty-five and he's going steady, his girlfriend's expecting. Martin's twenty-three, he wanted to go to college but ended up working up the factory like his dad." Stubbing her cigarette out she pointed at the family photos. "They took it hard. Want a cuppa?"

"No, thank you, I've just had lunch. There is a way you could help, Mrs Richards. Some people in the village are very concerned about the speed of traffic and have asked me to get up a petition to lobby the parish council. Hopefully then the councillors will have a go at the highways people. It's so dangerous on that bend, and they're too frightened to cross the road near the church."

"You'll never get that lot on the council to spend any money, just wasting your time," Jacky Richards retorted.

"It may seem cruel but apparently someone has to be killed or injured before they'll take notice." Maggie felt uncomfortable, "That was so tactless of me, I'm sorry."

"Funny really, p'raps my son will prove to be a blessing for the place after all."

"I was really wondering whether you could possibly write a letter, Mrs Richards? I know it would help, a letter from you to the council?"

"You can call me Jacky, you know. You'd never read my writing, girl, and I can't spell, never could."

"Perhaps I could write it for you, and you sign it? What if I call by next week and we do it together?"

"I'll think about it, see what my Len thinks."

"Thank you, Jacky, I really appreciate it."

Maggie lifted the cat off her lap and got up to leave. Instinctively she put her arm round Jacky Richards's shoulders. "I'm sorry; the older people have been very worried since the accident. I've been thoughtless, forgive me."

Jacky gulped, "It's alright, maybe I'll get over it one day, not yet though, my lad shouldn't have died that young. It helps talking about it actually."

"In that case I'd really like to come and see you again."

"I'd like that but you need to avoid my Len if he's about, he can be –," her voice trailed off, "well don't come if he's here that's all, you'll see his motorbike."

Maggie nodded; Charlie had warned her about Len Richards. She left, weaving her way past the dog, piles of scrap metal, old lawnmowers and car body parts. A sharp contrast to mown lawns and neat flowerbeds fronting the adjoining houses. The Richards' family had become outcasts, but Maggie felt that was even more reason to involve them.

CHAPTER 7

PARISH AFFAIRS

The village hall filled rapidly. The parish councillors, huddled in anoraks against the prevailing chill, watched in astonishment.

"Needs another fifty pence in the meter, Chairman," whispered the clerk. "Shall I pass some extra agendas round?'

"Thank you. Yes, on both counts." Major Gibson retired, was beginning to feel a little flustered. In ten years as Chairman of the parish council he had never seen so many members of the public. Normally they only made an appearance if a planning application bothered them.

Charlie leaned forward from the front row. "When are you going to start, Major? These chairs aren't made for sitting long. My backside's numb already."

"Quite so, Mr Watt." Major Gibson cleared his throat. "Ladies and gentleman, honoured as we are to have you with us, I must ask for quiet in the room, thank you. I'll start the proceedings, and in a moment I will close the meeting to allow you to address the council on the matter of concern. Traffic matters I believe?"

"I'll tell you what's concerning us right now. We want..." Edna

PARISH AFFAIRS

stopped as the Major glared at her.

"I'm afraid you will only address the council when I say you can, kindly remain seated Mrs Newbold."

Edna sniffed. "Who does he think he is?" she muttered, pursing her lips in a thin red line.

Maggie, sitting between Charlie and Edna, touched her arm. "Ssh, he's the Chairman, Edna, we want him on our side."

"Don't need to tell me who he is girl, never bothered about us before in all these years."

Major Gibson glowered at Edna. "Now then, I trust you have nominated a spokesperson. I will close our meeting so that one of you may address the council."

Maggie stood up and handed over the petition. Her written notes shook in her hand. "I represent everyone here, Major. I've gathered together a petition to show the council the very real concern we all feel about traffic speeding through our village." After her opening sentence she felt calmer. "There have been so many near misses, particularly on the bend. We really do need a speed limit. The accident in which a young man died, and which almost caused the death of a young woman, made us all realise just how lucky we have been so far."

"We are more than aware of the problems. Unfortunately, we don't seem able to persuade the highways authority that a speed limit is the answer," Major Gibson responded immediately and eyed the other councillors. "Do you all agree?" They nodded silently.

"Now there's been a fatality, Major, I think you must try harder to get something done and we are hoping for your help."

Mrs Reed, a retired schoolteacher, spoke quietly, shivering in the cold. Maggie thought she could hear her teeth chattering. "I think we should ask our County councillor to assist in this."

More questions followed. The Major agreed to consider the matter as urgent as a death had occurred and deliver the petition personally to the County councillor.

"In honour of my poor bloody son, is it?" The blonde head of Jacky Richards rose above the seated villagers at the back of the hall. "Use my son's death as an excuse. You should have seen to this years ago. Pity more haven't died then you could be in the running for a bloody flyover."

Major Gibson's face reddened. Shakily he grabbed the table. "Madam, may we offer our sincere condolences? The council has for years tried to..."

Maggie stood up.

"Thank you, Major. You've all been most helpful."

"No, they'aint." Charlie joined in, "Major, if it weren't for this young lady nothing would have happened. Reckon we should have her up there with you lot. You don't help us much in Little Fordham. Never 'ave."

Shouts and nods of agreement rippled round the hall, making the sitting councillors wriggle with discomfort.

"Well, that's kind of you Charlie, but I think it's time we all went home now." Maggie got up and pulled at his sleeve, "Come on," she hissed gently. "We're upsetting them and we need their help." She helped him up and slowly the disgruntled audience followed them.

Leaving the hall Edna confronted Jacky Richards, "If you kept your sons in order there'd be a lot less trouble in this village, I can tell you."

"Edna, please, you mustn't – ," Maggie urged as more villagers gathered round.

"Your lad nearly killed two other people, not just that young girl's horse." Edna continued.

Len Richards, his face puce with rage pushed forward towering over her. "You dare say that again to my bloody face, you old bag!"

"Please, please, everyone, please, we haven't come here to fight each other." Maggie was frightened, "Edna, please, it was a terrible accident. Let's all go home now, the council has promised to help." She gestured urgently at the villagers to move on before a fight broke out.

"If anyone wishes to stay for the rest of the council meeting they're more than welcome," blustered Major Gibson to the few remaining, relieved that there had been a rush for the exit.

Outside the village hall an ugly scene was developing between the Richards family and some of the villagers. Edna might have been knocked unconscious had not the local publican intervened.

"Cool it, Len, come on Jacky, have one on me, mate. Free drinks all round."

A small group set off for the pub as Maggie helped Charlie into her car and Dawn Creasey's husband hurried Edna away.

CHAPTER 8

CALLOUT

Maggie lay in Roberts's arms on the sitting room floor. She gazed out of the French windows at a star-filled sky thinking about her conversation with her sister, Eleanor, who'd phoned that afternoon. Their chatter had been all about babies. Eleanor was helping out in a play group. She had a new boyfriend, might move in to his flat, and was applying for a teaching post at their old primary school. Like Maggie she still hadn't managed to conceive and was putting all her maternal energies in to the play group.

"Mum's fine, she's really in to her art classes now." Eleanor had assured her. "Dad would have been amazed at some of her work. She really misses him, don't we all? I think she's sorry I've thought of moving out again."

"She's supposed to be coming down for a weekend soon. She hasn't been since we finished all the decorating," Maggie said. "You must come, Elly, I'm thrilled with my kitchen and the new Aga. The cottage is so pretty now, just the garden to sort out properly but Robert likes planning that. Our bedroom has now got what they call an 'en suite' and the bath foams at the touch of a button, brilliant, so good when I'm feeling haggard after a long shift. They said it helped aching muscles and I promise you, it really works. "

"Lucky you, I'll come down in the holidays for a weekend perhaps. You produce a grandchild for Mum and she'll be down like a shot," Eleanor said, laughing. "She's forever moaning to her friends about us two, both unmarried and having no little ones for her to fuss over."

Poor, Mum, no babies for her to be proud of, thought Maggie, gazing at Robert snoring gently beside her, having resisted all her earlier advances.

"Look, Maggie, we've tried every position I can think of, save hanging from the light switch, just give me a rest," he'd pleaded. Moments later he had fallen asleep. Travelling and extra work had taken its toll.

She eased herself up; it was getting cold as she piled more logs on the dying embers of the fire and covered Robert with a blanket. He was right of course, she thought. Sex dominated her thoughts; a feeling of desperation began to take hold as she yearned to get pregnant again. The moment Robert appeared Maggie pounced on him. They made love in the bath, in the garden, in the car, in the countryside, and just about everywhere she could undress him, to no avail.

Maggie found some degree of solace in other people's babies and was on duty in the hospital early the next day. She had stopped running her classes in the cottage as her midwifery duties had increased. During one slack night on duty in the hospital nursery she had dared to contemplate what it would be like to 'borrow' a baby. She felt a wave of pity and understanding for women who resorted to such desperate measures. Maggie reflected on her feelings that night as one of the babies stirred. Maggie picked it up and held it close to her face. She studied the tiny features and ran her finger over the delicate soft cheeks. The baby's face creased in to a smile, accompanied by the familiar sounds of a nappy being filled.

"Thank you, Jessica, that's the second time in an hour; now I suppose you're hungry again." She changed the nappy and carried the howling, hungry baby to her mother.

"I'll let you keep her," Maggie said, smiling as the baby latched on to the welcoming breast.

Maggie's temporary hours of work alternated between hospital shifts and the district, as she waited for a more permanent post. It was proving to be excellent experience.

One autumn evening she was called out to the cottage where Jacky Richards lived. Jimmy Richards, the eldest son, had turned up with his girlfriend and Jacky was worried. Tracy was thirty-two weeks pregnant, bleeding slightly and in pain. Maggie examined her and was relieved to detect the baby's heartbeat but recognising the danger of premature labour had made hasty arrangements for an ambulance.

"Haven't seen you since that council meeting, Maggie," said Jacky, as she boiled the kettle and passed her a mug of tea.

"No, you're right, nothing's been agreed yet though. These things take such a long time I'm told."

"My Len says he's going to sort out the old cow who runs the shop one day."

"Really?"

"Yea, really. Will everything be alright for Trace and the baby?"

"Everything's going to be fine," said Maggie, re-arranging the equipment in her bag.

"Leave her resting in the bedroom till the ambulance gets here. Sometimes babies decide they want to come a bit sooner unfortunately. Tracy will be given something to stop her labour if possible. They'll do what they can to stop her baby being born too soon, it's far better off inside its Mum."

"S'pose your right. What's wrong with my tea then?" Jacky said. "Letting it get cold."

"Oh, sorry," Maggie added more sugar, "it was a bit too hot."

"I told them to leave off; always at it. I can hear them in there." Jacky nodded in the direction of the bedroom. "Sex mad my boy, just like his father."

"Well it's okay for them to have sex, Jacky. Perhaps he was too rough? I wouldn't let Jimmy think it was any of his fault though, he's worried enough."

"That's a relief then--." Suddenly Jacky shrieked, "Oh, my God!" and pushed Maggie to one side as the kitchen door burst open and Len Richards's bulk filled the doorway. Maggie noticed the grubby shirt hanging like half-pulled curtains, barely concealing the pendulous stomach beneath his leather jacket. Swaying, he leered at them, belching beer fumes in to the room.

"Come here, woman," he lurched towards Jacky. "What the hell's going on, what's she doing 'ere.?"

"Give over, Len, you're drunk. Tracey's been having pains," Jacky nodded in the direction of the bedroom. "Maggie's been seeing to them, we're waiting for an ambulance."

"They ain't having no fuckin' kid in my fuckin' bed," he said, slurring the words as he made towards the bedroom.

"Mr Richards, please." Maggie tried grabbing his sleeve as Jimmy appeared.

"Leave off, bitch. What's going on, Jimmy?" Len Richards

staggered down the narrow passageway.

"Give over, Dad, I'll kill you if you touch my Trace."

Relieved, Maggie saw the flash of blue lights coming down the lane. "Thank heavens, the ambulance is here, Jacky."

The ambulance crew re-acted swiftly as Maggie yelled for help. Len Richards had fallen on top of Tracy. Swearing, the crew dragged him aside and rapidly stretchered the distraught young girl to the ambulance. Within minutes they were on the way to the hospital and Len was left out cold on the bedroom floor.

Maggie and Jimmy accompanied Tracy in the ambulance. Maggie just managed to stay upright supported by the strong arms of Bill, the ambulance crewman, as they swerved and swayed in the race to the hospital.

Five minutes into their journey Tracy suddenly screamed, "It's coming, it's coming. My baby's coming."

"Breathe the gas, Tracy, breathe, breathe," urged Bill, "Good girl, Maggie's going to help you, you're doing just fine."

Maggie stayed calm, aware now that they were not going to make it to the hospital in time. "Tracy, you're right, baby's coming, and you're going to be alright. Just listen to me and do exactly as I say. I need you to pant, Tracy, pant for me – like a dog. Good girl, keep it up." Maggie's voice rose above the roar of the engine as Amy Louise, eight weeks premature, delivered herself in to her waiting hands, halfway between Little Fordham and Cambridge

"Well done, Tracy, you've got a little girl and she's tiny but you've done so well." Maggie managed to show her the baby and control the overwhelming urge she felt to cry with relief despite the lurching ambulance. "I need to wrap her up. Can you see her, Jimmy?"

Jimmy, visibly shaking hung on tightly to Bill, "Blimey, she's small ain't she. Are you sure she's alright?"

"She'll be fine; we've got to keep her very warm. We're almost at the hospital, Tracy, you'll both be quite safe soon." Maggie hastily enveloped the baby in foil and blankets, thankful to hear Amy's high pitched cry, a weak but re-assuring sound as she tucked her in beside the young girl. "Here, have a cuddle while I sort you out."

"She won't die, will she?"

"No, she's a strong little baby, she needs a little oxygen but she'll make it." Maggie assured her with silent prayers winging their way heavenwards. "We're here; you're going to be alright now."

The ambulance, its lights still flashing, slowed to a stop at the hospital entrance.

"Thanks, Bill, for keeping me on my feet, they're ready for us," Maggie said with relief as the doors opened allowing the waiting group of doctors and midwives to take control. Maggie stayed to pass on her hastily written notes and gave a verbal report of the events leading to the baby's birth.

"Tracy's in the best hands, Jimmy, they'll put your baby in an incubator and keep her in the special unit for now." she said, giving him a brief hug as they parted.

"Thanks, nurse. I'll kill my bloody father if our baby doesn't make it."

"Forget your Dad; he was too drunk to know what he was doing. You'd better go and see how your new family are getting on."

Jimmy shook Bill's hand. "Thanks, mate."

Len Richards was lucky to avoid a conviction for an assault which could have caused the death of his grandchild.

"So you see they're out to create trouble. With a father like that it's not surprising the boys go off the rails." Angela, seated in Maggie's kitchen, listened to the story. "Promise never to repeat anything, especially to Charlie."

"Maggie, you should take care. Of course I won't say anything. Are you really expected to go to places like that on your own at night?"

"Oh yes, I'm not too happy about Len Richards but there aren't many families like that round here, thank goodness."

"It really makes me nervous," said, Angela. "I worry about you and I'm sure Robert does. Anyway, let's not dwell on that awful man. What's happening with you?"

"We'd better keep an eye on Edna, even if she is an old bat." Maggie said. "Her tongue gets her into trouble, always moaning and complaining about the Richard's family. Right, I haven't told you about my last hospital visit have I?"

"No."

"We've been referred to another obstetrician; apparently they've been doing a lot of research into recurrent miscarriages. Physically we appear to have no problems getting pregnant, Robert's sperm count's fine, excellent in fact, it's what goes wrong with me."

"Would you two ever consider adopting if you couldn't have your own?" Angela was uneasy, "I shouldn't ask really but it's such a shame, you two would make better parents than Gordon and I."

"Don't be silly."

"I mean that. Look at us. Gordon's only interested in business. He hardly bothers about James and just clams up on me if I dare mention having another."

"D'you want another?'

"Sometimes I think it would be lovely, especially for James."

"Is Gordon still seeing that woman?"

"I think he is. Says he's not. I just can't trust him anymore, and he's not exactly all over me. I'm just waiting for him to admit it or tell me he's going to leave us."

"Oh, Angela, I'm sure it won't come to that."

There was a cold gust of wind as the back door opened.

"Mind if I join you?" Charlie said, ambling in to the kitchen.

"Oh thanks, Charlie, they look good." Maggie took the basket of apples and pulled the large rocking chair up to the Aga. "Coffee or tea?"

Charlie sat beneath a swirl of smoke as he lit his pipe. "It's like a furnace in here. You two young ladies gossiping?"

"Not like you and Edna," Maggie chuckled, "have you been collecting sloes for your gin?"

"Got a load. We'll have plenty to keep us going this Christmas."

"Don't you get me tight again." Maggie picked up an apple. "Nice Cox's, Charlie, thanks"

Angela collected her coat from the hall, "Well, I'll love you and leave you. See you Saturday, Maggie. D'you think it'll rain today, Charlie?"

"Not today, girl." Charlie jumped as the phone rang.

Maggie grabbed the receiver, "Yes, yes of course. How far on is she?" she scribbled on the notepad, "every five minutes are they? Not leaking at all? No blood loss? Baby moving ok?"

She smiled at Charlie and mouthed to him that she needed to go. "I'm coming now. Don't worry, she'll be fine. See you in about twenty minutes."

The front door slammed. Robert stirred, he'd fallen asleep in front of the television. "Hello, darling, everything go okay? I've got an early start again," he muttered drowsily.

Maggie, elated, was eager to chat, "I had such a lovely delivery this afternoon. A first mum, she just popped it out." Maggie put her arm round him, "I'm making coffee, want some?"

"No, it'll stop me getting back to sleep. Aren't you on call?"

"I'm second on, you get the bed warm," she laughed, squeezing his arm.

Robert grimaced, "Please, darling, give it a rest. Not tonight."

Maggie smiled and kissed his forehead, "I don't know many men who'd turn down such an offer. Don't you like the way I make love to you?"

"I love the way you make love to me, darling, but I've had a hell of a day. G'night," Robert said, escaping up the stairs.

CHAPTER 9

REVENGE

"**E**very year I promise myself that I'll start shopping early and what happens? I end up panicking at the last minute." Maggie surveyed the packed shelves in the village stores. "Nice Crackers, Edna. Christmas stuff already, goodness me it's only October."

"It gets earlier every year." Edna sniffed audibly. "Mind you, I told Jennifer to keep them out the back. She doesn't listen that girl, gets carried away buying up all the Halloween stuff too. Don't agree with it myself, sinful all that trick an' treating."

"Market forces, Edna, that's the problem."

"So I'm told, cater for the customers or lose the trade. Keeps Charlie Watt happy growing them pumpkins. That one by the door is the biggest he's grown in years."

"Did Charlie cut the face out?'

"Yes, he's like a little kid. By the way he's been telling me that the police are expecting a lot of trouble makers in Waldersby for All Hallows."

"What sort of trouble?"

"Yobs, tearaways. Need a good clip round the ear if you ask me."

"Oh, I meant to say," Maggie changed the subject before Edna could start on one of her pet subject to reinstate hanging, "Angela and I really enjoyed doing up the church for the Harvest Festival. Did the vicar approve?"

"Yes, you did a good job, I'll give you that. I've put you on the rota for Christmas. Vicar was well pleased, he likes berries, never seen so many."

"We started in our lane and then went round all the gardens in the village, everyone was happy to let us pick what we liked, really helpful."

"When it gets near Christmas I'll tell you how the vicar likes it done. Need a decent tree too."

"OK, I'm glad we're in your good books."

Maggie took Edna's sniff and pursed lips as a sign of approval as she wiped her hands hard down her apron front, before turning away to tidy the newspapers. "You've settled into our ways all right, which is more than can be said for some." Edna said.

"Well, that's a relief!"

—※—

Maggie recalled the conversation in the pub that evening. "I don't think Edna means to be such a misery really, look how wonderful she is with Charlie. He thinks the world of her and she looks after him so well." Maggie glanced around, sipping her gin and tonic with relish. "You haven't said whether you like my new hairstyle, Rob?"

"That old boy knows which side his bread's buttered," said Robert, studying the menu, "I thought you looked different, what have you done?"

"I've had three inches cut off!"

"Whoops, sorry, you know I think you always look beautiful. Now, your choice as it's your birthday soon, Maggie. Looks as if we'll have to start without them. "

"I wonder where they've got to? James was really poorly yesterday but Angela was filling him up with medicine, poor little chap. They're usually very prompt. I'm starving too."

They were half way through their meal when Angela phoned the pub. The barman reported that she was crying and that her husband had gone to London for the weekend. He also said that she'd had to call the doctor out for her little boy.

"The bastard, fancy leaving her when James is ill," said Maggie, spearing a large chip, "I know he's seeing that woman again. The two of them were together in Waldersby last Tuesday, the day Angela had to stay at home for the plumber. I saw them."

"What were they doing?"

"Having lunch in the new wine bar behind the market square. I was celebrating with a couple of the students who'd passed their exams and Gordon was too busy ogling her to see me. I didn't tell Angela."

"Well, it's been going on for a while now," Robert said, waving to the waitress. "It's a hell of a shame but don't let it spoil our evening – we'll have another drink, one more won't hurt."

"Did I tell you that Mum rang to say she can't come next weekend, she might come down with Eleanor next month?"

Robert leant across the table and put his hand over hers. "Gives us more time to ourselves then, doesn't it? I fancy you even more with short hair."

—m—

No one heard Edna's screams as she was pulled in to the room at the back of the shop. Rough hands tied her to a chair and gagged her mouth with a tea towel.

"That should keep your trap shut. Been watching you for weeks." Spittle smeared her cheek and a large fist smashed into her thin face.

Edna could hear men laughing and throwing things around, sounds of the paper stand and displays crashing to the ground, breaking glass. They grabbed the cans of lager and sandwiches, before triumphantly urinating in her trembling lap.

The larger of the two bent close to her ear. Edna recoiled from his sweat and foul breath. "Not your lucky day. You're not worth shagging, you old bitch. Been watching you and planning to do this place over for weeks."

The second man pulled him away, "C'mon, Len, you've made your point, mate. Let's go."

The rain was light but the fall of leaves made it slippery. Doreen Creasey pulled on her wellington boots and called out to Kate, "Just going to get some more milk." She crossed the green to the village shop and narrowly missed being knocked down by a motorbike. The rider was laughing to his companion, revving alongside him. Still shaken and annoyed she thought it was odd that the shop door wouldn't budge. It was cash and carry day and unusual for Edna to lock up early. She retraced her steps and noticed the beer cans and a half eaten sandwich on the path. 'That'll upset Edna. Bet it was those bikers,' Doreen muttered, picking up the cans and returning them to the waste bin by the side door. She peered through the windows again and gasped in horror at the sight of the smashed up interior.

PC O'Sheridan looked at the clock on the dashboard, thirty minutes before his shift ended. He would drive through Little Fordham on his way back to the station and look in on the 'Dog and Duck'. He swerved to avoid the two bikers as he approached the green, swearing in annoyance as he parked the car and hurried towards the pub. Startled by a scream, then shouts of 'murder, help, murder,' he looked in the direction of the shop. He had never had to deal with a murder in Little Fordham. Burglaries yes, but murder? He pulled out his truncheon and ran as fast he could.

Edna was lifted gently in to the ambulance. She was badly bruised, her mouth swollen, one eye closed. She stank of urine.

Doreen Creasey, breathless and sobbing, described the awful scene to PC O'Sheridan. She'd run round to the back of the shop and spotted Edna on the floor tied to a chair that had toppled sideways. She could see blood trickling from her mouth.

PC O'Sheridan instantly knelt down to see if Edna was breathing. Two of her teeth lay in the pool of blood. It was his job and he was thankful to find her alive, but the scene shocked him profoundly.

—·—

Charlie waited for Maggie at the end of the lane, dressed in his Sunday best. He admired the bright autumnal colours of the hedgerow, the berries like garlands of jewels, the clear blue sky overhead, and the crows cawing loudly as they feasted on the big walnut tree in the meadow. It was a scene he had witnessed many times, an Indian summer before the cold and frosts of winter. But today his life had been turned upside down; he was filled with a great sense of unease and fear made him tremble.

"Poor, Edna," he dabbed at the tears spilling down his rough cheeks. "They'd no right to attack a poor defenceless woman. Cowards, that's what they are, wicked cowards." Doreen Creasey had not spared him the details. "I'd have killed them if I'd been there."

Sitting next to Maggie as they made the journey to the hospital he tried to control his emotions. The tears ceased but his body shook. Doreen had warned them to 'expect the worst'. A remark Charlie could not forget as he gripped Maggie's hand at the hospital entrance.

They bought flowers and Edna's favourite violet mints in the hospital shop and filled with apprehension made their way to the ward. The bed was curtained off.

A nurse took them aside and whispered, "The doctors have checked her all over. She'll need a lot of peace and quiet to get over the shock. That's what often kills them, you know."

"It'll take a hell of a lot to kill our Edna," Charlie muttered to her retreating back.

Edna's face was mottled blue and black, one eye gleamed through the swelling of her cheek. Charlie held her hand and squeezed it, "You'll be all right girl, you'll be alright." The tears had soaked through his shirt front.

Her voice, barely audible, seeped out of the swollen mouth, "Stop snivelling, I shan't be ironing you another shirt for this Sunday, Charlie Watt."

CHAPTER 10

THE SEASON OF GOODWILL

The villagers of Little Fordham took stock. They were shocked and rumour ran rife as to the culprits. It was common knowledge that the name Len had been overheard by Edna during the assault. PC O'Sheridan had visited the Richards house on more than one occasion. Eventually Len Richards had been remanded in custody.

"Now you just take it easy, girl. Jennifer's running the shop, and her boyfriend's doing all the fetching and carrying for her," Charlie said. He was sitting with Edna in her small flat.

As they waited for the district nurse to leave Edna thought to herself over and over that if only Jennifer hadn't been held up at the Cash and Carry none of this might have happened.

"You'll be fine. Edna. You've only been home a week and you need time to get over the shock. Weeks maybe. The bruises are going fast, and those cuts on your head are healing nicely. Your lip has healed very well." Gill, the district nurse, patted her arm, "I can tell you don't like being a patient so I'll pop in next Wednesday and discharge you then. Remember to call us if you need anything beforehand and keep that appointment with the dentist. Our friend Maggie Edwards has promised to keep an eye on you."

"All this darned fuss. People poking their noses in where they don't belong."

"Maggie don't poke her nose in, Edna, as you well know." Charlie set the potted cyclamen down on the coffee table next to her armchair. "She sent you this; we've both been invited to Christmas dinner with her and Robert. You'll be able to try out your new teeth."

Edna watched from the window as the villagers prepared for Christmas. The tree was put up on the green and decorated by the village hall committee, with Dawn Creasey in charge. Maggie and Angela called on Edna, at Charlie's request, to seek her advice about decorating the church so that she did not feel too left out. The air of festivity brightened the village as coloured lights, stars and streamers were captured in windows. The shop was busy selling supplies of mistletoe, sprigs of holly and Christmas trees. The Dog and Duck was fully booked up for Christmas dinners, and Edna could hear the sound of carol singers practising for the church choir.

—m—

Christmas Day came with a hard frost that gripped the deep ruts of the lane to the main road. The surrounding fields glistened with a covering of ice crystals. Robert and Maggie were packed with the other villagers into the small Norman church. They nodded to Edna and Charlie in their privileged position of a front row pew. Steam rose in the air from dampened clothes as warmth from the gas heaters penetrated the congregation. The vicar beamed with delight, giving Edna a special welcome, and gave thanks for the work done to decorate the tree and the church. The first carol was sung with such enthusiasm by the choir and congregation that Maggie felt overwhelmed with happiness. The smallest children were then asked to stand in front of the congregation and sing 'Away in a Manger' and, like many, Maggie felt moved to tears. She noticed James jumping up and down beside Angela, pointing eagerly at the packed toys beneath the tree. He was well now and a very active toddler. She leant forward to hear Angela whispering to him, 'They're not for you darling, they're for the poorly children in the hospital."

"Can I be poorly, mummy?" a little girl sitting next to him asked. Angela tried to hush them but James had other ideas. He started to chatter eagerly and soon both children had the giggles and were trying to clamber under and over the pew as Angela, embarrassed, prepared to leave.

"Please don't go." The vicar leaned forward from the pulpit. "You sit still, James and Abigail and I'll tell you both a story.

Startled by the grownup's attention the two children remained motionless as the vicar addressed his short sermon directly at them. He then interspersed several of his own comments on the state of the modern world with questions to other children. Parents beamed when their offspring answered correctly. The congregation, so sparse at most services throughout the year, basked in the warmth the vicar created and sang the familiar carols with enthusiasm. Finally, with a general sense of well-being, the congregation filtered slowly out into the winter chill.

The vicar patted James on his head, "You were a very good boy, and I'll give you a gold star when you come to Sunday school next year." James jumped for joy; like all his little friends he loved getting gold stars and stickers.

Most of the villagers wandered over to the pub after the service, as Maggie and Robert hurried back home to prepare for their visitors. Robert was in charge of the dinner and Maggie knowing how much he enjoyed entertaining had let him spend most of Christmas Eve preparing vegetables and stuffing the turkey. She had been quite content to leave him to it. He opened the champagne as Maggie prepared the table and Charlie and Edna arrived to find them in a very cheerful mood.

That evening Robert, half asleep, gazed at the dying embers of the fire and reflected on the pleasure it had given them to entertain their elderly friends. Charlie and Edna had left after the Queen's speech. He chuckled, "You know, darling, I think those two should move in together, even Edna's appreciated how much Charlie cared for her after she was attacked."

"Funny, I've been thinking the same. He really does seem to love her, doesn't he?" Maggie smiled, "I'm glad she managed to eat with her new teeth. Did you notice how he helped her pull the crackers, and he had his hand on her arm throughout the speech. Charlie doesn't approve of 'living in sin' though, it'll have to be a proper wedding. I can't imagine Edna in a wedding dress."

"That would be good, how about you and Angela as bridesmaids? Can't you just see yourself? I can be best man, and James could be a page boy!"

Maggie chuckled; they were both weary and had consumed rather too much champagne. "I think they'll want the locals, not us townies. After all we only make changes –," Maggie knew she sounded tipsy and Robert started to choke, as both started crying with laughter.

"Oh my, we need some fresh air." Robert made for the door.

"Hey, wait, let's go round the woods." Maggie, still giggling dragged on her boots. It was very cold as they buttoned up their coats and headed down the lane, frost gleamed in the ditches like sprinkled stardust. They opened the field gate and skirted across the meadow, clambering over the stile toward the thick woodland behind the cottage. Pheasants warned noisily in the trees, a solitary Muntjak broke cover, and a small group of roe deer bounded away. The sun was setting, and the sky appeared brush stroked in scarlet as the two of them walked towards it, arms entwined. Deep in the woods tiny shafts of light pierced the branches and filtered on to the small lake. They were in their favourite spot surrounded by the tunnels of a badger's sett.

"Babes in the wood." Maggie cuddled closer to Robert. "If we keep still and don't make a sound we just might see them this time."

"Hush then."

—m—

Charlie rubbed his knees and eased his stiffened body to a standing position. His head ached. Not used to champagne, he thought; funny stuff, don't know why people make such a fuss about it, "Give me a drop of carrot whisky any day, eh Mary?" he said glancing at the photo on the mantelpiece. Charlie felt her presence in the room as he often did and found it comforting. The light was failing fast as he put the kettle on the stove and filled a fresh pipe. Edna had gone off in a taxi and would spend the rest of Christmas with her niece.

He picked up a card. 'Season's greetings, trust you are well, we are. Your ever loving son'. He gazed at the picture on the front, of a snowman. "Poor bloke hasn't even got a pipe," he muttered. They hadn't written 'wish you were here'. Not a word about visiting or inviting Charlie up North. The relationship had altered when his son's new girlfriend had dissuaded him from visiting Mary during her illness and he had only just made it to her funeral. "Never cared about us did they, love?" He tore the card into tiny pieces and dropped it in the hearth. "Good riddance. Better fill this up 'fore it's dark," he spoke aloud, glancing inside the stove and picking up the coal scuttle.

Charlie stood on his doorstep and sniffed – he could smell smoke. Chimney on fire somewhere he thought, as he made his way round the cottage to the coal bunker.

It had been a beautiful evening as the last rays of the sun glowed red in the woods, the trees starkly silhouetted against the remaining light. He stood looking at the woods, relishing the distant view and sniffed again. The smell of smoke was coming from down the lane and there was only one cottage in that direction, something was not quite right. Charlie's heart lurched as he hurried inside to phone Robert and Maggie. There was no answer. Back outside he could hear a distant crackling sound, the smell of smoke was getting stronger. Then a flame exploded into the air above their cottage about thirty yards away, the smoke spiralling and the crackling getting louder. He knew now where it was coming from – their thatched roof. Panicking, he started up the lane, then steadied himself and hurried back to his kitchen, 'Now you think sensibly, Charlie Watt, call the fire brigade.' He dialled 999.

—※—

Robert pulled Maggie to her feet. "I'm sure these animals can smell us, that's why we never see them. I'm frozen stiff, come on, darling," he said. Maggie realised they'd both fallen asleep whilst waiting once more for the badgers to show themselves.

"I'm sober anyway. Let's go and watch the box."

Maggie hugged Robert's arm as they felt their way back through the darkened wood. "Great way to spend Christmas. Ouch! We should have brought a torch for goodness sake," she said, tripping awkwardly as the two of them slipped on the carpet of wet leaves. "Damn. All we need is broken legs. You know, I often come here on my own, hoping to see a fox, or the badgers. Watch out, Rob, there are rabbit holes everywhere, hang on I'm caught up here." She picked at the brambles in the gloom. "Can you hear bells ringing?"

As they approached the meadow, they saw them, two vehicles in the lane, headlights blazing and voices shouting above the noise.

"Oh, my God, I think it's the cottage, our cottage, look there's smoke." Robert started to run across the meadow. "They're fire engines, where the hell's the fire?"

Maggie tried to keep up but felt dizzy and breathless, "Hurry, Robert, you go on. I'll catch you up, run, quick, run."

They were both tripping and stumbling towards the lights. A third fire engine turned in to the lane. As they reached the field gate they could see the smoke and flames clawing at the sky, hear the snapping crackle of their burning thatch. Maggie, shaking and terrified, wanted to be sick.

"Stay here." Robert stopped her at the gate. "I think you should go to Charlie's darling."

"No, I'm coming with you, I've got to see what's happening."

Nut Tree Cottage was surrounded by firemen, hoses snaking in every direction across the lawn. The fire engines throbbed, mirroring the throbbing fear in Maggie's own heart as they ran to the back of the cottage.

"You're bloody lucky mate, that's all I can say." The leading fire fighter, called Ray, pulled Robert aside and showed him how the embers from the wood stove had most likely caused the fire to re-ignite and sparks from the chimney had caught the thatch. "Your front door was wide open, as if you'd left in a hurry. The draught set the fire up again nicely. If your neighbour hadn't realised what was happening, you'd have lost the ruddy lot."

"Charlie, our neighbour got hold of you?"

"Yes, poor old bugger nearly had a heart attack. One of my men is seeing to him now. The thatch at that end will need stripping back and redoing but the rest of the house is in one piece. We'll fix a tarpaulin up 'fore we go. Bit muddy and messy I'm afraid, but we had to act fast. It could have been a lot lot worse."

"Thank you. We really can't thank you enough. Maggie, d'you want to go and see how Charlie is?"

Maggie was still shaking uncontrollably as Ray put his hand on her shoulder, "Let that wait. Could do with a cup of tea if you've got one going, love. Your kitchen's okay and I see the Aga's pumping out a fair bit of heat as well."

The firemen were a jovial lot and despite the call out interrupting their own Christmas celebrations they were in no hurry to leave until Ray was satisfied that the fire was out and a makeshift tarpaulin was covering the end of the cottage. As soon as the last engine had gone Robert hurried along the lane to check on Charlie and thank him whilst Maggie stayed to survey the damage. He returned fifteen minutes later.

"He's fine, darling, just glad we're ok. Gave me a shot of whisky, great stuff. Thank goodness he realised what was happening, it really doesn't bear thinking about what could have happened here. It's always been Charlie's greatest fear he said, as we're both thatched."

"At least we're all in one piece." Maggie choked on the words, near to tears. "I suppose it's taught us some sort of lesson. I've never been so scared and, as you say, the worst bit is imagining what might have happened."

"Well it didn't. You know I spoke to your mother yesterday and said I wouldn't be visiting that furniture showroom up in Leeds now so I won't see her over the New Year. You could go up on your own if you like, while I sort out the mess here?"

"I think we'd better sort the mess out together. The smell's the worst."

"I rather thought you'd say that."

"Angela rang, the whole village heard the engines of course and a lot of them have been checking on Charlie, thinking it was his cottage," Maggie said. "She wants us to go and sleep there tonight. I said we'd be alright here."

"I'd rather stay here, so 'Happy Christmas'," he whispered, hugging her. "We've got each other, no lives lost, and that's really all that matters, darling."

CHAPTER 11

NEW APPROACH

Maggie huddled behind a magazine in the corner of the doctor's waiting room. It was filling up with patients and she had no desire to talk to anyone, least of all any of the parents she knew. A conversation about the baby she had last visited would cause her even more distress. Nothing seemed to matter now. A tear trickled down her cheek as she gazed at the blurred writing on the page in front of her.

"Can I help? Sorry, I didn't mean to make you jump, it's just that you looked so unhappy, Maggie. I must say your thatch looks fine now it's been redone, I saw it yesterday. Terrible thing the fire, such a shock." Maggie acknowledged Dawn Creasey. "I can sit somewhere else, dear."

"I'm alright, really, thank you, just tired. How's Kate?"

"She's fine, getting on with her studies, needs a little boost every now and then that's all. She goes riding at the weekends with her boyfriend I'm pleased to say. I don't think she'll ever get another horse though, not to own I mean. I don't think she could bear that." She looked round at the waiting room. "Busy today isn't it? My doctor's running twenty minutes late, the receptionist said, or muttered, I should say. She's a funny one that girl, always a bit surly, no need to be rude is there?" She picked up the magazine Maggie had been holding. "Finished this, dear?"

"Yes."

'MAGGIE EDWARDS PLEASE. MAGGIE EDWARDS FOR DOCTOR SOUTHGATE.'

Maggie breathed a sigh of relief. She liked Dawn but was in no mood to chat and she knew Dawn had a tendency to gossip to Edna, who soon spread every word around the village.

Dr Southgate took hold of Maggie's hand, "I think it might be a good idea to refer you, young lady. There's a good chap I know in Cambridge who's been leading the research they're doing into recurrent miscarriage."

"I'll see anyone now, Doctor. I knew I was pregnant and didn't bother to do any tests, I guess I'm about eight or nine weeks?"

"Can't be sure but I'll send you in, if the bleeding persists. Haven't needed a scrape before have you?"

"No."

Doctor Southgate was the senior partner in the practice. A kind man of the old school who never hurried a consultation. He looked at her thoughtfully before he spoke again, "There can be many reasons why this happens, as you well know, Maggie. I realise it's too easy to say it's nature's way or that you should have avoided intercourse. The new research is quite promising so I think in your case it would be very helpful to investigate the possible cause a bit more." He patted her arm in a fatherly way and walked round his desk as she rose to leave. "Would you like to discuss anything with our counsellor, Maggie? I know how low you feel just now."

Maggie fought the tears welling up again as he put his arm round her shoulders.

"Don't want to give you any happy pills my dear, but I think you need to take a couple of weeks off. Think about it, you might like to bring Robert with you for your next appointment. You both need to talk this through."

"I'll be okay, thanks."

—⁓—

Maggie stared at her swollen red eyes in the bathroom mirror. She had cried herself to sleep the night before. Robert was due home late so the puffiness should have gone by then. She would tell him of course. They had comforted each other on Christmas night after the thatch fire, by making love. She must have conceived then. Now she had that familiar feeling of desperation. She wanted a baby so much it was gnawing away at her every day. All her friends, apart from her sister, seemed to find keeping babies so easy. And was it really necessary to put so many adverts on television about nappies? Did every radio programme have to be about starting a family? Did every book she read have to have a pregnant woman in it? It was all so unfair. Even her work which she'd always loved was beginning to upset her. She coped with delivering other peoples' babies, but now she found herself actually feeling envious and resentful.

"It'll be so nice to have you here dear, it's ages since we saw you. How is it by the way, the roof I mean?"

Maggie let her mother chatter away on the telephone about the fire and thatch repair, mumbling a reply every now and then. It was balm to hear her voice. A strange longing to be a little girl again often overwhelmed her when she heard her mother talking gently; she was so pleased she'd decided to go back home for a few days. "Mummy –,"

"Yes dear, what did you say dear?"

"I've forgotten. I'll see you Saturday,' bye now."

The train rattled along past fields of sheep and newborn lambs. Maggie gazed out of the window. Spring and a world bursting with new life, she reflected. "Every creature on earth is managing to propagate the species except me, useless Maggie Edwards."

Robert had been upset with her for not telling him about this latest pregnancy. He had encouraged her to go home to her mother and sister and had seen her off that morning in a state of excitement about how busy he was at work, new openings in Europe, going to meet clients in Brussels at the weekend.

"Stay as long as you like darling. I've got a conference in Prague after the Brussels trip. It's all taking off over there. We need to get one shot ahead in Europe."

Maggie found his enthusiasm for his work annoying. "I don't think you care about me at all."

"Come on, you know that's not true. It's business I'm afraid, can't ignore it. Frank is really pushing me to clinch these contracts."

"I thought we moved here to make babies."

"Oh Maggie, come on love, that's just silly." Robert seized her arm, "Listen to me, please stop crying. I love you very much and I want a baby too. At the moment you're not pregnant, and it looks as if we need to get hold of good advice. When I come back we'll see that specialist in Cambridge."

Maggie thought back to the office party when Frank Sutton had whispered in her ear about Robert being a very reliable director and that his faith in him had been more than justified. After that show of praise he had left his hand lingering rather too long on her thigh, she recalled resentfully.

Elizabeth Edwards took one look at her daughter standing outside the station, and decided that this week would be devoted to some extra special mothering of her own.

It was a short drive to the house in the small village in the Lake District which had been Maggie's home since childhood and where her father had died, following a stroke, three years before.

"Eleanor has found herself another man. She'll be staying with him this week so I don't think she'll get over here." Elizabeth said, as they unloaded the car.

"Oh, that's a pity, I really wanted to see her." Maggie said.

"Well, I've got you to myself which is a real treat for me. Now you get unpacked while I get supper ready."

She left Maggie to settle in her old bedroom where there were strong reminders of her childhood. Dolls and books unmoved, as if in wait. Later Elizabeth listened while her daughter unburdened herself, in between serving up too much cottage pie.

"Mum I'm not starving." Maggie's protests were in vain.

"You don't look to me as if you've had a proper meal in months. Eat it all up." Elizabeth chided.

Maggie knew her mother was firmly of the view that she should get married and give up work in order to concentrate on having a baby. She was grateful that her mother was choosing diplomacy this time, as she basked in being treated like a child. Robert phoned regularly to see if she was feeling better and she told him that she was revelling in being mothered once more.

—◊—

A fortnight later it was time to return, she heard she was needed due to staff shortages. Hardly had Maggie set foot back in Nut Tree cottage before Charlie arrived and presented her with some fresh cut vegetables.

"Saw you go past. The hens are doing grand," he said proudly. "Just look at the size of this one." He produced a large brown egg from his pocket. "Have that for your tea, girl," he said, placing a box containing half a dozen more on the draining board.

"Charlie my mum's been spoiling me rotten for two weeks, so don't you start."

"Well, you go careful," he said, "it's none of my business and I know I shouldn't say this but I've seen you unhappy, and it's my guess you're still hankering after a baby, so I was wondering whether you might like a little pup?"

"A what? A pup?"

"A puppy. Dawn Creasey's neighbour put an advert in Edna's window. Seems like the farmer's terrier got at her Labrador. There'll be pups needing a good home." He slurped loudly on the mug of tea.

Maggie looked bewildered, "Charlie it's a baby I want. I've never owned a dog in my life."

"It'd be good company, that's all." He started twisting his cap in his hand before slapping it on his head. Sucking on his pipe he heaved himself out of the chair and moved to the kitchen door,

"Seen the tadpoles? Lots of frog spawn in that pond this year." He lumbered off towards the gate, "Enjoy them eggs."

Maggie smiled to herself. Darling Charlie, just wanting to help. It would be something to cuddle, she supposed...'

CHAPTER 12

RAPID DESCENT

Another staff shortage at the hospital and a plea to work an extra shift was not what Maggie had planned for Saturday night. She was looking forward to a meal with Robert at the Dog and Duck, expecting Angela to join them. Unfortunately, her colleague Susan, persuaded her otherwise; as she always did.

"We really are short tonight, Maggie. Be a dear, we can catch up on all the news, if we get a break."

It was sheeting with rain as Maggie opened the garage doors. Soaked and irritated she drove the car through deep puddles in the lane, tooting her usual signal as she passed Charlie's cottage.

The labour ward was a war zone. Harassed midwives acknowledged her briefly and Sue gabbled instructions down the phone. The information board indicated that there was a baby being born, or about to be born in every room. Complications were listed and one mother was on her way to theatre for caesarean section. A doctor and a registrar argued quietly at the desk while a large heavily pregnant woman shuffled past, her flimsy dressing gown partially covering her large bulk.

"I need a fag," she muttered, disappearing in the direction of the waiting room.

"You really shouldn't, it's not allowed in here," said Maggie hurrying after her.

"Stop me then."

Duly rebuffed, Maggie returned to the main desk.

Susan finished her phone call and gave Maggie a quick hug, "Thanks for coming in, you're a star. Don't tell me, I saw you speaking to Carol, she's not worth the hassle. She's your patient by the way, it's her sixth, so it should be quite straight forward, trouble is we haven't got a room for her at the moment."

"Well thanks a lot! She doesn't look as if she's in labour though, has she been assessed yet?"

"Difficult to tell, she's had a few twinges and a bit of a show. Told me she wouldn't have any internals, and she'd let me know when the baby was coming. Last one apparently dropped out in the Co-op!" Susan chuckled. "Nothing to worry about, we checked everything when she arrived, much to her disgust. The baby's fine."

"Who sent her in?"

"The district midwife 'cos she couldn't find a heartbeat and can't come in herself, she's busy with a home birth. Carol told her that the baby didn't seem to move much. With all that flesh it's difficult to find anything."

Maggie returned to the smoke filled waiting room to properly introduce herself.

"Should have let me have it at home, trouble is I bleed like a stuck pig. The Co-op looked like a bloody slaughter house last time round." Carol coughed violently, clutching at her stomach.

"Something for me to look forward to then?" Maggie laughed.

Carol coughed again and almost choked. "Bloody awful fags, these, he knows I don't like 'em tipped. I could do with a drink."

"I'll get you a cup of tea. Now ring this buzzer if you feel anything's happening. What about your husband? Is he coming in?"

"Not my Gary, he's on the taxis, the kids are with his mum. I'll be ok."

"I've got another lady in early labour to look after, Carol, but I'm not far away. I just need to check on that baby again and we'll get you in to a room as soon as possible.

Midnight came and went with Carol demanding to be allowed back home. "My hubby's finished his shift now, he can easily come and get me."

Maggie watched her prowl up and down the hospital corridor, stopping every now and then for another surreptitious smoke. "If that doctor doesn't come and say I can go, I'm going anyway." It was early morning and they were arm in arm ambling back to the room that Carol had finally been allotted when she suddenly stopped still. "Christ, it's coming, mate."

A gush of fluid hit the floor. Maggie, far from a buzzer, yelled for help at the top of her voice as she urged Carol to lie down. As she did so Maggie was just in time to catch the baby that shot like a canon ball in to her out stretched hands. Carol was convulsed with laughter as Maggie carefully placed the baby boy onto her stomach where he lurched like a small boat in a storm-tossed sea, snorting and snuffling on the vast pink fleshy cushion. "Bugger me, beat your brother that time, matey."

Midwives appeared from nowhere as the separated afterbirth landed with equal speed and accuracy in a well-placed kidney dish.

"Watch out she's liable to bleed," Maggie urged as helping hands loaded mother and baby on to a padded wheelchair and the baby began crying lustily; much to Maggie's relief.

At the end of the corridor a young couple stood transfixed amid the commotion, having arrived for the birth of their first baby.

"You'd better scarper before they deliver yours in the kitchen," Carol hooted as she was wheeled past.

Carol did not bleed, and before dawn Maggie waved 'goodbye' to her and baby, Freddy. Gary taxied them home to join the rest of their brood. Carol had insisted on discharging herself against the wishes of Sue and the duty doctor.

It was quiet in the labour ward and as dawn broke Maggie was despatched to a busy post natal ward, where she sat in the nursery and cuddled a baby who'd been fretful since birth. The mother was disinterested, and had no wish to feed her baby, Daniel. Maggie pacified him with a small amount of bottled milk. The trusting gaze and the tight grip the baby had on her finger stirred strong emotions, making her want to cry.

"Can't understand it can you, Maggie? She should be grateful she's got a healthy baby at all," muttered Karen, a young nursery nurse busy changing another. "Says she wanted a girl because she's got three boys already. She won't even hold him, it makes me really mad."

Maggie loved the distinctive new born smell of baby Daniel as she put him up on her shoulder, gently patting his back. This and the soft downy cheek pressed against her own brought her to tears.

An idea was forming in her mind that made her tremble. What if she took this baby home with her? The mother wouldn't care; she had rejected him. She had access to food and clothes, she had the ability to care for this little boy. She began to think of other cases of child abduction, but this was different. This mother didn't want her baby, so why should Maggie not have him? She knew how irrational she was being but it felt so unfair. Here she was, desperate to have a baby, losing every child she managed to conceive, and here was this mother who couldn't even be bothered to look at her own small son because he wasn't the little girl she'd ordered. It was easy. She would walk down the corridor, tell Karen she was going to see Susan in the labour ward, pick up her things in the locker room, and walk out. Simple. It was questionable whether anyone would challenge her, after all the midwives were always walking around with babies in their arms en route to somewhere. She held the baby tightly now wrapped in extra blankets and picked up her bag in which she quickly secreted several nappies and a supply of milk powder.

Susan opened the nursery door, "Oh there you are Maggie, you wouldn't be a dear and come back to the labour ward would you? Sorry, I know you like cuddling the babes. By the way Karen told me to tell you that Daniel's mother is asking to have him now. It seems she's over not wanting him and is feeling ashamed of herself. Karen will take him for you. I'd be really pleased if you could scrub up for a section that's just coming in."

Maggie was barely able to breathe and hoped Susan would not notice she was trembling.

"Hey are you all right Maggie? Sit down a minute." Sue knelt down in front of the chair. "You've gone very white. Here, give me the baby."

"No I'm all right, really I am. Just rather tired." Maggie whispered.

Susan gathered Daniel in her arms, "I think he's filled his nappy, Karen can change him and take off some of these blankets, he's far too hot." She knelt down again, "Look, go and have a cup of tea or coffee, we don't need you for another half hour, eat something too. The registrar is coming back at six, that'll give you time and then you'll feel better. You know we've still not had that natter have we. I have to get back, Maggie, so I'll see you shortly."

Maggie drank some water and tried breathing deeply in the way she taught her mothers in class, anything to calm herself down. Did she really think she could have taken Daniel? Could she really have done something so dreadful? Leaving Karen with baby Daniel she went to boil the kettle in the ward kitchen. Her throat was dry but the trembling ceased, as she clung to the hot sweet plastic mug of coffee.

CHAPTER 13
CUPBOARD LOVE

Maggie fondled the blonde puppy, its warm coat soft to her touch. Trusting eyes gazed at her with curiosity, a tiny pink tongue licked her hand.

"Trudy, my old bitch, is getting a bit fed up with them now," smiled Linda Clark, the Creasey's next door neighbour, as she rearranged the remaining sleepy heap of puppies. "Wonder they don't smother each other more often; sorry to say the littlest did get squashed the first night."

"Oh dear, how awful," said Maggie, instinctively tightening her hold. "Did she realise what had happened?"

"Not really, well not that she was too fussed about it. One less for me to home as well. I've found places for all these five, except the little chap you've got there. Trudy's getting on a bit you see."

"You know, Linda, I've never had a dog in my life."

"Need one round here, love, they make good company. You'll have to walk it mind, that one's getting long legs on it. You can have it for nothing if you like. I just need to know he's got a good home. I dare say I'd take him back if you really couldn't manage."

"I know nothing about feeding them, or anything."

"You'll soon learn if you go to puppy training classes. They have a class at the village hall here every two weeks. Anyway I can always tell you anything you need to know."

Maggie bent down and tucked the puppy in next to its mother. "Poor Mum. She does look a bit fed up, doesn't she?"

"Well, she's had three litters and this lot were a mistake. The terrier from the farm got to her. She hasn't really had time to get over the last lot have you, Trudy?" Linda stroked the Labrador gently. "So what d'you think then? Charlie said he'd watch out for him if you got stuck on duty."

Maggie bent down again, "I'll need to have a think about it. Thanks very much for showing them to me," she said, preparing to leave and hesitating at the door. She looked back at the puppy she'd been holding, who was trying hard to clamber up the side of the bed by standing on his mother's head.

"You see," Linda said. "He doesn't want you to go."

The puppy, now hanging over the side by its front paws started to whimper.

Maggie, overwhelmed with a feeling of tenderness, retraced her steps and stooped down. "Okay, you win," she said.

—⁂—

Robert settled in to the armchair, switched on the television and waited for the weather forecast for the next day. It was mild with rain in the West; he could relax. He was leaving early in the morning for Scotland, as Frank Sutton had been complaining about some of the company reps and he urgently needed to sort their problems out. Business was not as good as it could be up North, but sleep overtook him as he planned his first visit.

Maggie, returning from an evening visit, nudged him awake,

"Darling, keep very still, I've got something to show you."

Robert was used to Maggie's habit of springing surprises on him lately, mainly new clothes, encouraged by Angela. Her desire to make love every other night had diminished, much to his relief, for he was not in the mood and needed an early night.

"Close your eyes." Maggie had fed the puppy and hidden him in the cupboard under the stairs while she visited a new mother with feeding problems. Tucked in a cosy bed with a small hot water bottle he had slept for over two hours. "Meet Woody!"

"Woody?"

"Isn't he cute, darling?" she said, placing the sleepy puppy on his lap, "It's all Charlie's fault, he suggested having him, and the poor little thing had no home to go to." She was babbling now. "He's only ten weeks old, half Labrador and half terrier, and we're booked in to classes next week in the village hall. Charlie says he can stay at his place if I'm on duty, and he can sleep here, in the kitchen next to the boiler, and he'll be fine after a few days. He just needs a ticking clock and a hot water bottle and he'll be all snug and cosy." Maggie stopped to draw breath as Woody, now being held at arm's length by Robert, peed in mid-air.

"You do like him, don't you? Please say you do." Maggie mopped up the small wet patch and knelt in front of Robert. "You don't seem very surprised; did Charlie tell you about his reasons for suggesting we had a puppy?"

"Why Woody?" said Robert, secretly delighted that he and Charlie's ruse had apparently worked. They had discussed the idea together several times since the puppies had been born. "Charlie did mention something about puppies for sale last week."

"The name just sort of came to me."

"If it helps you, darling, then I'm all for it."

The puppy gazed up at Robert, snuggled his head under the thick cardigan, and closed his eyes.

Woody was soon the centre of attention at Nut Tree Cottage, but the toilet training was not going well. Small puddles appeared, soaking in to the tiles and carpets. Sheets of newspaper littered the floors.

Robert became increasingly exasperated as he tripped over chew bones and squeaky toys and slithered across the kitchen tiles. "Don't they teach them anything in classes, Maggie?"

"It's my fault, he only seems to lose control here. He's top of the class for 'sits'."

Maggie thought her heart would break when Woody had cried and whimpered the first night they had left him alone in the kitchen, but Robert had been the first to give in and allow the dog in to the bedroom.

Woody soon became Maggie's shadow. He delighted her when he outshone the others in his class with a trick she had taught him. He was learning to obey the simple commands, amply rewarded by treats. His certificate for completing the beginner's course was proudly displayed on the kitchen wall. Given the all clear to go for walks beyond the confines of the garden, Woody soon learnt the route to Charlie's; and more treats.

Woody was excited by everything the outside world had to offer. They found footpaths and bridleways and met other dog owners, new friends. They encountered dogs with different temperaments; shy, timid, or over friendly, some aggressive and even muzzled. Mrs Griffiths passed them daily on her set walk, she and her small blind cairn terrier, reliant on each other. "Got the time, dear?" was her regular refrain. A young man often sprinted past with his 'rescued' grey hound. "Have you seen a puddle anywhere?" he called, indicating his thirsty dog. The major's wife, Mrs Gibson, hung on to what appeared to be half the canine world, with a tiny dachshund lording it over the pack, as Woody shrank behind Maggie's legs.

Maggie developed favourite routes, along hedgerows and ancient tracks; the rise and fall of the land taking her to different vistas where she studied the drama of the skies above them; the cloud formations captivating her interest. New walkers appeared, strangers to the village, to gather in the late summer harvest of sloes, elderberries, blackberries and mushrooms. Woody scented the rabbits and deer and as the alarmed partridge and pheasants took off like fighter planes, Maggie learnt to take firmer control of the dog.

One late afternoon, walking past the terrace of houses where Jacky Richards lived, Maggie saw her gathering in some washing.

"Nice dog that," Jacky said, as Maggie approached. She patted Woody, whose lead wrapped round Maggie's legs as he retreated from her whining Alsatian, straining at the end of its chain next to the house.

Maggie looked at the sad eyes of the older dog, its tail wagging hopefully at the cowering Woody.

Jacky smiled, "I do bring him inside if the weather gets rough. Len would never have him indoors though."

"How is Len?"

"Doing his time. He's not complaining, he should get parole if he keeps out of trouble. Got time for a cup of tea?"

"I'll make time, Jacky. How's your grandchild? Maggie picked up Woody and carried him in to the kitchen, as the cat took flight between her legs, and disappeared.

"Oh, she's a lovely little thing. Tracy and my Jim are well

settled in their council flat in Waldersby."

The place was as Maggie had last seen it when she had attended Tracy in labour. The draining board groaned under a pile of dirty dishes, ashtrays spilled their contents on to the sticky plastic tablecloth. Piles of magazines spilled off the edge of the table. Grime and a smell of damp added to the unkempt surroundings. As Jacky made a space for her on the old settee, her arms jangling with bangles as she moved, Maggie observed her heavily applied make up and smelt her sickly perfume.

"I hear you're working at the Dog and Duck?"

"Yeah, doing a few evenings in the bar." Jacky looked uncomfortable. "I need the money."

"I'm sorry. It must be really awful for you on your own here too," said Maggie. "Are the neighbours friendly?"

"Not really, they keep themselves to themselves. Excuse the mess, this place needs doing up a bit," she said, moving a pile of newspapers on to the floor. "The council keep saying they're coming to put in a new boiler and do some paint work, but they never turn up, so I don't bother. I quite like my own company and the kids call by. The old people complained to Len about the garden but they leave me alone. Joan, at the end house, brought me some veg from her garden the other night." Jacky poured the tea and lit another cigarette. "Len's not that sorry for that old cow from the shop you know, despite his sentence. She said some bad things about our boy after the accident. She had no call to speak badly of him. He'd done some petty crime, I know, and I clipped him round the ear more than once, I can tell you. Dying like that though, that's what's really eating away at me."

"I can't imagine how you must feel about losing your son in such a terrible way. It must be dreadful for you both." Maggie stumbled over the words, anxious not to re-awaken the memories of that tragic scene. "Am I holding you up?'

"Don't mind if I do a bit of ironing, do you?" Jacky spread a cloth on the table. "I'm working tonight." She stubbed out her cigarette and handed Maggie a mug of tea. "So what made you get a dog then?"

"Charlie, my neighbour suggested it. You see, Robert and I have been trying hard for a baby. I manage to get pregnant but then I lose them. I've had four miscarriages now."

"Blimey, four, that's not fair. So what's that to do with a dog?"

"I think Charlie thought I needed something to love." Maggie stroked the soft head of Woody nestled in her lap. "I must say I didn't realise just how much this little chap would mean to me. He follows me everywhere, and I'm getting to know this area well by walking. I've also lost a lot of weight, which won't do me any harm."

"Funny, you being a midwife and not able to have a baby. Well, I don't mean funny but you know what I mean. Never had any problems myself, shelled them like peas when my time came. Nearly didn't make it to the hospital for the last one." Jacky dragged on another cigarette and peered at Maggie through the veil of smoke. "So what are they going to do about it?"

"Nothing they can do really, there's research going on but it's not going to help us right now." Maggie relaxed and found herself enjoying the company of the older woman, the way she listened to every word.

The light was fading as she looked at her watch.

"Gosh, is that the time? We must get going in a minute." Maggie nudged the sleeping dog. "Thank you for listening, Jacky, it's been a real help to get things off my chest."

"Any time, love. Anytime."

"I'm going to the Parish Council meeting tonight, to see how things are progressing with the speed limit. Charlie Watt always comes with me just to have a go at the Major. If Robert's back we might call in at the pub after. He's so busy these days, travelling all over the place."

"What's his job then?"

"He's a director of Suttons Scenario in Waldersby, the soft furnishing company, that's what brought us here. He really loves his job."

"I know Frank Sutton's, one of my boys worked there for a bit." Jacky opened the back door to shout at the whining Alsatian. "He's a good bloke to work for."

Maggie suddenly felt a need to confide in Jacky again. She felt that she would keep a confidence. The thought of her night in the hospital the week before and remembering that she really had wanted to steal a baby from the ward haunted her still. She had been unable to confide in Robert; she didn't want him to know how desperate she had felt that night; he blamed himself enough for their inability to have a family. Jacky would understand and she needed to tell some-one.

"If I tell you something, will you keep it a secret? I would hate anyone to know. Only I've kept this to myself for so long," Maggie said quietly.

Jacky offered her the pack of cigarettes. "Want one?"

"No, no, thanks."

"Go on, then, what else d'you want to tell me."

Maggie told her what she had become close to doing at the hospital; Jacky listened carefully, occasionally blowing smoke out of the side of her mouth in the direction of the open window.

"So you see," Maggie ended, "I could have been joining your Len and doing time myself. I can't say whether I would have gone beyond the hospital entrance. I really don't know what came over me."

"I can understand it." Jacky turned off the iron. "I can, love, really." She sat down next to Maggie and put her arm around her shoulder. "If it's made you feel better to get it out then that's all right by me. You can have a bloody good cry, love."

The heavy perfume and smell of tobacco were almost suffocating, as Jacky held her tightly. "Does no good to bottle things up. Anyhow, you didn't take that baby and no one's any the wiser. You best forget it, if you ask me and I'm no expert on these things but I do hear that if you stop thinking about something all the time, it can just happen, like getting pregnant. You hear about women adopting babies and then suddenly they are in the family way, after years of trying. P'raps if you get pregnant again you should just ignore it and it might hang on longer. Stands to reason you wanted that little baby, its own mother not caring like that."

Maggie wept at the relief of having told this comparative stranger about something she knew she could not divulge at home. Some of the guilt was fading and Woody, anxious to get going was jumping up eagerly.

"Anytime you want to have a little chat you come by here. I won't tell a soul, and if it helps, I'll gladly listen."

Maggie's step was lighter as they left, a burden had been lifted. She continued her walk along the old cart track and skirted the edge of the woods. Jacky had understood and made no judgement. Maggie quickened her pace, one day she would tell Robert also, but not yet.

CHAPTER 14

PAROCHIAL AFFAIRS

Preparations for the church fete were underway. Maggie had agreed to run a tombola stall with Angela, giving them another means to get to know more local residents. Maggie called at every house and cottage, with Woody in tow. She collected bottles and tins, and any unwanted gifts, and was easily drawn in to conversation at each front door. Kate Creasey, virtually recovered from the accident, had apparently fallen in love with her college tutor. Kate's mother, Dawn, tut tutted about the blossoming relationship. The boyfriend had a sports car that roared into life in the small hours, disturbing all their neighbours, she told Maggie. Kate, Dawn sighed, excluded her parents whenever he came, disappearing in to the back room, to get up to goodness knows what.

"He's far too old for her," Dawn muttered crossly.

Maggie grasped the tins of baked beans being offered. "Edna said you liked him."

"I did when he was just her tutor but I don't like to think he's taking advantage of our girl. Last thing we need is her pregnant before she finishes her studies."

"Oh, Dawn, you trust her more than that surely, Kate's not that irresponsible."

Maggie, irritated by the older woman's suspicious nature, thanked her and moved on to her neighbour.

"We're off to Manchester tomorrow, our daughter's got a 2:1. Never thought she had it in her," smiled Mrs Nelson, handing Maggie more unused tins, soups this time.

"Well, don't tell her that, will you?" said Maggie.

"We won't, dear, we're so very proud of her. Dad's over the moon, aren't you my love?" Mr Nelson smiled and proffered Maggie some bottles of his home made wine.

As she circled the village, Maggie listened to complaints about the local council, trouble with the dustbin men and the litter they dropped, noisy barking dogs, nosy neighbours, the postman's late deliveries, the milkman missing a round, too many squirrels in the gardens and moles in the lawns. Top of the list were speeding motorists, and unsatisfactory septic tanks. Several villagers knew of Maggie's nursing background, so discussions also developed about minor ailments. Old operation scars were revealed, socks hitched up, shirts unbuttoned. When the women discovered she was a midwife she was treated to long accounts of their labours.

The more interested Maggie appeared the more prizes she got, she also began to get the feeling that having supported the villagers in front of the parish council on the need for a speed limit, the villagers hoped she would take on more of their complaints. They'll be suggesting I become a parish councillor next, she thought.

Maggie compared her collection with Angela and was delighted with the approval of the fete committee.

"I'm beginning to feel we belong here at last," said Angela. "It's a nice feeling."

The day of the fete was bright and sunny. Crowds swarmed around the vicarage gardens, heading for the tearoom, the various stalls, and pony rides. The vicar succumbed to being bombed with wet sponges in the stocks, the Waldersby High School band played until it was time to call the raffle. Only then did the rain come down.

"Charlie, that was good fun, our stall was a great draw." Maggie walked home with Woody and Charlie, laden with his and her raffle prizes, aftershave gained from the tombola and an assortment of bric-a- brac.

"Quite the country lass now aren't you? I never thought you'd settle down to our ways so well."

"D'you remember, you called me a Townie the day we met?"

"Well, you were all tarted up," said Charlie.

"Yes, and then you got me completely sozzled, you wicked old man!" she laughed as they reached his gate. "See you later, Edna's bringing you over a chocolate cake, so save some for us."

"Right'o. You get that little dog his dinner now. I'm sorry Robert couldn't make it. "

That evening Robert was noticeably quiet when he and Woody joined Maggie, Angela and the rest of the fete committee in the pub. The day had proved to be a great success and the vicar was delighted with the boost to church funds.

"Mind if I don't stay?" Robert picked up her glass, "I'll get you another then I'll take Woody back."

"How odd," Maggie whispered to Angela, "Robert's being so unsociable. Just because he couldn't be here for the fete this afternoon doesn't mean he has to be so 'po faced' about it."

She sipped her second gin and tonic, and felt a stab of irritation as Robert muttered a brief farewell, saying he had some urgent business calls to make. She had noticed that he had been getting a bit moody of late but now flushed with their success at the fete, and a little wobbly after a couple of drinks, she made herself forget her annoyance and joked her way through a darts match with the Vicar.

"Can I see you girls home?" Major Gibson's florid complexion had a taken on the shine of a ripe plum, as he bought himself and the committee more celebratory drinks.

"No, no thanks, we'll be fine. We'll walk together."

Arm in arm, Maggie and Angela left the pub, and circled the duck pond on the village green.

"Hope he's not driving his old jeep with all that booze inside him." Maggie giggled, Damn fine, 'what'? She mimicked the Major's deep baritone, as they walked unsteadily towards the road, tripping up with laughter.

The dark silhouette of the giant oak stood out against the sky and startled ducks cruised in to the protection of the reed bed, illuminated by a full moon.

"Are you okay going down the hill on your own? I'm sure if you come back with me, Robert will run you home." They had reached the end of the lane and could see the lights of the cottage.

"No. I'll be fine, I'll stick to the path. The baby sitter will be keen to go so I'd better hurry now," Angela said as they hugged.

"You haven't got a torch. Ring me to say you're back safe and sound then."

Maggie made her way past Charlie's darkened windows. A fox like shadow flitted across the meadow, visible in the moonlight.

Woody barked as Maggie crunched the shingle path. An owl hooted in the wood and more distantly another sound, a screech owl perhaps. She felt light headed and decided to sit on the bench by the front door for a few seconds, relishing the night's stillness and calm. Woody whined, sensing her outside.

"Alright, I'm coming Woody, don't wake your master up, or you'll get me in to trouble," Maggie whispered loudly, failing to notice that Robert's car was not parked in the drive.

The note on the pillow was brief, "Sorry, Maggie, I'm going away for a bit. Not sure how to handle things anymore. Need some space. Lots on my mind, I'll be in touch, Rob."

Maggie screwed her eyes up to focus as she read and reread the scrap of paper. She began to shiver, her legs giving way as she slumped on to the bedroom floor, head pounding. What on earth did Robert mean? It was nearly midnight and too late to contact Angela who had apparently forgotten to ring when she got back home. He must be feeling ill. Maggie knew his work had been getting on top of him and there had been some arguments recently, but he would never go just like that, he would never leave her; would he? She hauled herself on to the bed wishing she hadn't drunk so much. She felt queasy and the room swirled, dizzying her thoughts.

No, they weren't married, but then neither were lots of her friends; they loved each other. He must be ill. And they had been trying for a baby, though admittedly the urgency was not so acute after she'd seen the consultant in Cambridge. There was, she had been informed, no obvious cause for her miscarriages. There would be further investigations. Now, Robert, the man she had planned her life around had apparently moved out. He had left her a scrap of paper with no explanation and no sign that he loved her after all.

"Robert, don't do this to me," she sobbed, holding on to a perplexed little dog.

Maggie woke, cold and shivering and not sure where she was. She was lying on top of the bed and had been disturbed by Woody scratching at the bedding and whining. The luminous dial on the bedside clock face showed it was two o'clock. The persistent ringing of the telephone aroused her.

"Yes, yes, of course, I'll come right away." She trembled, despite the policeman's reassuring tone telling her he would call for her in five minutes. How could Robert have left her and now Angela was in some sort of trouble, Maggie had never felt so frightened.

Angela clung to Maggie as if she would never let go. The police car had left with one of the officers, arranging to return later.

Maggie learned that Angela had not telephoned her to say she was safe home because her walk down the hill had been anything but safe. In between sobs Angela told her how she had almost reached the bottom of the hill when she had tripped. She was still a little drunk and knew she was lucky not to break any bones. The passing car must have spotted her in the moonlight, sitting, nursing her grazed knees, on the side of the road and it stopped, Angela thought, to offer her help. Young men, in their late teens, there were three of them and they had probably also been drinking hard in Waldersby, got out.

"You didn't recognise them?" Maggie asked.

"Two of them, no," Angela looked scared, "I'm sure the third was a Richards' boy."

Maggie shuddered, "Oh heck, I hope not."

Angela continued, "One of them started goading the other, saying things like 'do her up mate' and 'she's a posh fuck'. I heard one of them yelling at the others to stop, telling them I was the friend of the nurse." Angela clung to Maggie, trembling. "Oh, Maggie, I was so scared. They were pawing at me, trying to rip my jeans off, too strong for me. I realised I had to get away, but my legs wouldn't move, I was terrified, I felt paralysed. Then one of them grabbed me and I must have been screaming because he put a hand over my mouth. He reeked of alcohol."

Maggie guided her back to the kitchen and poured them both some more black coffee. If only Robert was here, but she couldn't tell Angela about the note now. She cried with her friend, guilty that her tears were for herself. Please come back Robert, we need you, she silently begged.

"I was dizzy with drink and didn't have any strength, I just felt limp." Angela stopped to mop up more tears. "Then I heard another car coming down the hill and they ran back to theirs. I thought they would drive off, but they didn't. I was waving frantically and saw it was Kate Creasey's new man. He stopped when he saw me, offering help. Just as I was trying to tell him what had happened two of the boys rushed back across the road. Oh, it was so awful," Angela gripped Maggie and sobbed, "I couldn't help him, I was screaming and useless. The thugs beat him up so badly."

Maggie's head was spinning; vivid pictures of what had happened to her friend mixing in with the note from Robert. She could not begin to tell Angela that Robert had moved out and add to her distress. The happy gathering in the pub felt like years ago. She persuaded Angela to rest on the settee in the lounge and returned to the kitchen on the pretext of making some coffee before leaving a message on Robert's office phone for him to contact her urgently. She needed him so much and was at a loss to imagine how she would cope without him. She could hear Angela crying in the other room. Gordon had been contacted by the police and despite their estrangement was on his way home and the nanny had offered to stay the night.

CHAPTER 15

REFLECTIONS

The gathering in the vicarage was a sombre one. The vicar and his wife, the Major, Edna, Dawn Creasey and her husband joined other residents to ponder over the attack on Angela and Kate's boyfriend, while Charlie alone fretted about Robert's absence and Maggie's unhappiness. The knowledge that another Richards's boy may have been involved with the assault made the Creasey family particularly angry.

Local reporters roamed Little Fordham taking photographs of whomever and whatever they found to enhance the story. Angela requested police protection when James's nanny found a reporter questioning the little boy in their garden.

Maggie attempted to cope with Robert's strange behaviour and absence by offering to work more shifts. She hoped exhaustion would numb her pain and give her less time to dwell on her feelings.

"Charlie, could you possibly have Woody again?" became her daily plea, although Charlie was only too glad to be of help.

Maggie was finishing an afternoon clinic at the surgery the following week when a call came.

"Could you come please, I think the baby's on its way."

Christopher, a young father well known to Maggie, sounded agitated.

"I can be with you in about ten minutes."

"Hurry, you know what Emma's like, I'll try and keep her calm."

Maggie couldn't help smiling at the panic in his voice. Emma had delivered her last baby at home with relative ease but her husband, Christopher, had passed out at the birth.

The drive through narrow country lanes took Maggie to Christopher and Emma's remote thatched cottage. It was late afternoon, lights blazed from every window. She ran up the creaky staircase and soon discovered that his panic had been justifiable this time as grinning broadly, Christopher handed over his newly born baby son, delivered shortly after speaking to her at the clinic.

"I put the phone down and Emma shrieked that baby was coming. She was absolutely brilliant, Maggie. She panted and panted, trying to hold on, didn't you darling." Christopher sat down on the bed and cradled Emma. "You had to let go in the end and I just managed to catch him. He cried straight away, didn't he?" Christopher beamed, "To be honest, Maggie, I've never felt calmer in my life. Emma told me not to cut the cord, but it snapped anyway. If you wouldn't mind, we've left the afterbirth to you."

"Too late," Emma said, "It's out now, Maggie. Chris was wonderful, a brilliant midwife, he did everything I told him to. I hope I don't need stitches this time, I'm in a bit of a mess I'm afraid," she grimaced. "Isn't baby a dream, Maggie? We really wanted a boy."

Maggie cleaned Emma up, assuring her that no damage was done before bathing the baby, newly named Elliot, in the sink.

"Goodness me, he's nearly nine pounds!" she exclaimed, hoisting the protesting baby up in her weighing net.

Warmly wrapped, the baby attached himself eagerly to Emma's breast as Christopher re-appeared with a tray of tea and biscuits.

After more hugs and tears Maggie drove back through the quiet lanes remembering the look on Chris and Emma's faces as she left them admiring their new baby, Elliot. It was a happy end to a long day until she started to think of her own empty home. Chris and Emma would have lots to tell their family and friends. Their toddler, Joanna, had woken before she left and Maggie had taken a photo of the family and the toddler proudly cuddling her new baby brother. Overwhelmed with envy and sadness for her own plight she cried all the way home.

When she arrived Woody was whining for a walk and the doormat was covered with circulars and bills suffocating any attempt at a normal cheerful welcome. Maggie shivered in the cold air of the cottage. The kitchen looked desolate and she knew the fridge was empty, as she hadn't had time to shop -it would be an omelette for dinner- three nights on the trot. She longed to come home to a message from Robert, a mess in the bathroom, dirty wellies at the back door, a bonfire, anything, but most of all Robert in her bed. The phone rang. It was eight o'clock.

"Hi, Maggie, you are on call aren't you? One of your mums thinks she's in early labour, she's had a show anyway, can you give her a ring?"

Maggie's heart sank. "What's the name?"

"Right, here are her details…"

Maggie gave Woody his supper and phoned the young couple. She hoped that as this was their first baby she would have time to eat. She watched Woody wolf down his food as she buttered some toast before checking on their progress, reassured them and arranged to visit as soon as Woody hah had a quick run.

"Come on, Woody. Once round the block."

She felt guilty leaving him alone again especially when he cocked his head to one side as if listening to her explanation. "I won't be gone long."

It was a long, slow, difficult labour. Sarah and Tom, the young couple, were determined to have a natural birth. They had attended local classes with the NCT and Maggie had got to know them well at the clinic. Tom's attitude changed as his wife called out in pain.

"I'd like a general anaesthetic, Maggie, please." Sarah implored, all resolve fading fast.

"You're doing so well, now listen to me and breathe as I tell you to." Maggie soothed her forehead with the cold flannels that Tom provided and gently but firmly massaged Sarah's back. Together they were on all fours rocking back and forth. They walked and listened to music. Candles were lit and the aroma of lavender filled the air. As the dawn chorus made itself heard Maggie became increasingly concerned – the baby was large, in an awkward position and tiring. She called a colleague for support as the morning sun streamed through the windows.

"So you see, Woody, in the end we had to get her in to hospital. She'd never have made it on her own. She had to have a forceps delivery, and all the drugs she hadn't wanted." Poor Sarah, thought Maggie. Tom, however, was simply relieved to see his wife and baby survive. Sometimes women set their sights too high, especially with a first baby, Maggie reflected. I hope she realises that all that really matters is that she and her baby are alive and well. "Thankfully, Woody they had a lovely little baby girl who weighed eight and a half pounds, and they're both doing well."

Maggie bent down to hug him. The dog resembled a tiny child listening to her every word, his big brown eyes on hers. If only Robert had been here to comfort her. An admission to hospital of a mother hoping for a home delivery always filled her with a sense of failure. She ate her way through a bowl of cereal, weary and depressed.

The phone rang. "Hi Maggie. You couldn't possibly do a labour ward shift could yo

"I'm sorry, Sue, I'm heading for bed."

She'd never felt so alone and so exhausted and made no attempt to stop the tears streaming down her face. She couldn't go straight to bed without seeking some form of comfort and so despite the early hour Maggie called her mother, Elizabeth, who agreed immediately that a brief trip North for her was overdue and would take place the following weekend. Maggie slipped upstairs and crawled under the cold duvet, but before she could drop off the phone by the bed rang.

"Maggie, it's me."

Her heart jumped as she struggled against the drowsiness overwhelming her. "Look I can't explain all this really. I'm having difficulty explaining to myself, let alone you. I'm all messed up, Maggie."

"Rob what's the matter?" She was fully alert now. "Please tell me. Is there some one else?" Silence greeted her, "Robert please, please, come back, you know I love you so much. It's awful without you and so much has gone on that I need to tell you about. Something horrid happened to Angela and Charlie is so upset he can't bear to talk about it. I need you, we need you."

"Give me more time, Maggie. Look something's cropped up."

"Where are you living? Don't you need more clothes? I've been so worried. Can't you come home so we can talk?"

She heard him sigh, "Maggie, d'you remember that war time picture that hung in the hall? You know the bomber my Dad painted. I know you never liked it. If it's okay by you I'd like to pick it up in the week, I've got the key if that's alright? I won't be stopping."

He hadn't even asked how she was. Snapped out of her slumber, wide awake and now filled with anger, "How dare you treat me like this," she shrieked, and slammed the phone down. Enraged she pulled her dressing gown on and ran down stairs, Woody barking excitedly at her heels.

The picture was considered to be an accomplished work of art she recalled as she wrenched it off the wall, opened the front door and flung it outside. After slamming the door to and reassuring Woody she changed her mind. Opening the door again, she grabbed the picture despite its heaviness in its gilded frame and tossed it into the pond, where it floated for a while before dipping soundlessly beneath the water lilies.

"Sorry Robert," she mouthed. "Afraid your bloody bomber has just landed in the drink."

Returning to bed after soothing the trembling Woody she sobbed angrily, cursing Robert, before falling in to the deepest sleep since he had left her.

CHAPTER 16

SWEET REVENGE

Tapping the green leather desk top with his forefinger, Frank Sutton gazed round his wood panelled office. Swivelling his chair, he rose and walked across to the photographs, depicting his three Directors, and the Managers of Suttons Scenario. He lifted the picture of Robert Groves, Technical Director, and placed it face down on his desk.

"Such a pity," he murmured, undoing his top button and loosening his tie. "He could have been running this place for me in a few years." He buzzed his secretary. "Sally, did you know that Robert has left that girlfriend of his, the midwife?"

"We all knew, Frank, it's so sad, she's such a nice young woman."

"So why then? He's also just handed in his bloody notice. Come in here and tell me about it."

"Oh dear, I'm not surprised," said Sally, hurrying in and pouring them both a coffee. "One of the reps saw him dining out with a Swedish girl he met at the Brussels conference last year. D'you remember her?"

Frank was irritated, "No, should I? I don't usually miss a bit of glamour, do I?"

"Apparently things had been getting difficult for him, and, Maggie." Sally continued, "It seems she's been pretty desperate to have a baby, and suffered a couple of miscarriages. Robert confided in me about all that, asking my advice, you know. He seems to blame himself which is silly and Maggie's been neglecting him a bit. He told me last week that she was working hard and he was fed up with getting his own meals. He said she thinks more of their little dog than him. He sounded rather sorry for himself."

Frank looked surprised. "What's he want, a servant? Well they don't make wives like you anymore. My wife lives on the bloody golf course." He was pacing. "This company needs people like Robert Groves. He's damn good and between you and me I had him lined up to take over eventually. Who the hell am I going to get to do his job? I'm not promoting Derek Jacobs; the man's a bloody idiot and gets right up my nose."

Sally opened the corner cupboard and poured a small brandy. "You drink that up, Frank."

"I'll go and see his girlfriend, Maggie, tomorrow," Frank said. "He said he's moved in with an old friend of his in London. Didn't say who it was." He thumped the table. "We've got to get him back somehow."

Maggie wandered around the cottage, flicking a duster. She'd not done any cleaning after Robert's departure and the neglect was beginning to show. She sorted out the washing and set the machine as Woody followed her from room to room. It was a sunny morning but as she took in the views across the fields to the woods she saw signs of autumn tingeing the leaves - a new season without Robert.   So much of themselves had gone in to making this cottage, that the thought of having to give it all up was too much. They'd both loved it on sight, dilapidated as it was and had had so much fun painting and decorating, browsing through local sales to buy old furniture that he loved. Choosing the best soft furnishings that Suttons Scenario designed to make the rooms warm and inviting. She wandered in to the spare room which she'd hoped to make into a nursery, now a shattered dream. Aimlessly she dusted down the stair rails and returned to the kitchen, her favourite room, warmed by the Aga and where she entertained Charlie on an almost daily basis. It would be too sad to lose it all. After the fire in the thatch the whole roof had been patched up and now looked better than ever. Maggie retraced her steps to the small bedroom Robert used as an office, which overlooked the front garden, and the lane past Charlie's place. Sitting down at his desk she picked up an old photo of the two of them on holiday in Majorca the year they first met, arms wrapped round each other, in love. She began to sort through his papers, not sure what she was looking for, uncertain if she wanted to discover evidence of another woman or not. She didn't hear the wheels of a car crunch on the gravel leading to the garage. Woody started barking at the front door as she jumped and peered out of the window. She didn't recognise the gleaming silver Mercedes, but peering down at the front door she saw the dapper figure of Frank Sutton, stroking his hair into place, adjusting the knot of his tie.

"So, you see, I felt I had to come and see how you are." Maggie thought Frank Sutton looked extremely awkward sitting in the middle of the large, rose-coloured sofa. It couldn't have been easy for him to visit her in this situation.

"One of ours?" he queried, patting a cushion, before grasping the cup of tea she proffered, looking uneasily round the room. "I'm so shocked that Robert wants to leave, he's quite the best director I've got you know, I've always felt he was destined to take my place one day. Damn shame."

"Unfortunately, we've not had the chance to talk things over," said Maggie. She recalled his chat-up lines at the office party and wondered whether he saw her as easy prey.

"Look, Maggie. Don't mind me calling you by your first name, I trust? I think you and I should work this out together. My secretary tells me Robert's confided in her quite a bit recently. She mentioned how cut up you were at losing another baby. Seems Robert was beginning to see it as his fault. Then you got your dog and I gather he felt a bit rejected."

"Rejected? So he's been telling the whole office about our private affairs has he?" Her hand shook with fury, as she banged the cup in its saucer.

"No, no, nothing like that. Sally's a motherly soul and takes us all under her wing. She told me because she thought it would help."

"So perhaps you can tell me why he's left me then, as you all seem to know so much? I suppose you haven't any other little secretaries that my partner fancies tucked away?"

She was ashamed at the sarcasm in her voice, but more furious at being exposed and humiliated by Robert.

Frank Sutton was staring at her, disturbed by her reaction, as her face flushed with anger.

"Look, I'm sorry to have upset you, Maggie, but your Robert means a hell of a lot to me and my company. I'd just like you to know that so if either of us can engage him in any sort of conversation soon, we can get him to reconsider. I'm not accepting his resignation till I've had chance to talk to him face to face. Do you have any idea where he's staying?"

She forced herself to focus on what he was saying, hearing a genuine concern in his voice.

"No, I'm trying to find out. I know he's in London with some art dealer friend."

"Art dealer?"

"Yes, he told me that much," she said.

"Well, I think I might know where he is then."

She watched him put his cup down, after slurping the contents, knowing the hurt was written on her face, watched him brush at his jacket to remove imaginary specks of dirt. "We met an art dealer at the show we put on in London last year, needed our advice for his studio, and wanted some of our ultra-modern stuff. Nice guy, Robert and I met him at his flat near South Kensington. He might be there, it's worth a try."

She wanted to rush straight up to London and confront him and she knew Frank Sutton guessed as much, getting up to leave.

"Look, Maggie, I'll get the details and ask Sally to give you a ring. I do hope you'll forgive me for calling on you like this. Both of us have different reasons for wanting Robert back, of course. I really do care about the pair of you, you know. We'll put up a good fight together."

She showed him to the door and he put his hand on her shoulder.

"Forgive me, Maggie, your man's just too good for me to lose."

Maggie travelled to London the following day, leaving the cottage early after dropping off Woody with Charlie and catching a fast train from Waldersby station to Liverpool Street. Sally had been on the phone before nine o'clock that morning giving her clear instructions about the flat Frank Sutton had visited. She bought a street map to study on the underground to South Kensington and sat in a café a few hundred yards from Onslow Gardens. She would walk and work out what to say on the way there.

But as she neared the flat her confidence faltered and she hesitated a few doors away from the tall imposing building, containing a block of four flats. What on earth was she going to say to Robert if he was in she wondered, identifying the name of the art dealer Frank Sutton had given her printed on a neat brass plaque.

Taking a few deep breaths, she tried to compose herself, her heart was beating fast as she rang the doorbell. 'Come on, come on, breathe for a baby,' she chided herself, amazed the tactic actually worked.

A voice sounded from the slatted brass plate, "Who is it, please?"

Maggie jumped, she had fully expected to hear Robert's voice. She took another deep breath and was pleased her voice sounded assured as she spoke again, "Hello, I've an appointment with Mr Andrews. I have some art work to discuss."

"Please, come up."

The door opened slowly and Maggie entered a large imposing hall with a marble staircase. She gripped the banister hard to stop herself trembling as she mounted the stairs.

"Mr Andrews has been delayed, he should have been back an hour ago."

Maggie stared at the beautiful Oriental girl who ushered her in to a large high- ceilinged sitting room.

"I do the cleaning. You like some tea? I can get it for you?"

"Oh that would be lovely, thank you very much," said Maggie, smiling with relief.

She studied the paintings, mainly oils, hanging everywhere and propped up against the furniture. Abstract art adorned one wall.

Then she noticed a separate group of paintings, depicting war scenes and thought of the painting she had pitched into the pond."

"I'm sure Mr Tony will come soon," the girl said, returning with a tray of tea, before disappearing again, explaining that she had to go out to the bank.

Maggie was aware of voices in an adjoining room as she poured a second cup of tea. The door opened and for a brief moment she thought she would faint. Robert, first through the door, opened and shut his mouth with an expression of shock and surprise before exclaiming, "Maggie!"

A blonde woman also entered the room and smiled at her, as Maggie spilt the tea in her lap.

"Hello," she said. "Can you introduce me, Robert?"

—⁂—

Hunched in the crowded train Maggie held a newspaper in her hand but her mind spun over and over the last few hours. Robert had been spared too much discomfort by the arrival of his art dealer friend, Tony Andrews and his rapid departure with the blonde woman in tow, leaving Maggie and Robert together.

As the door had closed behind them the silence was broken only by the trembling tea cup in the saucer.

"Would you like a cup?" she asked.

"Maggie, you didn't come all this way to pour me tea?"

"No, I came to try to find out what's going on. Are you having an affair with that woman? Is that the problem?"

Robert sighed, "Oh, Maggie, no. We've been out together with friends." He looked so unhappy that it was all she could do to remain seated. "I really needed to get away to think about us, you and I. I needed some space and time to think, from a distance."

Maggie tried to pick up the cup again but her hands were shaking too much. "What d'you mean?"

"Would you believe me if I said I feel guilty that we haven't had a baby yet? After all that was one reason for moving to Little Fordham. It's not easy and we were drifting. I love you, I always have but I kept thinking it was my fault somehow."

"Oh, Rob, I'm the one that loses the babies, not you. It's not your fault. Why didn't you say something before? I'm so miserable without you. I can't live in the cottage on my own. It's you I love, I know I dearly want children, we both do don't we? But even without them I can't imagine life without you. Please come home, please?" She was shaking as the tears ran down her cheeks.

Robert knelt in front of her and reached for her hand. "Maggie, we can't really talk here. I want us to understand each other."

The door opened, "More tea, Mr Robert?"

—⚬—

Maggie collected her car at the station and drove straight to Angela's house.

"So, what's his problem? Is he in love with another woman?" Maggie knew Angela had been longing for her return. It was early evening and the wine flowed freely as her friend listened.

"He assures me his relationship with the blonde I saw is just platonic. She's an artist and they met in Brussels last year. She used to have a business in Sweden in interior design."

"You don't believe that nonsense, do you?" Angela snorted. "Maggie, he's having an affair with her I bet. Just like Gordon. They're all the same these men, it's just too easy to ditch us."

Maggie looked at her despairingly. "Look, I've got to believe it.

I just can't bear to think of him in bed with her or anyone else. Anyway, we talked, which is all that really matters at the moment. I don't think he's that keen on the art dealing side of things. He really loved his job with Frank Sutton and seemed relieved Frank wanted him back. You know, Angela, I'm sure he loves me, it's just that he's all of a muddle inside. We talked about me losing the babies and he actually cried. He sobbed. I've never seen Robert show emotion like that. He kept saying it was all his fault, and he felt he'd failed me as a man."

"How come?" Angela looked puzzled. "It's not as if you and he can't make babies. Hardly his fault that your body rejects them, is it?"

"I know that. He still seemed to think that if he left, and I maybe found someone else I might have more luck."

"Goodness, he is mixed up. He's the one that's found someone else, not you. He knows how much you love him, for heaven's sake. How many more excuses does he have?"

"Don't be hard on him. I'm really glad I got to see him and talk things through. That's a problem we've had, not talking together. I think he's been a bit jealous of Woody, too."

"Jealous of your little dog? That's daft. Okay, so where does this leave you?"

Maggie downed the rest of the wine and poured them another. Raising her glass she grinned at Angela. "Well, my friend, I've got him to agree to come back to the cottage for the weekend." Her speech slurred. "Yes, I'm going to prove that I can outdo the Swede or any other woman at their own game. By Sunday night Robert Groves will be begging for mercy." Maggie giggled helplessly and then burst in to tears. "I love him so much, I've got to make it work."

CHAPTER 17
NEW VOWS

Robert's car bounced in the pot holes, mud splattering the windscreen, he was nervous enough without being shaken about, he thought, slowing near Charlie's gate and realising how much he had really missed the old boy. He swerved to avoid another puddle and just avoided knocking Charlie's fence down. "Drat, what's the matter with me?" He'd been in two minds whether to come but his heart to heart with Maggie had affected him deeply – he was relieved she understood how he felt about their failure to have a child. "Anyone would think it was our first date," he muttered.

Robert regretted that the night he'd left Maggie he'd allowed Brigitte to give him what she referred to as a 'demonstration of sympathy', the sex they had had was unfeeling and perfunctory. Brigitte's real lover was their friend, Tony Andrews. It had been so different making love to Maggie, at least in the early days – a roller coaster of fun, lots of play and laughter, but during the last year their lovemaking had become less joyful, it's only purpose to get Maggie pregnant, which had reduced their natural spontaneity. He had found himself treating her with care and consideration, frightened to hurt her body in any way, aware of the fragility that lay within her.

He reflected on the weeks before he made his decision to move out, aware of his own deep longings to have a child. 'Am I inadequate, less of a man, somehow to blame for her miscarriages?' He had constantly questioned himself. Perhaps they should have had counselling but that idea had also filled him with a sense of failure. So he had withdrawn and run away. Deep inside his love for Maggie remained unaltered and he was relieved and grateful that she had come looking for him. He slowed as the cottage appeared. How could he have left all this? They had worked hard together to make it a home, random flower beds interrupted the spacious lawn wrapped around the building, water lilies flowered in the pond, a rose arch over the front door, lavender edged the path. The newly-thatched roof already blended with the old. 'I'm home', he said out loud, prickling with excitement as he turned the key in the door.

Maggie had asked Charlie to look after Woody for the weekend. She needed Robert alone if her plan was to succeed. Before he arrived she prepared herself, soaking in the bath filled with expensive oils, before dressing with care. She and Angela had made several purchases at the new lingerie shop in Waldersby. The sales assistant had been full of good advice, "Not black lace, too obvious, something a little more subtle, more elegant and mature?"

Maggie examined her reflection. She felt deliciously feminine for a change and grinned as she patted the uplift of her breasts, and felt the delicate satin underwear embracing her body beneath the loose fitting dress. She was ready.

Before the meal awkwardness surrounded them, as they tiptoed around each other with polite remarks. Gulping down

Charlie's sloe gin in the kitchen, Maggie sprinkled more cheese on the lasagne, once Robert's favourite, and poured him an equal measure of the rich ruby liquid. The dining room glowed with candlelight and Charlie's brew, plus an expensive bottle of wine began to take effect. By the end of the meal all formality had vanished and Maggie's plan to seduce her partner followed immediately after the first course.

Robert gazed at her face and ran a finger across her brow, "I've missed those freckles," he murmured.

"Promise me you'll never run away again," she whispered, smiling.

An emerald dress lay crumpled on the path from the dining room, the satin underwear trailed across the bedroom floor. Theirs had been a joyful act of love making, laughter had filled the bedroom as they wrestled together, and then had come a moment of complete awareness for both of them. They were reunited. Robert caressed her, renewing his love for her body. He explored her as if it was their first time. The sweet smell of her perfume, the small blemish on her thigh, the zones that aroused her the most.

Maggie ran her fingers lightly down his back. Nothing had changed, the fine down on his shoulders, the strength of his muscles, the firm buttocks. She held him tightly as her hand reached for his groin. Thrusting gently, he entered her. Elation and a profound happiness overwhelmed them both.

"Come on, darling, please don't cry. I'm here for good if you'll have me?"

Maggie was sitting on the edge of the bed. "I'm crying because I love you so much, it hurts."

"Can I stay?" he murmured, slowly running his hands over her back. "Maggie, this may sound odd after what's happened but will you marry me now, I really think it's time we did?"

"Marry you? Really marry you, Robert?" She stood up, "Say that again."

He stood in front of her, revelling in the beauty of her nakedness, "How shall I say it?" he whispered, gathering her to him. "Will you be my wife?" Robert knelt down and took her hand, pulling her to her knees. "Will you?"

"Hold me tight, darling. Of course I'll be your wife; I've wanted to be your wife for far too long." She was laughing now, heady with joy.

"Now make love to me again, and again, and again."

Relief and delight surged through her as they tumbled back on the bed.

The following day they sat in Charlie's tiny kitchen and discussed their decision to finally become man and wife, knowing it would gain his approval.

"Well, there'll be no stopping Dawn Creasey, and Edna, if you decide to get married in our church. There hasn't been a wedding here for a few years."

Maggie could tell how relieved Charlie was to see them both together again and felt a glow of happiness surrounding her.

"I'd love to get married in the village, we both would," said Maggie, half-heartedly sipping elderflower wine. "I'm still not sure I should be drinking this after last night."

"Can't have a cup of tea to celebrate your wedding, girl. It'll do you good, drink up." He bent down and patted Woody. "This little chap's glad you're back, Robert. He's missed you, you know."

Maggie smiled. Dear Charlie, he made a good accomplice.

"We thought we'd go for a walk before lunch. Clear our heads a bit." Woody's tail banged the table leg. "Yes, I know, you're coming too." Maggie said.

They took their favourite route through the meadow to the woods and sat down near to the badger set.

"D'you think Mummy would mind if Charlie gave me away?"

"We'll ask her later, darling."

"She'll just be so relieved that you're going to make an honest woman out of me." Maggie called Woody to heel. "We could have my sister as a bridesmaid, and James will make a cute page boy."

"Hey, hang on a minute. You said a small quiet wedding last night."

"That was last night," she laughed. "Come on it's getting chilly, let's go to the Dog and Duck tonight. I'll call Angela. She might like to join us."

"Good idea, wife to be," Robert said, hugging her.

CHAPTER 18

IN PREPARATION

Once Charlie had told Edna about the wedding the news spread rapidly. Despite Robert's preference for a small private affair Edna and the villagers decided otherwise. The shop was re-stocked to cater for unknown numbers of well-wishers. Edna and Dawn Creasey pestered Maggie to allow them to do the flower arrangements for the small church and villagers' gardens were earmarked to provide the best blooms and foliage.

Maggie sat in her kitchen pouring over yet another list among a pile she had already discarded. The guest and present lists were now complete, whilst a general one of who was doing what was in constant need of alteration.

"Can I come in?" called Charlie, pushing open the back door and ambling towards the kitchen and his favourite seat as Woody fussed around him.

"Of course, guess you smelt the coffee?" Maggie said, acknowledging her most frequent and favoured visitor.

"Edna's taking me to Waldersby this afternoon. Seems they've got some decent suits in the gents' outfitters near the market square," he said.

"What's wrong with your best Sunday suit? That's smart enough isn't it?"

"Not for this wedding, my girl. Can't give you away with my cuffs all frayed. I could do with a new one for best."

"We'll pay for it, Charlie. But it would be no trouble to get new cuffs you know, Dawn Creasey is a good seamstress isn't she? I don't want you splashing out at our expense."

"No you won't pay for it young lady, I'll not accept charity."

Maggie filled his coffee mug. "Sorry, I didn't mean it like that."

"Edna wants a new hat, too. Mind you, it'll be from the Oxfam shop 'cos she knows a bargain. We're going in on market day when the farmhands bring the cattle in for auction. You know I used to drive my geese in regularly a few years back? We'll stay for a bite to eat after."

Maggie nodded, "Here's your coffee. You'll enjoy yourselves then. It's amazing to think that geese would follow you all that way, which must have been quite a sight. I wish I'd known you then. Just one spoonful of sugar, remember Edna said you were to cut back. Now I must sort out the music for our grand entrance and phone the vicar." Maggie ticked items off her list. "The village hall is booked, and I think Dawn has found some helpers among Kate's college friends."

"She and Edna will be pinching more flowers from everyone's gardens, same as they do for the funerals," he said, repacking his pipe and sucking vigorously. Sparks flew from the small furnace. "I've put by two bottles of my best sloe gin. Robert said it would go down well after all the speeches."

"Oh, Charlie, don't let me near it too soon, you know what it does to me. By the way did Robert tell you that Frank Sutton has insisted on paying for our honeymoon?"

"Must think a lot of you two."

Maggie looked thoughtful, "You know, Charlie, I never dreamt I'd be this happy again. It's wonderful to know I'll have Robert for keeps now. I was so scared when he left me, I couldn't imagine the rest of my life without him, or bear the thought of losing this cottage and not seeing you so much. I'd never have been able to stay here on my own."

Charlie shifted his pipe from side to side. "You had me worried I can tell you. Robert's lucky to have you. You're like my family, you two."

"You know you're right there, I feel that way."

"It cut me up properly to see you both running adrift."

"Well, thank goodness it's all behind us." Maggie refilled the kettle, "Strange how things often seem to happen for a purpose don't they? You don't realise it at the time of course; Robert and I are so much closer now."

"When does that Sutton bloke want Robert to start again?"

"He's back there already, Frank's so pleased to have him that he's also given him a pay rise. As for the honeymoon, Robert has only hinted so far but I think it might be the 'icing on the cake', as Edna keeps saying. Ooops, the cake, I promised to ring Jacky Richards and tell her what decoration I wanted."

"You haven't asked that woman to make it, have you?"

"Now then, Charlie. I know you and Edna don't like her but she's becoming a very good cook. She's turned the catering round in the Dog and Duck and given the chef some new ideas. It was her husband who hurt, Edna, not her, remember? Jacky was as upset as we all were." She patted his arm. "Come on, give her a break, Jacky's alright."

"Edna won't like it."

"Well, it's my wedding and I really don't feel I need to get Edna's permission, Charlie! It's our cake after all."

Charlie sniffed, "P'raps I'd better not mention it then."

Maggie smiled to herself knowing Charlie would find it impossible not to tell. She could appreciate their feelings against the Richards family well enough; Edna had suffered badly from Len's beating. But hopefully, once they'd seen what Jacky was capable of, even the worst tongues in the village would admire her skills and give her another chance.

"Thanks for offering to have Woody tomorrow. Angela and I will be leaving for an early train so Robert will bring him round first thing if that's okay? I know I'll spend far too much, especially if we go near Harvey Nichols. Pity I've agreed to do a shift tonight as there are a couple off sick. I'll sleep this afternoon and who knows, with a bit of luck they'll cancel me."

Maggie helped Charlie ease himself out of the chair and rearrange his walking stick. Charlie patted the dog's head. "Good boy, down now, I'll see you in the morning. I'll pick you some veg and leave some eggs indoors. They're laying well at the moment."

Maggie kissed his rough cheek. "I love you, Charlie Watt. If you really have to get a new suit get a navy one, it'll look so smart with a white shirt and you can have one of Robert's silk ties – he has far too many."

"Don't worry, I won't let you down, girl," he ambled slowly to the door. "I'll shut the gate."

"Woody, stay." Maggie caught at the dog's collar, "You'll see Charlie again tomorrow and you mustn't pester him for treats all the time."

Blowing Charlie a kiss, Maggie returned to her lists. Wondering if Jacky could design a replica of Nut Tree Cottage to go on the cake, she picked up the phone.

Maggie and Angela caught an early train packed with commuters. Maggie recognised a new father she'd last seen changing a nappy in the hospital nursery under her guidance. They acknowledged each other as she squeezed herself in to a remaining space. Tired, after the busy night in the labour ward, she was asleep before the train reached the first stop, her head lolling and jerking.

"You have to feel sorry for these chaps, squashed together like sardines in a can, twice a day," said Angela, nudging her awake at their destination, "I did it for two years and it nearly killed me."

"Mmm, I'm so glad we moved out of London," Maggie yawned. "It's great travelling up for a days shopping though. Just think, I might have had to leave the cottage and go back to a London hospital for a job. We're so lucky aren't we?"

"And so is Robert to have you."

Maggie agreed with a nod, remembering that Charlie had said the same. They were both right, she and Robert were lucky to have each other.

Maggie's prediction had been correct. They shopped in Harvey Nichols and treated themselves to lunch in Harrods. By mid afternoon, laden with carrier bags they were more than ready for the return journey.

"Thank, God for Little Fordham. I just love getting back to its peace and quiet," Maggie said removing her purchases from Angela's car boot, "It's been such a great day hasn't it, even though we've spent far too much. Thanks for the lift."

"Must rush, see you later." Angela waved as Maggie undid the latch on Charlie's gate.

Opening his front door, she was greeted by a very excited Woody. A large bag of spinach and a dozen eggs were on the kitchen table. 'Gone up road, back soon. Woody okay.' said the scrawled note.

"Woody, down, down, I know, I'm glad to see you too," she said, kneeling to ruffle his coat, "I've really got to train you not to jump up though. Come on, let's take you home and I'll come back for these bags."

Robert returned two hours later and found Maggie asleep on the sitting room sofa with Woody curled up beside her.

"Down, Woody."

"It's my fault, Rob," Maggie yawned easing herself up wearily I'll take him out for a walk in a minute, "Daddy's being horrid isn't he?" she said, as if to a child, patting the dog.

Robert sighed, "You spoil him, darling, there are dog hairs everywhere."

"So, aren't you going to ask how we got on then?"

"Yes, of course, I'll get us a cup of tea then we'll all go for a walk and you can tell me about your day. I could do with some air after being stuck in the office all afternoon, we had such a long meeting with the suppliers. Where's all the shopping or have you hidden it?"

"I left the bags at Charlie's, we can pick them up on the way back. I've lots to show you and you can tell me about your meeting. I've collected his eggs and lovely fresh spinach for our supper."

"That's good, I'll change before we go."

They crossed the meadow in time to admire the setting sun, a glorious blaze of fiery red and orange. "We'd never see such an expanse of sky like this in town," Maggie said, gazing in admiration as it sank below the horizon. "Just look at that, I never tire of watching it." Hurrying on in the chilly air she recalled the trip to London. "Angela spent a fortune, well come to that, we both did. Luckily I've done so many extra hours lately that I've managed to save a bit."

"I suppose you'll be demanding a dress allowance when we're married?"

"I don't think that happens these days, Rob, unfortunately. Now tell me about your day."

"Well, Frank and I had a working lunch in that new bistro, off the market square before meeting up with the Irish chaps for the afternoon. It so happened that Gordon was in there. He and I have arranged to meet up next week."

"Did he say he was definitely coming to the wedding?"

"He seemed anxious and obviously wanted to tell me something, but with Frank there it was a bit awkward. I'll be able to find out more when I see him."

Woody scampered ahead scattering leaves and scenting rabbits. "Good boy, Woody." Robert joined in the chase, "He'd do really well on a shoot you know, helping the beaters."

"That's just what Charlie was saying."

Charlie was snoozing in his favourite place by the warm range when they collected Maggie's shopping.

"Thanks, Charlie, we'll not stay, see you tomorrow."

Cleaning their boots outside the kitchen door Robert ran the hose over Woody's protesting paws. "Now you're really hungry, I bet," he said, roughing up the dog's coat.

"Omelettes and spinach won't take a minute, and it's my only speciality." Robert said, filling two wine glasses, "You feed Woody, darling. Did Angela say anything today about Gordon? I mean, d'you think they'll ever get back together? I know he tries to be at home most weekends. Is that working?"

"Well, they lead separate lives really. Angela still works in the office and they're on speaking terms; just. He comes home and sometimes stays for the week end, but he's not very hands-on with James. To be honest, I think she finds it easier without him. James certainly seems happier with her, or the nanny. How come your omelettes are always lovely and fluffy?"

"Good, aren't they? Can't beat Charlie's fresh eggs either, I don't think I've ever seen egg yolk this yellow."

Maggie cleared their plates and carried the tray to the sitting room. "Coffee?"

Robert admired the new clothes and was tactful, Maggie thought, in not asking the cost.

"This is my favourite skirt, a real bargain," she said, smiling to herself as she remembered Angela's shock at the price she'd paid for that particular one.

"Angela didn't say anything today but, I've got a suspicion about the new man in her life. She's being very coy though. I'll let you know when she spills the beans. Now, enough about them, come on, Rob, you're keeping me in suspense, you've got more exciting news for me? Any more details about our honeymoon? No secrets, please."

"Alright, I was going to tell you later. Frank is still absolutely insistent that we go at his expense, he won't hear otherwise. He's telling everyone I'm his prodigal son! It's going to be fantastic I think. Apparently the hotel complex is very grand and set in an old sugar plantation. We'll have our own little cottage on a hillside overlooking a bay in St Lucia."

"St Lucia? You mean the island in the Caribbean?"

"Yes."

"Oh, my, that's amazing."

"What's even more wonderful is that Frank's absolutely insistent that we fly first class." Robert grinned. "And there's more."

"Wow!" Maggie relinquished her hold on his arm. "I don't think even these new clothes are going to be smart enough for a place like that," she chuckled, "I'd no idea it would be so grand."

"We get picked up at the airport by helicopter and flown across the island. Apparently a friend of Princess Margaret owns the place and lives nearby."

"What a dream. We can go snorkelling; the water will be so warm won't it?" Maggie hauled a bemused Woody on to her lap. "Are you listening Woody?"

"Get this, we can have as much to drink as we like, and it's all free apparently." Robert said, obviously enjoying that bit of information.

"I expect we'll have to dress up a bit in the evenings?"

"Maybe, which reminds me, Maggie. Can we go to Cambridge on Saturday? I need some more casual shirts and we have to choose our wedding rings, and I need to talk to that art restorer."

"Yes," Maggie moved Woody back to his basket. "Oh dear, your father's picture, I'm glad it's not totally ruined, darling, unforgiveable of me but I was so angry with you that night. Let's forget that, I said I was sorry. I'll need a couple of even smarter dresses now and a new bikini. Also d'you think we can buy Charlie a shirt without offending him? He and Edna were going to trawl round the shops yesterday. He was a bit upset when I suggested I get him one. You could ask him if they found anything and if not offer to get one in Cambridge. I don't want them out of pocket for us."

"Sure. By the way I forgot to tell you that your mother rang while you were working last night. Elizabeth wants to come down for a couple of days before the wedding. She also wondered if Angela could put your sister and her new boyfriend up?"

"I expect so. I'll ask her. We haven't given much thought to your family though have we?"

"Not many of them around are there. D'you realise, it's almost ten years since Mum and Dad died. Strange how we three brothers have drifted apart since their terrible car accident, no parents to hold us together somehow. Odd that."

"You don't like remembering it, Rob, and I don't suppose they do either. Being together brings back too many memories for you all. I'm just sorry that I never got to know your parents. It would be good if one of your brothers could be with us though wouldn't it. I realise it's a bit much to expect, Ben, to come over from South Africa?"

"Ben says he wants to come if he can. He's got some business to do in Europe and it could coincide. It would be great to see him." Robert's voice trailed off, "We last met up just before we moved here, remember? Mum's sister, Auntie Jenny, is certainly coming, but she'll only stay for the day. I love her but she's quite eccentric isn't she?"

"Right, I know she can't leave all her animals for long. I've never met Chris though, have I?"

"No, you'd like my little brother a lot." Robert smiled. "He's a complete scatterbrain. Chasing women most of the time. I think he really would like to settle in Edinburgh now. I've told him all about us and he'll probably come. Perhaps we can put him up on the settee if he turns up? Edna and Mrs Creasey have offered their spare rooms but Ben might prefer a hotel in Waldersby, he likes his comforts," he said, pouring more coffee. "Chris was really screwed up about Mum and Dad. He was the baby of the family after all and never really got over the shock of losing them both. Well, that's silly of me, I suppose I haven't either and I don't suppose Ben has. Life moves on." Robert shivered, "I'd rather not think of it tonight, darling."

Maggie put her hand to his cheek, "I haven't got over the shock of nearly losing you either," she said, kissing him tenderly. "I'm sorry if that sounded a little callous, Rob, it wasn't meant to. You know something, I rather fancy an early night with the man I love." Maggie stood up and stretched out her hand. "Forget the coffee."

CHAPTER 19
NEW BEGINNINGS

"**M**ummy, do stop crying," Maggie smiled at her mother. "We're very happy you know."

"I know dear, that's why I'm crying. Excuse me," she sniffed and pulled a pink cotton handkerchief from her handbag. "I'll just go out to the Ladies."

"I'll join you." Maggie said, extricating herself from Robert's embrace. "Mum and I are just off to the loo, darling," she whispered. "She's finding it a bit overwhelming."

Maggie and her mother walked across the empty wooden dance floor of the village hall. The wedding speeches were over and the younger guests were keen to start dancing. A small local jazz band were beginning to limber up at the end of the hall. She and Robert would lead the dancing as soon as they were ready and all the tables had been cleared.

It had been a very happy day from the moment that Maggie woke. The weather held and the sun had shone. Eleanor, her sister had kept her laughing most of the morning. She was the only bridesmaid and was to be dressed in the palest blue satin. Angela arrived early to help arrange their hair whilst Elizabeth helped them to dress. Maggie's dress was a cream satin gown that she and her mother had chosen together. The florist from Waldersby arrived with perfect bouquets of mixed freesias and cream roses and two buttonholes for the men. Finally, the wedding car jolted its way up the lane on the short ride to the village church where the whole community stood waving and whistling cheerily, as Charlie escorted Maggie inside looking proud and almost dapper in his new navy suit. They proceeded very slowly, his walking sticks banging inadvertently against the pews as he tap, tapped down the decorated aisle. The slow progress gave Maggie a chance to acknowledge all her colleagues, hospital friends and family. Even Woody, handled by Eleanor and sporting a satin collar, managed to walk sedately behind.

"I just love the way Robert looks at you, darling. It makes me well up inside. Silly I know." Her mother smiled, watery eyed.

"You can be silly on my wedding day, Mummy. It's allowed."

"How d'you think it all went in the church?" Maggie said, leaning forward across the basin to apply her lipstick. "The vicar's nice, isn't he?"

"Charming man. I thought it was a lovely service and the church looked and smelt beautiful with those gorgeous flowers. I've always been fond of freesias and the two ladies had managed to get some in all the arrangements, such a lovely aroma. I'm very impressed with the way they've decorated this hall too, the tables look pretty don't they? They went to so much trouble for you darling," she said, removing her large pink hat.

"Hold this a minute, there's a dear. The church flowers matched your bouquet to perfection. You look quite wonderful in that cream satin," she said, drying her hands and peering at her own reflection, I felt very proud of you both. Robert looked smart and so handsome. Eleanor suits blue so well and I can see that Andy is very smitten. As for dear Charlie, words fail me, darling. Daddy would be grateful that you asked him to give you away. I quite see why you love him," she said, giving Maggie a fleeting kiss. "I hope you approve of my outfit by the way, you haven't said so?"

I've always liked you in pink, Mummy. Where did you get this amazing hat? Are these real ostrich feathers?"

"Yes. To be truthful darling, I hired it." Tears trickled down her cheeks again. "If only your father could have been with us."

Maggie fingered her hair back into place and made for the door, "You know, Mummy, I'm very proud of you too. Don't start me crying as well. Daddy is here in spirit, I feel it somehow, and I'm sure you do. Come on, Robert's waiting. Incidentally I think Eleanor has made a real catch this time don't you, with Andy? What a handsome guy!"

"Oh, he's such a nice lad. I do hope this one lasts, they're always changing, and I can't keep up. Look I'll sit with Frank Sutton, he's been so kind to you two, and I want to get to know him better."

"You've been ages, everyone's waiting for us," Robert said, dragging Maggie towards the dance floor to loud clapping, as the guests stood up to cheer.

The band started playing 'It's a wonderful world' with one elderly crooner trying to mimic Louis Armstrong. Maggie looped her arms around Robert's neck. "Look, Charlie and Edna are fast asleep, don't they look sweet like that."

Edna's head rested on Charlie's shoulder, her face covered by the veil of her new straw hat. His head had fallen forward on his chest and his best cap rose and fell on his stomach in unison with a very loud snore. Woody was asleep and curled up under the chair, the satin collar still in place.

"The Creaseys all look a bit sleepy too, none of these oldies are used to champagne."

"It's not the champagne. Jennifer brought in Charlie's sloe gin and they've been guzzling that happily. They all tucked in to Jacky's cake too I noticed."

"I was impressed with that, I'm glad you asked her to make it, it must have taken her hours."

"I expect so, I'll tell you what it cost later! I've suggested to her that she sets up a little business in wedding cakes, hopefully ours will bring in some orders for her."

"Good idea, that'll help her."

Maggie studied the other guests. Several of her colleagues from the hospital were getting merry in the corner of the room, encouraged by Dr Southgate, their hired hats beginning to tilt at crazy angles as the giggling increased. A solid group of young men hovered around the bar area under a haze of smoke. Two little boys and one little girl from the village were playing chase. It was good to see that her older guests were mingling and making a move towards the dance floor. The little girl broke away to waltz with her father. Angela had joined Ben and Chris, who had managed to get to the wedding in time. Maggie had heard Ben talking about his business with Gordon after the speeches, unaware of the tension between them. Young James was fast asleep, cuddled by his nanny.

Maggie glanced at a couple who had recently moved to the village with their new baby and felt sentimental and near to tears as Robert whispered, "You realise, darling, we'll have to leave here in about half an hour?"

The music stopped and the spontaneous cheering and clapping woke Charlie and Edna. Woody, immediately alert, started to roam the room for scraps.

Maggie leant against Robert's shoulder and enjoyed the admiring looks of all her friends and family with a sense of overwhelming happiness.

"I can't wait, husband," she murmured.

Robert jumped as Frank Sutton tapped him on the shoulder just as Maggie was distracted by Sue, her colleague who had to hurry back to the labour ward and wanted to say goodbye.

"Sorry, Robert, I need to give you a few tips about the resort."

Finally, it was time to leave for the journey to Heathrow airport; all the arrangements were in place. They thanked Frank profusely and kissed and hugged their way around the hall, anxious not to miss anyone out whilst making hasty arrangements for their return.

On board their flight Maggie preened herself in the luxury of First Class, enjoying the sense of importance and sipping the free champagne.

"Here's to us, darling," said Robert, leaning across to hug her. "You've no idea how lucky I feel."

Their small whitewashed cottage in St Lucia overlooked a turquoise sea, the bed adorned with rose petals; a magnum of champagne and a bowl of exotic fruit welcoming their arrival. Surrounded by palm trees in the warm tropical surroundings they discussed every minute detail of their wedding day. The church service, the guests, and the clothes they had worn, the presents they had been given, their vows to each other. With a sense of abandonment in the sultry heat they made love.

"Robert, I'll try and be a good wife," Maggie cried after one tender session. "Who knows, we may be able to have a baby one day, but really I wouldn't want to live my life with anyone else. Please don't ever frighten me and leave me again. Promise?"

"Never, never ever. Thank you for being so understanding. I can't say how sorry I am for what I put you through, darling, it was unforgiveable," he said, hugging her tightly. "I'm so lucky to have you now and forever, mine for keeps. We may not have a baby yet, but sure as hell we're going to have a great time trying," he laughed. "Come on, I'm going for a swim."

Attentive white-jacketed waiters attended to their every need as they lay lounging on the silver sand, drinking brightly-coloured fruit cocktails. They snorkelled in warm water where bright tropical fish darted around them in the crystal clear sea. They discussed the future, revisited the past, and reflected on their joint sadness at being childless, and the effect this had ultimately had on their relationship.

"I frightened myself as much as I did you, running off to London," Robert said, pausing, "I also need to tell you about a phone call I had just before our wedding. It was from Tony Andrews."

"At least you know I'll come and get you," Maggie laughed, "What did he have to say? I thought he was abroad? Incidentally, Rob, I think we could have had a double wedding."

"Why's that?"

"Charlie and Edna are really good for each other, especially now she's mellowed a bit."

"So we're going to marry them off in their old age, are we?" Robert smiled, "You know Frank seemed to be having a good time with your mother, didn't he? Pity his wife couldn't make it. Not that Frank cares much really, as they seem to live separate lives". He paused to spread more sun cream on her reddening arms.

"This is my news, Tony apologised for not being with us and told me that he and Brigitte are planning to marry."

"Really? That's a relief! I thought you might have had a bit of a fling with her when I saw her in London. So now she's got her man and I've got mine. Let's forget her." Maggie didn't want to revive too many memories of almost losing Robert and changed the subject to nearer home, "I thought Angela looked pretty didn't you? Did you notice that she was getting smoochy with the new boyfriend, even though Gordon was a couple of seats away?"

"James looked cute in his sailor suit, didn't he? Gordon and Angela really have hit the rocks you know." Robert massaged her shoulders lovingly. "He told me when we met for lunch that they've agreed to separate officially, with a view to getting a divorce later in the year. He's still involved with that woman, and he also told me that Angela was seeing the new chap on a regular basis. He didn't seem at all interested in what happened to James."

"Well, perhaps James is better off without him. Gordon's never been that interested in him, has he? Angela has been a bit secretive about Tom. I know she's been worried that everyone is saying that she pinched him from Kate." She drew her knees up. "That's enough, darling!" she giggled. "We're so slippery we'll be making love like a pair of seals. Let's go and see that chap at the end of the beach about you having a diving lesson later."

The days passed quickly and they developed a routine. Beach combing, swimming and sunbathing before retreating to their cottage for a siesta after lunch. In the evenings they sauntered to one of several restaurants, indulging in limitless supplies of colourfully presented exotic dishes, and danced into the early hours.

Too soon their honeymoon was coming to an end, it was time to return home, but Little Fordham seemed a world away.

"How will we ever be able to thank Frank for all this?" Robert said, gazing across the bay from their small balcony, drinking in the magnificence of another fiery sunset. This is magical."

"One day we'll come back here, promise?" Maggie clinked their glasses. "Here's to our marriage, the good times and bad."

"Maggie, you're really all mine now, please God it will only be good times," Robert said, turning to embrace her.

CHAPTER **20**

MAN'S BEST FRIEND

A ngela waited anxiously at the airport. She was going over and over the manner in which she could impart the worrying news. She knew Maggie would react badly and wanted to tell her as gently as possible.

Irritated at the plane's delayed arrival, with an extra hour to hang around, she wandered round the small boutiques and bookshops, purchased one of the glossier magazines and a newspaper, and sat in the nearest cafe. The paper was all gloomy headlines; reports of two murders and a case of child molestation did nothing to lighten her mood. Her thoughts strayed to the previous day spent in London with Tom Farrow. She and Tom had met at the Tate gallery to discuss their affair, her thoughts on divorce, and how James would cope without Gordon, from whom she had now officially separated. Angela was aware that it had become common knowledge, having had far too much to drink at the wedding and not been terribly discreet. She recalled how Dawn Creasy had taken her aside, and their strange conversation. Dawn actually thanked her for taking Tom away from her daughter, Kate.

"I really didn't intend to, Dawn," Angela had said. "He was so kind to me after I was attacked on the hill, and I felt so terrible at the way those louts turned on him."

"No need to explain, he's far too old for my Kate," she'd said, her mouth a tight indication of her disapproval. "Without him as a distraction my daughter can concentrate on her studies more."

"Is Kate very upset with me?" Angela had asked.

Dawn sniffed righteously, a habit she appeared to have adopted from Edna. "She'll just have to get over him. Out of sight out of mind, I say."

Angela had bumped in to Kate in the village hall. They had both returned to help with the cleaning and clearing up of the wedding celebrations and she recalled their conversation.

"Kate, I really don't want to cause you any pain. Can I talk to you about Tom Farrow?" It was out. She'd felt a sense of relief.

"Don't worry Angela, really. Tom's tried to explain too. I know my mum's pleased as she never liked him much and was always going on about his age, and his noisy sports car." She'd actually chuckled, "I'll really miss going out in that. I'm off to University in Edinburgh soon, so I'll be far away. It was never going to work out between us. I ended it, not Tom."

Angela had felt even more contrite as Kate was being so pleasant. She knew how courageous the girl had been following the terrifying ordeal she too had been through and how well liked she and her family were. Tom had been genuinely fond of Kate and it appeared that she had ended the relationship, not him. Angela couldn't see why anyone might resent her taking up with him now.

"No doubt you've heard that Gordon and I are planning to divorce?"

"Yes, you can't do anything in this village without my mum and Edna knowing it all," Kate had muttered, as she polished. "To be honest I can't wait to get away."

She's hurting and I've added to it Angela thought, hearing the bitterness in her voice. Instinctively she'd put her arm round the young girl's shoulders, "Thanks Kate."

"Tell him I'll miss him though, he's a nice guy and we had some good times together." Kate had murmured as they parted. "Good luck."

Angela scooped up the remains of the coffee froth and smiled to herself. I'm not sure Tom wants to be thought of as old! Is twenty-seven old? He'd confessed that he was falling in love with her. A shudder of pleasure ran through her; she too was attracted to him – strongly – but love? No, she wasn't ready to fall in love yet. Gordon, with all his faults, had been the man she'd fallen in love with, and he was the father of their child. She was deeply saddened at Gordon's inability to show real affection for James, and wounded by his continued affair with Leanne, which he had made no effort to hide. So why had it all gone wrong? They had both wanted to start a family but somehow Gordon had found it difficult to be a parent. He never had been blessed with patience. It was comforting to realise that she had proved to be a good mother, at least. It boosted her morale also to know she could still attract another man and despite her misgivings she would let the affair take its course. James would benefit as he and Tom had hit it off straightaway and their attraction for each other went beyond the 'brmm brmm' of his powerful sports car. For James it was football, and Tom played football as much and whenever the little boy wanted him to.

Angela wandered back to the Arrivals area where the board

indicated that the plane had landed twenty minutes before.

"Angela, we're over here," Robert called, as he and Maggie grinning broadly, pushed their baggage in her direction.

"Sorry you've had to hang around for us," Maggie said, as she hugged her.

"Don't worry, I've been having a good read. My word, what fabulous tans you've got, you both look so well," she said, as they headed for the exit. "So has it been a wonderful time in paradise? I can't wait to hear all about it."

"Angela I'm so happy; we both are." Maggie tripped over her words. "It was a fantastic place. Our cottage near the main hotel was beautiful. Can you imagine a bed covered in petals?"

"No expense had been spared," said Robert.

"The views were stunning, across a fabulous bay to the mountains. I've taken loads of photos to bore you with." Robert loaded the suitcases in to the car as Maggie chattered on. "I learned to snorkel properly and Robert did some deep sea diving. We spent a bit of time looking round the island, but we were both so tired that we really didn't feel like touring much. I've put on too much weight again." She grimaced as she patted her stomach. "It's really kind of you to collect us, I thought you'd have James with you?"

"You can do the same for me one day. James is with the nanny and she's taken him for his swimming lesson."

"You know we would. Now what other news have you? How's Little Fordham surviving without us?" Maggie smiled. "Tell me they all enjoyed the wedding."

"They certainly did." Angela hoped she could delay the bad news a little longer, as she eased the car through the traffic and swung off down a side road.

"We'll go the scenic route. I can't bear the motorway. The traffic's been causing a real jam in Waldersby lately too. Not much better in the village either. You'll be pleased to know that we've had the speed limits installed. They've started the 30-mile limit just beyond our barns."

"Oh, that's really good news. Good old Major. When did they do that?"

"The day after you left. They've put up a 'Ducks' crossing sign as well!"

"I bet motorists will slow down more for ducks than humans, that's what made me suggest it to the Major," Maggie chuckled. "All we need now is one for the toads and I'll be satisfied."

"Now, that's getting silly, darling," said Robert.

An hour later the car turned in to the lane and bumped down the rutted track. "Home again. I have to carry you in, remember." Robert said, lifting Maggie over the threshold, accompanied by so much laughter that the pair ended up in a sprawled heap in the hall.

Angela continued asking questions about the honeymoon, as Maggie brewed the tea.

"Did you wear all those clothes we bought?" she asked.

"I lived in the summer frocks and my bikini. It was quite casual dress in the evenings, though one of the restaurants liked you to dress up well. We did on the last night."

They walked out in to the garden, "Everything has grown so much," Robert examined the vegetable patch he had attempted. "Weeds mainly."

"It's incredible, you'd better mow the lawn tomorrow, Rob. I'm dying to collect Woody now, I bet he'll have changed a bit too. Stay and have supper with us, Angela? We could go up to the pub, if you like?"

Angela gazed hard at the flower border. This was the moment she had been dreading. How on earth was she going to tell them the awful news?

Maggie slumped on the settee, tears pouring down her cheeks. "We've got to find him, Robert. I can't accept that he just disappeared. Woody would never run off that far, he'd always come back," she grabbed at the remaining tissues. "Whatever happens we mustn't blame Charlie. He must be in a dreadful state, poor man."

It was a sad tale that Angela had to tell them: hare coursers had been seen in the district quite frequently during the last few weeks. PC O'Sheridan had warned people to take care, after a local farmer had tried to confront a group of men on his land and been abused and threatened by them. The coursers came from London and coursed for money; thousands of pounds were involved. The dogs were mainly Lurchers and terriers that the police believed were used for badger baiting in other parts of the district. Woody had been outside in Charlie's garden, whilst Charlie had a nap indoors. The policeman, Angela told them, was convinced that somehow Woody had been enticed away, because remains of fresh meat had been found by the gate. The hare coursers had been known to steal dogs and were also capable of abandoning any dog that was injured. Friendly Woody would have been easy prey.

Angela left them both visiting Charlie, who was inconsolable. "He was always in the garden or in the cottage, never left my side," he repeated constantly.

"Did you hear any sound, Charlie?" Robert asked, as they discussed the incident again.

"Must have pulled him over the gate. I never heard the latch or anything. The police think the van stopped up by the road so they could have carried him back to it, knocked out somehow, maybe drugs." Charlie's body sagged. "They're wicked people them coursers," he muttered. "A real bad lot."

"So they tell me," Maggie said wearily. "It's the not knowing I can't bear. I'm imagining such awful things. We'll put notices up everywhere. Edna can ask everyone who goes in the shop to look out for him, can't she?" Maggie put her arm round the old man's shoulders. "Robert and I will search in all his favourite places."

"I've spoiled your homecoming well and proper. Spoiled it rotten," Charlie sobbed.

"Charlie, we know it wasn't your fault." Maggie said, endeavouring to comfort him. "I'm so sorry it happened while Woody was with you, but you mustn't blame yourself. He couldn't have been with a better person and he loves you as much as we do." Her soothing words only served to increase the old man's distress.

Maggie made him a strong cup of tea which helped to calm him a little before they wandered back up the lane, "I'll be back shortly," said Maggie. "Please don't fret, we'll find him."

"I couldn't care less if the whole house is covered in dog hairs," Robert said, kicking at the empty dog basket in their kitchen. "Just let me get hold of one of those bloody louts."

The sadness and fear was overwhelming.

For days Maggie retraced their favourite walks and searched the woods in and around the badgers' sett, calling the dog's name repeatedly. Robert had returned to work and Maggie found herself reluctantly agreeing to do a night shift at the hospital.

Throughout the long night Maggie's thoughts returned to

Woody. Where was he sleeping? Was he cold? Had they fed him? How frightened was he? The thought of his small trusting face and the memory of the look of love he gave her whenever she arrived home was breaking her heart. She had never felt happier on her honeymoon; but their happiness had turned to misery in a moment. The night on the ward was interminable. It was quiet, and she had too much time to think about her loss, instead of coping with women in labour. There were no new admissions and the babies in the postnatal ward slept soundly.

"You know, Maggie, we didn't stop once last night," said her young colleague. "We must have delivered a dozen babies at least, well it felt like it. None of us got a break."

Maggie wished something would happen to distract her thoughts.

"By the way, I'm sorry to hear you've lost your little dog."

The kindness of her colleague was well meant but it unlocked her emotions once more. She was relieved when the shift ended, and she could drive home quickly.

The stillness and silence in the cottage was intense. Maggie decided to walk round the village and retrace the route that she and Woody enjoyed the most, before she went back to bed. She needed to settle up with Jacky for the wedding cake, too and tell her that the novel idea of replicating the cottage had been well received. As she walked down the lane towards Jacky Richards' house, the tethered old Alsatian rose up, and growled menacingly.

"It's only me," she called, approaching him with caution.

Jacky appeared at the open door, wiping damp hands down her trouser leg.

"Well, this is a nice surprise. Come in, Maggie, fancy a cup of tea?"

"Thanks, I'd like that. I won't stop long."

"I'm really glad to see you," said Jacky. "I want to hear all about your honeymoon. You look as if you've been up all night, despite the tan."

"I have," said Maggie, clearing a space between piles of ironing on the settee. "I did a shift at the hospital last night but it was too quiet. I like to keep on the go at night"

Jacky filled the kettle. "D'you mind a mug?"

"Not at all, thanks. It's much more tiring at work when it's slack."

"So what brings you here? Where's that dog of yours?"

The chance remark hit home.

"Oh dear, you mean, you haven't heard?" Maggie broke down and once more found herself being supported by Jacky, as she told her the sad story.

CHAPTER 21

EXCITEMENT

"You'd make a lovely, Mum, Maggie," said Clare, watching from the comfort of her bed.

Maggie, on one of her morning visits flinched at the innocent remark from the young mother, which for a moment hung painfully in the air. A first bath for her baby was a new experience for her and Clare watched carefully, as Maggie demonstrated how to cope with bathing two-day-old Thomas. He was angelic and thankfully did not cry. The remark had been well meant and Maggie was careful to ensure that her mothers were not made to feel uncomfortable by her own deep longing for a baby.

She gently patted dry the area around the baby's clamped umbilical cord. "This little bit will drop off in a few days' time, I'll put a ligature round it and you can sprinkle it with the powder like I'm doing as they can get a bit smelly, I'm afraid." She noticed the look of concern on Clare's face. "It really doesn't hurt, they hardly know it's there; the last bit of Mum."

The baby was eager to feed and Maggie's guiding hand helped him to latch on with ease. "You make a lovely mum too, Clare.

You're not frightened of him, you're doing so well." She stroked the fine hair on the baby's head. "You can bath him next time and show Dean how it's done."

Who knows, she thought wistfully, my turn may come one day.

Maggie paused to fill in the notes before letting herself out of the flat. "I'll see you tomorrow morning, ring me if you get worried at all – about anything, I can always call back here after clinic."

"Thanks, Maggie; my mum should be here shortly. Dean's hoping his boss will give him a few days off." Claire tucked Thomas in closer, "We're so lucky aren't we? He's a little darling. I know they'll spoil him rotten, Dean always hoped we'd have a boy."

Maggie drove quickly. She had had a busy morning with five home visits all at some distance from each other. Feeding difficulties took a while to sort out, particularly with the first mothers. Frustration and helplessness were a strong mix and Maggie wished she could give them all much more of her time. She was happier working in people's homes, away from the charged atmosphere of the hospital, so she had made arrangements to meet her manager the following week to discuss her future. She didn't mind the occasional shift in the hospital to help out, but was anxious to get a permanent job and her own caseload, and build up stronger relationships with the couples she already dealt with on the district.

Arrangements had been made for Melanie, a student midwife, to accompany her for a couple of days and she was expected to start at the clinic. Arriving back in a rush, Maggie found that Dr Chandley's session was fully booked and her student had not arrived. With no time for a lunch break she gulped down a mug of coffee, while getting the room ready and calling in the first mother on the list. She tested urine samples and weighed each mother as they arrived and was pleased that Dr Chandley trusted her judgement as much as his own, when it came to listening and palpating their swollen abdomens to locate a baby's position. For one mother there was the added relief of knowing that her baby had 'turned' and was now head down in a better position for the birth. She confessed to Maggie that she had been dreading the examination, as Dr Chandley had forecast that she might have to have a caesarean section if the baby stayed in the breech position. He'd tried to reassure her that breech births were not uncommon, but admitted that some of his medical colleagues were more inclined to operate, seeing it as less risky for the baby, which had worried her.

The mother was leaving as the student, Melanie, arrived. She was a large, jolly girl and Maggie took an instant liking to her.

"So what kept you? We've got quite a number of women to see and the one that's just gone would have been interesting for you, a baby that was breech last week and has turned just in time." Maggie pulled up a chair beside her. "Did you enjoy your experience in the labour ward yesterday?"

"Yes and no. I'm sorry I'm so late, Maggie. I lost my way here, I'm not used to narrow country lanes." Melanie pulled a face. "I don't think I would say I enjoyed yesterday that much. It was so busy and I really didn't like watching a forceps delivery."

"That's a shame," said Maggie. "Perhaps you'll be able to get to a home delivery, you'll enjoy that, it's much more relaxed at home. I must say I couldn't really describe a forceps delivery as fun for anyone. Was the Mum okay, and baby?'

"Yes, fine, I had a chance to go and see them both in the ward later. The mother was thrilled with her little boy, and said she was just relieved to get it all over with. She also said she would have asked to be shot if they'd left her any longer."

"Poor thing, when they're so exhausted, it has to be a relief," said, Maggie pulling a clean sheet over the couch.

Maggie was pleased at how willing and adept a student Melanie was, listening to the babies' heartbeats and how much she seemed to enjoy talking to the mothers. In turn they were obviously making an effort to put her at ease, happily answering all her questions.

When the last mother, Jane Blighty rang in to say she'd been delayed, Maggie was grateful for the break.

"So, d'you think you'd like to work out here?" she said, searching the kitchen cupboard for more biscuits.

Melanie looked dubious, "I'm not sure really. I know I didn't like watching the forceps delivery but funnily enough I did enjoy the sense of excitement you get in hospital."

"I think being on the district is more rewarding than exciting," said Maggie. "You get involved with the whole family in a personal way, it's a more intimate relationship altogether. You're not just dealing with parts of their body knowing nothing of their real circumstances back home."

"I can understand that," Melanie said. "I won't make up my mind until I've done everything. I've got so much more to see and experience, haven't I?"

A receptionist peered round the door, "Nicking the cream biccys again, Maggie. Your patient, Jane Blighty's waiting and Dr Chandley has had to go out to a call," she said, firmly replacing the lid on the tin. "He asked if you could deal with her?"

"I'm ever so sorry I'm late," apologised Jane. "My littlest fell over in the playground, so I've left him with my neighbour. Lots of tears but no real damage, thank goodness. He'll be the death of me that one, always getting in to scrapes he is, covered in bruises. Got me in a right sweat, done my blood pressure a power of good, I'm sure."

Maggie decided to wait before examining Jane and let her chat to Melanie about her wayward brood of four little boys. When she finally took her blood pressure Maggie tried hard to look unconcerned. It was dangerously high.

"Can you wait in reception for ten minutes, and then I'll check it again?"

Jane nodded, "Just give me a good magazine, love, I need a rest."

The second reading was still too high and Maggie informed Jane that she would have to go in to hospital to rest. Dr Chandley agreed when she phoned him, instructing Maggie to get her admitted as soon as possible.

"Well, there's no way I can go to the hospital today. Who's going to look after the kids? My old man's on night shift and doesn't take kindly to being woken." Jane stood up to leave. "Sorry, love, I know you mean well."

Maggie held her arm. "Jane, I'm sorry but I shall have to speak to your husband. I'm serious; you will have to be admitted for observation. I don't want to alarm you, but you will be putting yourself and the baby at risk if you don't take my advice. Your blood pressure's high and your urine test's not good, I'm afraid. If anything happens to you, then there really is no one to look after the family, is there?"

Maggie saw the shock on Jane's face as she gave the ultimatum. "Dr Chandley insists we get you in straight away."

Jane's husband, Ron, was a very unhappy man. He swore at the receptionist and brushed aside Maggie's attempts to explain her concern. "She's not going in any bloody ambulance, I'll take her and I'll bring her back, sharpish. There's four kids wanting their tea right now and I've got a job of work to go to later."

"The hospital is expecting you, Mr Blighty and Dr Chandley is on the phone for you now," Maggie said, passing him the receiver.

Ron Blighty snatched it angrily, breathing hard as he listened to the doctor informing him of the seriousness of the situation. "Right bloody carry on," he muttered, slamming the phone down, before hurrying Jane out to his waiting car.

"Well, you should never have got me pregnant again," Maggie heard Jane shout as they went out.

"I think I'll have another coffee, Melanie, before we go," said Maggie. "See what I mean about getting to know the whole family?" she chuckled. "He'll get her there quicker than the ambulance if he listened to Dr Chandley."

—✽—

Ron Blighty drove fast. "Look mate, you look okay to me, what's that doctor and midwife going on about?"

"I'm sorry, Ron. I don't feel so bad really, just this headache's getting a bit worse. I kept seeing stars this morning, flashing lights you know."

"If I stop at home you can give the kids their tea, and then I'll take you in."

"We can ask Norma, next door if she can take them back to hers and give them their tea?"

"Alright, I'll ask her. I need to pick up my fags and the paper," Ron said irritably.

Jane could see a row coming. "Don't suppose another few minutes will matter."

—m—

Melanie, the student's eyes widened as she listened to Maggie. It was wet and windy as they drove through the narrow lanes and Maggie had to shout above the noise from the wipers. "I'm sorry I couldn't get hold of you, but really there wasn't any time and you'd have been half way back home then. Ron Blighty rang as I was leaving last night."

"Will their baby be alright?"

"Just about. I'm more worried about Jane. She's in Intensive Care and having a few fits. It's a long time since they've seen such a bad case. At least the ambulance got her in quickly. I'm really angry with myself for letting Ron Blighty leave the clinic like that, but we couldn't force him and he was warned. He decided to take his wife home instead of straight to the hospital."

"I thought he said he'd take her in?"

"He did, and I thought he would, but he took her home and decided that she should see to the kids' tea after all, as the neighbour was busy and wanted to go to the supermarket. Because Jane only had a headache, his words not mine, he went to see one of his mates and when he came back she was unconscious on the floor and the kids were huddled in the corner, too scared to move."

"How awful," Melanie looked rueful. "You do get some excitement then?"

"Yes," said Maggie, swerving to avoid a rabbit. "And we've got more excitement for you now, as there's a home birth brewing. Nice couple in the next village. I've a feeling she'll be quick, too."

—m—

Robert put his arm round Maggie's shoulders, and pulled her close, "Fancy walking up to the pub, darling?"

"If you like," Maggie yawned, "I really wanted to get to bed early tonight though; it's been a hectic couple of days."

"We'll just stay for one round, I've promised to play in the darts team," he said, smiling as he anticipated her surprise.

"Since when did you play darts?"

"I don't. They wanted someone to make up the numbers, so I've said I'd give it a go."

"I'll have to watch this."

"I think it's a good way to get to know a few more of the local lads and get a bit more involved in the village."

With linked arms they were soon side-stepping the potholes in the lane. "I might even stand for the parish council."

Maggie stopped him, "Has our Charlie put you up to this?" she said, glancing at his garden gate as they passed.

"Joking, darling, just joking, that's your sort of thing."

"I must say I'm pleased you're joining the darts team. You need to relax a bit more. Did I tell you that Angela and I thought of starting some Keep Fit classes in the village hall?"

"That's a great idea," he said. They started to jog slowly. "Can men attend? Tell me all about it in the pub."

Maggie found herself falling asleep as the darts match and muggy heat in the pub took hold. Robert was enjoying it so much, revelling in being man of the match, after scoring a bull's eye and seeing Maggie dozing he joined in a couple more rounds until Time was called.

"Charlie's still very depressed about Woody, blaming himself all the time" said Maggie, as they passed his cottage, with its bedroom lights still ablaze. "I'm finding it really helpful being busy now, it gives me less time to think about what might have happened to Woody."

"Me too. I was really fond of the little chap you know," he said, stopping to hug her, as they reached the cottage door. "By the way," he said, turning the key, "Don't be upset now but I feel I have to ask you. Would you like us to get another dog, darling?"

"No," Maggie said and ran upstairs.

She heard Robert pour himself a whisky, chastising himself aloud for his lack of tact.

Maggie threw herself on the bed, unable to stop the sobs rising in her throat.

CHAPTER 22

NIGHT VISITOR

"I suppose it happened after we got back from the pub?" Maggie said. "Have you lost them all, Charlie?" Charlie was sitting by the empty grate; his pipe neglected and unnoticed next to him.

"Found one cockerel behind the coal bin. Daft fox, I'd have given him that. Looks like he got all my good layers, and my little old Doris is missing," Charlie sniffed.

Edna plonked her teacup down on to the plastic tablecloth. "She weren't any good, you daft 'apeth, she hasn't laid a decent sized egg for the last two years. Eats more than all the others, mind. He should have had her and the cockerel and been satisfied, but no, he wanted to kill them all. Some say they do it to make a larder, stock piling, like. Beheaded the lot and left half in the run."

"I'm just amazed that we didn't hear anything."

"Probably had one drink too many and then slept deep," said Edna.

"Actually, Edna, I had one drink. I admit I sleep soundly after a drop of Charlie's sloe gin," Maggie retorted. "But I only had a glass of wine in the pub."

Charlie tapped his pipe on the fender, "Now don't start Edna. Maggie's got enough on her plate."

"We're not having a good time are we, Charlie?" Maggie put her arm round his shoulder. "What with Woody, then the deer nearly messing up your vegetable patch, and now this fox."

Maggie noticed a single tear run down his cheek, as he blew his nose into one of his bright yellow handkerchiefs. "No girl, we're not."

Edna brewed another pot of tea, while Maggie went outside to check on the damage and gather up the dead and injured chickens.

"What d'you think?" she asked on her return, holding up a bird for Charlie to see. "Two of them will survive, if I patch them up, but I'm afraid five are dead; we could pluck them and put them in my freezer, that'll make a nice meal for you."

"Leave 'em be," said Charlie. "The fox'll come back tonight. Pile them dead ones in the ditch at the end of the garden for 'im, he'll have taken the lot in a day or two."

Maggie laid the dead chickens carefully side by side in the ditch, having decided to let the two injured birds get over the shock before she bathed their wounds. As she walked back down the path to the kitchen she took a look at the damage the deer had done when they'd trampled on his vegetable patch and a slight movement near the hedge caught her eye. Curious, she crept closer and parted the leaves of a patch of marigolds to find a small brown hen, which blinked and squawked at her, before diving for cover again.

"Doris!" she called, grabbing at the trembling bird and gathering her up. "How did you manage to get away, you clever girl!" Maggie held the hen close, smiling with relief. "Charlie will be happy now you're okay, you're all right, don't be frightened. He'll look after you."

Despite his sadness, Charlie managed a smile, enfolding Doris in his broad hands, tucking her on his lap, "Well, I'll be darned, fancy you escaping old girl." Stroking her feathers gently he whispered, "You'd better sleep with me tonight."

"Don't be daft, you can't keep a live chicken in the kitchen, it's not natural." Edna gave a disgusted look.

"She may not be any use, but she's company," said Charlie, clutching Doris even closer.

Doris went everywhere with Charlie in the following weeks. She was tucked in to his large jacket pocket when he went to the shop and in his inside pocket when he attended church, much to Dawn Creasey's horror. At night the bird was given a bed of straw in the basket that had been Woody's, by the range. In return, Doris surprised Charlie, by laying an egg every other day.

Maggie couldn't forget the look of sadness on Charlie's face when he'd told her about the fox and the misery of the deer trampling on his prize vegetables and she bought six replacement chickens from a local farmer in the hope of bringing a smile to her old friend's face. As she drove back to the village with a cardboard box full of birds she looked forward to presenting them to him. She was treated to another of his rare smiles and a reluctant grunt of approval from Edna, but Charlie remained steadfast in his resolve that Doris would not be returned to the hen house.

—⁓—

"Are you still searching for the dog every day?" Angela asked Maggie.

They were sitting in Maggie's kitchen, drinking coffee, and bemoaning the loss of Woody.

Maggie nodded and decided to change the subject. She noticed

Angela had a new hairstyle and highlights, was wearing more make-up than usual and looked more relaxed and confident than she had seen her looking for a while. Noticing every detail of her friend's new look made Maggie feel dull by comparison.

"The consultant found no reason for my miscarriages," she said, moving on to her last hospital visit. "Oh, Angela, how I hate that word. In my mind I lose a fully- formed baby each time it happens. Rob suffers too, he tries to do the strong man bit in order to protect me, but he needs just as much help as I do. It tears us apart you know, we need to communicate closely, to try and rationalise this whole thing. The consultant was insistent that we would eventually succeed. He told us to stop worrying, don't they all?" she said with bitterness. "Apparently there is research going on in America and in this country into bio chemical pregnancies, but that's not helping me now." She poured more coffee. "It's all right for him to say don't worry, but it's almost impossible not to. We've also been going over and over the possibility of adopting a baby. Mum suggested it. Everywhere I go I see parents and children. Every book I read, every programme we watch. The world is full of families and everyone wants to know when we are going to start one of our own. There are days when I just want to scream. She paused, worried she might lose control in front of her friend. She couldn't tell her how it felt as if her heart was breaking every time she picked up a new-born baby. She couldn't describe how she longed so much to have her own baby and endured a physical pain every time she delivered someone else's child.

"People don't realise how desperately you want a baby. They don't mean to be hurtful," said Angela.

"I know, I know. It's just that everyone seems to care more for people with babies and a family, as if couples without children aren't as important." Maggie was trying hard not break down.

"How d'you mean?"

"Well, for example, it's always those with children who get first pick of the rota and taking time off, and so on at work. I'm sick of hearing: 'I'm sure Maggie won't mind staying on, after all she doesn't have children to worry about'. I know it's easier for me, but it hurts, all the same."

"So are you thinking about adopting, then? Seriously?"

"Before we heard what the consultant had to say, about me carrying a pregnancy to term, it made us think of other options you know, fostering, and adoption." She got up to switch the kettle on.

"Like another?"

"I'll just have half a cup."

"Biscuit?"

"No, thanks."

"Well you see, that said, I haven't managed to have a baby yet, have I? So I thought I might make enquiries, just in case, that's all."

"I know there is a need for adoptive parents for children from all sorts of backgrounds and from very different circumstances. Would it concern you if a child had a disability for instance? Have you considered that possibility?" Angela asked.

"No. I don't mean to sound heartless. Robert and I both know we could give a child, any child, a good home, but we are also aware of the problems of bringing up someone else's child and neither of us feels we'd cope with more problems, not to begin with anyway." She was near to tears again. "I'm sorry if that sounds really selfish."

"Of course not, it was thoughtless of me to mention it," said Angela.

Maggie got up and walked over to the pantry. "Fancy a slice of my ginger cake?"

"Oh, yes please. The last one you made was really good."

"I'm making a batch for Edna as we're all being asked to help out at the jumble sale next week. She likes to be in charge of teas and cakes."

"How is the old trout?"

"Fine. I want to get those two married off," Maggie laughed. "Poor Edna has to vie with Doris for Charlie's affection at the moment."

"Doris? Who's Doris?"

Angela shuddered at the tale of the headless chickens when Maggie told her about the fox and the discovery of Doris. "Poor Charlie, it was an awful shock for him. Mind you, I think Doris will be easier to live with than Edna," she laughed, before picking at the remaining crumbs on her plate.

"Oh dear, I've got to go unfortunately. This cake's excellent, you're becoming quite an expert cook, Maggie. Give Charlie my love and say how sorry I am about everything." Angela stretched her hand across the table, "Look, Maggie, if you want advice, and I think you do, it really wouldn't do any harm to make some enquiries about adoption, after all you may get turned down. Can't imagine it somehow, but you need to find out." She scraped back the chair. "I have to go."

"Yes, we will," Maggie said, looking round the kitchen. "And about fostering, but that's enough for now, you must go and collect James. You haven't told me all about you and Tom. Let's meet next week. Perhaps we could go to the pub and have lunch? I'll ring you when I know what shift I'm on."

"'Bye." Angela hugged her and hurried down the path.

Maggie sat on in the kitchen, oppressed by the sudden emptiness of the house. It was three weeks since Woody had been taken, and the police had no real leads; they didn't think the criminals had come from London, so perhaps they were local? Her heart ached for him. What if whoever had taken Woody was mistreating the poor little dog? For all she knew he might be dead. Maggie shivered; best not to dwell on what might have happened. She rinsed the mugs and gazed out of the window. One day, she determined, there would be a swing and slide on the lawn, and muddy little wellies in the hall.

Angela drove slowly, relieved that Maggie hadn't broken down completely but glad her friend had felt able to express her thoughts. Her heart went out to Maggie; she couldn't imagine what it must feel like to lose the little dog in such a cruel way – not knowing what had happened to him. If only Maggie could get pregnant again and carry a baby to term, have the child she was so desperate for. It was, of course, quite easy to find another puppy, but now was not the time to suggest that to her friend. She had had no difficulty conceiving James and was sure that for her, getting pregnant again would not be a problem. She had been bursting to tell Maggie her own news, but it had not been possible with her friend in the state she was in. She ran over in her mind what she would tell her next time, just for the thrill of it and because she could hardly believe the way things had worked out. Tom was planning to move in as soon as her divorce was through. Gordon was letting it happen and without any resistance from either party, it would soon be finalised. She was certain to get custody of James, and Tom had spoken of his own desire for them to have children. Poor, Maggie, it would be salt in the wound to tell her and so it must wait.

CHAPTER 23
LOST AND FOUND

"**S**hut it, will you! Bloody whining, it's getting on my nerves."

The Alsatian yelped as Jacky Richards cuffed it on the way back to the kitchen after hanging out a line of washing. Another pile of laundry was waiting by the machine and she sorted it into heaps on the floor, pouring herself a mug of tea. The dog continued to whine, pulling hard on its chains, before breaking in to a howl with its head laid back, wolf-like.

Jacky filled a basin with water and marched outside, "See if this'll shut you up," she shouted, tossing the cold water. The dog yelped, shook the water off and began whining again as she went back inside, going upstairs to put fresh sheets on the beds and distance herself from the dog's noise. She had been feeling unwell all day and her head ached. "I'm getting 'flu or something," she muttered. The dog was howling now, as she peered down from the open window.

"What the hell's the matter with you?" There was no one about, as it was market day in Waldersby. The bus had collected her neighbours from the end of the lane an hour ago and they wouldn't be back for ages.

The dog was wrenching and pulling now, barking frantically, as Jacky ran back downstairs. She was beginning to feel nervous now; the dog never behaved this way, the odd growl and bark at passers-by sometimes, but nothing like this. "Here, I'll let you off," she said. He was an old dog, and since Len had gone inside, she had taken to letting him off the chain in the evenings, feeling safer with him in the house and she knew he would never leave her, even if she did swear and curse at him. But the dog, freed from its chain, raced away down the lane, and disappeared into the undergrowth near the wood.

"Come back, come back," she yelled, retreating into the kitchen, surprised and fearful to find herself shaking. "Pull yourself together," she said. "Get your boots on and think straight." She wished Len was there with his shot gun; that always spooked any strangers.

The distant sound of the dog's barking drew her in the direction of the old gravel pit, where a track led off the path, skirting the wood. The pit was beyond an old iron gateway. The area had been a favourite haunt for her boys, when they were younger. The, PRIVATE, KEEP OUT sign, hung at an angle from the rusting bars. She swore at the brambles clawing at her bare arms. The track to the bottom of the pit was overgrown and the ground riddled by a rabbit warren, which tripped her every step, but the barking was closer now, more persistent.

"Here, boy, here. Here, boy, here."

The barking stopped and there was silence. Jacky didn't know which direction to take, listening, not moving, until she heard another faint sound.

The jumble was arriving by the bag load and the village hall was awash with old clothes, shoes, toys, books and bric a brac. Maggie and Angela were helping to sort out everything in preparation for the annual sale the following day, with Edna giving strict instructions to cajole as many people as possible to bake cakes and biscuits for her stall. The two had done the rounds and half the village now had a cake baking in the oven. Some of the jumble smelt musty and had been recycled several times but Maggie laid claim to several items, including a serviceable jumper for Robert to garden in, plus some trousers for Charlie, which she knew would be subject to Edna's approval. Angela picked out some children's books and jigsaws, together with a pretty pair of vases. Maggie finally struggled home with her bargains, picking her way down the lane with bulging plastic bags banging against her legs and when Robert arrived home he found the sitting room floor piled high with jumble.

"I thought you were helping at this event?" he said, as Maggie insisted he try on a red track suit.

"Oh dear, that's no good Rob, here try this on."

Maggie thrust a thick- knit, slightly frayed, jumper at him. "It's the perks of being a helper."

"That's cheating isn't it? Nicking all the good stuff first. Not that you could really call this good stuff, could you? This jumper stinks of moth balls."

"I've been told it's normal practice," she laughed, as Robert threw the jumper aside and tried a faded corduroy jacket. "It also means they get lots of helpers."

Robert swapped the jacket for another jumper. "So who comes to this event if everyone in the village is helping?"

"Jumblies, regular jumble sale followers. Apparently they come from miles around and queue really early. Some items have been stored since last year. What doesn't get taken away by a market trader is stored in Dawn Creasey's garage, 'til the next time."

Robert grimaced. "Are we so desperate that I have to wear this rubbish, just so that you can say we've got a bargain?"

"Don't be a snob. Just look at these books. I'll have that jumper if you don't want it, I can soon wash the smell out."

"That's fine, my love, it looks better on you anyway. Now, if you don't mind, can we eat? I'm starving."

"Two minutes. I just need to sort this lot out, and your dinner will be on the table," Maggie stuffed the clothing back in the bags. "Have a beer and pour me a gin and tonic, please – I deserve it."

—⁂—

Jacky Williams pulled at the undergrowth in the gravel pit. The whimper she had heard was barely audible, but she could see a face and two eyes staring up at her, surrounded by dense thicket.

"Well I'll be... however did you manage to get in there, silly boy?" she said aloud. "Don't fret, I'll get you out."

Excited at this discovery she barely noticed the prick and stab of the brambles now, as she plunged her bare arms into the thicket, working quickly until she had made enough space to kneel down and reach in. The old Alsatian sat whining and whimpering on the ledge above her, until Jacky finally managed to reach out her hand to stroke the small brown head, "Woody, isn't it? Woody? How long have you been hiding in here?"

The little dog stood up shakily and then fell again, his legs buckling. He was terribly thin and Jacky noticed a deep cut on one back leg, as she stroked him. But gradually the trembling eased and he gave a weak wag of his tail, as she coaxed him out of the thicket. He staggered, barely able to stand at all, as she lifted him into her arms. The Alsatian barked noisily as they drew near and Woody cringed.

"You're all right, he won't hurt you. You've lost a lot of blood from that wound, I reckon." She continued to stroke the dog, placing him on the ground, giving him time to gain confidence in her. Woody managed a few steps up the steep slope, but his progress was slow and half way up he stopped and flopped to the ground.

"You don't look as if you've eaten for weeks, you're just skin and bone. Well, I know someone who'll be more than pleased to fatten you up. Come on, little one."

Jacky let him settle in her arms before carrying him back to the top of the pit where she laid him on the grass. Woody trembled and whined pitifully as the Alsatian gently sniffed him all over and licked at his wound.

The second she got home Jacky picked up the phone, watching as her old dog lay down close to Woody as if to warm him, a catch in her throat when she spoke to Maggie.

"Yes, really, he's very weak and has a nasty gash on his leg but he'll be fine." She paused at the sound of sobbing. "Really, Maggie, don't cry, love. Honestly, I'm sure he'll be alright"

Maggie's sobs diminished as Jacky relayed the full story.

"You'll be right as rain now, Woody, they're coming to get you and I bet you'll get spoilt rotten," Jacky said, waiting for Maggie to arrive. She stroked the little dog constantly and even patted the Alsatian, "Thanks to you, mate, we found him. Got me really riled you did to start with. Here, have this," she said, giving the old dog a well-chewed bone.

—҂—

"You're holding him too, tight darling," Robert said, as Maggie hugged Woody and wrapped him in a large towel on the draining board.

"I must make sure he's dry."

"Goodness, he needed that bath and the wound looks a lot cleaner now," Robert said, gently lifting the injured leg and carefully inspecting Woody, who was shivering violently, despite the warm towels.

"Pass the bandage and I'll cover it up. We need to get him to the vet, but it doesn't look infected, thank goodness." Maggie lifted Woody to the floor, and Robert played the hair drier over the dog's damp hair. "He's always loved this bit, but it's awful to see him so weak isn't it? Look he's trying to play though."

"Better not feed him anymore. Jacky gave him a tin of her dog food and apparently he wolfed that down and then sicked it straight up. We'll see what the vet suggests; just small amounts to start with, I expect. Come on, that'll do, let's go."

On the way to Waldersby they discussed the comments from the policeman they'd spoken to on the phone.

"He thinks Woody tried to escape from their car or van and probably got injured jumping out."

Woody, snug in the blanket on Maggie's knee gazed at her. "If only you could talk to us," she said, stroking him.

"We'll never know," said Robert as they turned down Waldersby High Street. "I expect he's been lying low in that gravel pit for several days, licking that wound and whimpering, too weak to go on. Thank heavens Jacky's dog picked up the sound. He could have died there."

"I'm not letting you out of my sight," Maggie whispered in Woody's ear, as she carried him into the surgery. "Don't you ever speak to strangers again."

On their return they stopped, so Charlie could see Woody. Edna said he'd been pacing up and down since the dog's discovery, wearing himself out with anxiety. Now he sat with Doris the hen on his lap, tears running unchecked down his cheeks. "Well, I'll be darned," he repeated, over and over again. "Well. I'll be darned."

Robert and Maggie took turns to explain what the vet had prescribed. Even Edna lent forward without a word and stroked the little dog's head.

"We'd better take him home now," Maggie said.

"I just hope they catch them," Edna said in her usual loud manner. "They deserve to be shot them sort, wicked they are, wicked."

"Now, you can stop fretting, Charlie," Maggie said, stooping to kiss his rough cheek, "I'll bring him round tomorrow after he's had a good rest."

Charlie reached out and patted Woody gently on the head. "You're safe now, boy. I'll not let you down again." He blew vigorously into his yellow handkerchief before taking up his pipe.

Doris clucked and flew on to the table, startling Woody into giving a short bark. Robert smiled, as he opened the door, "There you go, Charlie, I think he's on the mend already."

CHAPTER 24

IN NEED OF CARE
AND ATTENTION

Dawn Creasey did as she was told and picked up the pen on the shop counter, as Edna pushed the clip board towards her.

"Right, sign there." Edna instructed. "Got to stop these houses going up somehow. Not bad, thirty signatures so far."

"A petition? So what will you do with this, Edna?"

"Maggie Edwards will get everyone else to sign up, and then she's giving it to someone on the council."

"The parish council?"

"Yes and that other lot in Waldersby and some in the village are going to send a letter to the MP. She's going to the council meeting next week to tell them what we think of this barmy idea. Charlie said she's trying to find out as much as possible about fighting it," she sniffed. "No doubt the Major's very proud of his grand plans, as it's on his land. Now we know why he wanted to sell that meadow. He'll be hoping to get permission for all them houses and do very nicely, thank you."

Dawn winced at Edna's sarcasm. "It must be nice to have spare land. I've often thought we could build a little bungalow in our back garden, where the greenhouse is, but hubby says the council would never let us. I agree it seems a shame to spoil that lovely meadow, though. Charlie won't like looking out at buildings will he?"

"It's daft," said Edna. "This village can't take all them new people. The school's full as it is. Before you know it they'll be wanting a supermarket here and I'll lose my trade."

"Surely it won't come to that, Edna? Most people like to do a big shop in Waldersby, they'll never have a supermarket here. Don't get het up before it's actually happened," she said, looking along the shelves. "How many houses will there be, d'you know? One or two won't hurt will they?"

"About ten."

"Ten? Oh dear. Now I've forgotten what I came in for, I'll take some tomato soup anyway." Dawn placed two tins on the counter. "I'll have some ham and a piece of that cheddar. I made a lovely macaroni with it last week."

"Ten big ones too, not for the likes of you and me you know," Edna said, vigorously wrapping the cheese.

Dawn rummaged in her bag for her purse. "It'd be quite nice to see a doctor's surgery here though, my arthritis is really getting me down."

"Well, that won't happen," said Edna, lifting the ham on to the slicer. "How many? Thick or thin?"

"Four, thick. Well, I know it won't, but now the bus only runs twice a week I have a devil's own job getting to the surgery when it suits me."

"Doesn't bother me, I can't be doing with doctors these days. Cider vinegar with a drop of honey in hot water seems to clear up my complaints." Edna handed over the wrapped ham. "D'you still want a dozen eggs on Friday?"

"Yes, I hear Charlie's hens are laying now?"

"The new lot are good layers, they're keeping me well supplied. I just wish he'd stop letting that silly old hen of his in the kitchen." She reached under the counter for a cloth.

Dawn smiled, "He's kindly like that."

"It's unhygienic." Edna pursed her lips, wiping and rearranging a few items as she spoke, putting Dawns money in the till and slamming the drawer shut.

"The little dog is doing fine, I hear?"

"Beats me how it ever survived," Edna said, "Charlie will keep on about it being his fault. It's beginning to pick up though and it's eating better. The vet said it was a miracle."

"I hope they catch the swine," Dawn said. "It was cruel, really wicked to take him like that, I cry every time I think of it."

"Police say they haven't a hope of catching the culprits. They move about the country, leaving dogs all over the place, just abandon them without a care." Edna turned her attention to rearranging some tins on the shelves behind the counter and blinked hard. She didn't want Dawn to think she'd gone soft.

"Disgusting, I'll be off, I'll come by Friday for my eggs. Give Charlie my regards, won't you?" The doorbell pealed loudly as Dawn went out.

With no sign of any more customers approaching Edna decided to close early for lunch. Before leaving she picked up a packet of dog treats, marrow bone biscuits, 'Woody's favourite', she murmured, placing the packet in her bag. 'Extra vitamins should do him good.'

When Charlie didn't answer her knock, Edna pushed open the cottage door and placed the box with his corned beef sandwich inside on the table. As she put the kettle on she called out to him, thinking he must be down the garden, shushing Doris the hen off the table as she did so, but there was no reply. Doris, flew up on to the draining board.

"Oh, no you don't," said Edna, brushing her off roughly.

Squawking, Doris retreated under the table.

As she set the kettle to boil she realised the range was stone cold and that there were no signs that Charlie had had his breakfast either. He always left his dishes to soak in the sink. She opened the kitchen door and walked down the garden path, calling to him. Perhaps he had gone to see Maggie? He was nowhere to be seen, anxious now she hurried back up the path and in to the kitchen. He knew she'd be bringing his lunch and wouldn't want to miss his sandwich. Just as she thought of phoning Maggie she heard noises coming from the bedroom above the kitchen.

"Edna, Edna, is that you?" Charlie's voice sounded weak.

She pulled open the half-shut door to the hallway.

"I'm up here," he called weakly.

Edna's heart was pounding as she climbed as quickly as she could up the creaky old staircase, pulling on the wooden rail, her arm brushing against peeling whitewash.

"What are you doing, Charlie?"

He was sprawled awkwardly against the wall next to his bed, shivering and cold to her touch.

"What on earth? Can't you move?"

Edna grabbed his arm. "Oh my, I can't manage you. It needs someone strong. How long have you been down there?"

"Since crack of dawn," he said, trying to help himself up, but sinking back down, "I keep drifting off but I'm cold, Edna, so cold. Can you put me a blanket on, old girl?"

His voice was thin and strained and Edna felt the tears in her eyes for the second time that day, as she yanked a blanket off the bed and covered him up as best she could.

"I'll call an ambulance; it's the only way we'll get you on your feet. I'll ring Maggie, too."

"She's not in. I heard her go out early. Baby on its way I expect. Robert's away on business."

Edna had to bend close to catch the whisper of his words.

The ambulance crew chatted away happily as they lifted Charlie on to the bed and wrapped him in red woollen blankets. They checked his heart and examined him before manoeuvring him with difficulty down the narrow flight of stairs and in to the waiting ambulance, with Edna watching their every move.

"He's very cold, Mrs," said one of the crew.

"I'm not his Mrs," Edna said. "I found him when I brought his lunch and he told me he'd been stuck there from six o'clock this morning. That's his normal getting-up time. I'm just a neighbour he relies on a bit, no relation."

"Lucky you found him then, 'cos he's probably suffering from hypothermia, and that can be a bit nasty, specially for old people," one crewman said, slamming the back door of the ambulance.

"Thanks for the call, young lady. You'd better ring the hospital in about an hour, and find out what's what. Bye love," called the driver.

"I'll give them love! Cheeky buggers," she muttered crossly, shooing Doris from the kitchen, before locking the cottage door and hiding the key under the flower pot by the front door.

Maggie stopped the car abruptly as the ambulance, lights flashing and siren sounding, rushed past her. Edna was shutting Charlie's gate on to the lane as she ran towards her.

"Edna, tell me please, is Charlie all right? What's happened? Has he had a fall? Is it his heart?"

"Seems he fell over that silly chicken!" said Edna, pursing her lips.

"Doris?" said Maggie, unable to think straight.

"It goes with him up to the bedroom, if you can believe it!"

"I can," said, Maggie.

"Well, it was clucking about when he got up first thing to use his chamber pot. It seems he got back in bed, but rolled off trying to pick Doris up and got himself stuck. Then he couldn't get up at all, he must have passed out and can't remember much after that."

"Oh my goodness, poor Charlie," said Maggie, listening to the full story as they walked back to the car.

"What did the ambulance crew say? He must have been perished lying there."

"They've taken him in to be on the safe side. Might get hyperpneumonia or some such."

"Hypothermia, I think they mean. I'm not surprised though. Poor, poor, Charlie. I was terrified when I saw the ambulance and its flashing lights."

"He was only in his vest and long johns. Trapped, between the bed and the wall."

"I'll ring the hospital in an hour or two's time, if you like, just to see how he is, and then I can go and fetch him home. Hopefully they won't want to keep him in too long."

"He hates hospitals," said Edna. "I'm going back to the shop, you can ring me there. He was upset at being taken in I can tell you, but they insisted. Quite right, silly old fool."

"It was a nasty shock for you as well. Let me take you home," said Maggie, noticing Edna's trembling hands.

"I'll be alright, I don't mind walking."

Maggie put an arm round Edna, pretending not to notice the tears she was wiping away.

"I don't know what I'll do if anything happens to that daft old man," Edna sniffed, searching her bag for a handkerchief.

"Here, take this," Maggie produced a tissue, "Charlie will be fine. Come back with me and have a cup of tea?"

"I'll be all right, don't you worry," said Edna, brushing Maggie's hand away.

"Come on, I insist. Charlie would be very cross if I didn't look after you, wouldn't he?" she said, guiding her towards the car.

When she opened the cottage door to an excited Woody she gave Edna a full report on the dog's progress, knowing that Edna had always had a soft spot for him. She was relieved also that Edna, or the 'old trout', as Angela called her, demonstrated that she had even more of a soft spot for Charlie.

"It's so good to see his mischievous spark returning," she told Edna. "At least he doesn't collapse every time he wags his tail and he's eating well, the vet's pleased with him."

Edna listened without comment as Maggie chatted on filling the awkwardness between them. She hated to leave him for even a short while, she told Edna, but the vet had advised her to live their lives normally and that slowly the dog would regain his confidence and feel secure in his familiar surroundings.

"All right Woody, all right, that's enough hellos," Maggie said, leading him back to his basket. "Do sit down, Edna, you can have Charlie's favourite seat. Let me hang your coat up."

Maggie made a pot of tea and pulled the lid off a big cake tin. "I hope you'll like my carrot cake," she said, cutting two slices and placing a strong cup of tea in front of Edna, who was unusually quiet. "Now I think I'd better phone the hospital, don't you? We'll see what time we can go and visit Charlie."

In the hospital, Charlie was pretending to be asleep as the

ward sister picked up the chart at the end of his bed and passed it to the consultant, Mr Hall, doing his ward round.

"So how is this old chap, Sister?"

"He seems fine. He got very cold of course, but we've warmed him up. He didn't like going down to X-ray this afternoon."

"You had a lucky escape, I think Mr Watt. The X-rays don't show any broken bones," he boomed, turning to the students gathered around the foot of the bed. "He can have what he likes to eat and drink now, and we'll keep him in for a couple more days, Sister." Mr Hall clipped the chart back on the bed end, and made to move away.

Charlie opened his eyes, "No, you won't. I need to be getting back to my cottage, thank you, Doctor."

Mr Hall moved back to the bedside, "Mr Watt," he said, patting Charlie's arm and smiling round at his students. "You've had a nasty fall, and a shock. I'm keeping you in for observation."

"That's very kind, I'm sure, Doctor" said Charlie, plucking at the blue cotton counterpane and shifting his stiffening legs. "You don't understand, Doctor. I've got hens to feed, and I need to water the veg. Beans don't like drying up, like I was telling Nurse here."

"Sorry Mr Watt. I'm afraid you're more important right now." Mr Hall said, ignoring the faint snigger from one of the students.

"Does he have any family visiting, Sister?"

"I believe a neighbour is coming this evening, I'll make sure someone gets to know all about his worries."

"Thank you, Sister. I'll see you tomorrow, Sir."

Before Charlie could reply they had moved away, and were surrounding the next bedside, but Charlie threw back the bedclothes, swung his legs slowly over the side of the bed, although he was too stiff to get far. The metal bed frame was cold and hard, and his feet didn't quite reach the ground.

"I'm going home when the visitors come," he called out, alerting a nurse who ran back just in time to stop him falling.

"You're a bit breathless, Charlie. Perhaps one of the doctors will listen in to your chest before they leave. I'd better let Mr Hall know. Now, don't move from there will you?"

"I don't need any more of them X-rays." Charlie said. "I'd like my clothes and I'm going home."

"Not possible I'm afraid."

The nurse plumped up a pillow and placed it behind his head, wrapping two blankets firmly round his knees. "There now, I'll organise a nice cup of tea for you, when the ward round's finished."

Charlie knew when he was beaten. He slumped in the chair, and tried to remember what had happened. He couldn't recall much, only how cold he had felt when Edna found him. He knew that hospitals were like prisons once they'd got you, and he'd been told that old people got confused when they were in strange surroundings. He had to make Edna take him home. Maggie would be able to get him out, he felt sure.

That evening Maggie and Edna found Charlie snoring loudly. The ward sister had spoken to them as they entered the ward.

"I'm afraid he's getting cross with us." she said, smiling. "I'd rather he was like that though, at least it shows spirit. Old people sometimes just fade away when they come in here."

"Has he eaten?" Maggie asked.

"He's had two bowls of soup and he's asking for cups of tea every time one of us passes the bed."

"That's a good sign," said Edna.

They both sat by the bed for fifteen minutes while Charlie snored.

"I know, I'll write him a note, and give him our love, and tell him that we'll be back tomorrow. He needs to sleep more than us chatting. What d'you think, Edna?" Maggie said.

Edna arranged the flowers for a second time. "I expect you know best."

Reluctantly, they left the hospital and spoke little on the way back to Little Fordham.

"Please don't worry, he'll be fine in a few days. I'll see to Doris later, and shut them all up for the night," Maggie said as she dropped Edna off outside the village shop.

She drove quickly alongside the green, rounded the bend and turned down the lane to the cottage, stopping at Charlie's open gate. "I'm sure it was closed," she said to herself, glancing up the path to the door of Charlie's cottage, which was wide open.

She got out of the car, and walked up the path in the dim light, certain that Edna wouldn't have left the door open.

CHAPTER 25
UNITED WE STAND

PC O'Sheridan scratched his head, looking puzzled. "In all my years on this beat we've only ever had three break-ins, and they were garden sheds."

"It's extraordinary that whoever did this chose the moment that Charlie was in the hospital, don't you think?" Maggie queried, "I mean, how could they have known?"

They were sitting on the bench outside Charlie's front door – the spot where he loved to rest in the evenings and watch the sunset over the meadow, puffing on his last pipe of the day, before turning in.

"Coincidence I think. Just so happened they were around when the ambulance left and saw an opportunity, which convinces me more than anything that this might be local villains."

"Goodness, I hope not," said Maggie. "We all know each other so well. I can't think of any villains who might be local."

"Well, you haven't been around that long, young lady. I think I could tell you a tale or two that would make your hair curlier than it is already."

"Have you spoken to Mrs Newbold yet?"

"I'm seeing her later. She can be a right old so and so if she chooses and no doubt Charlie Watt's accident and now this, will have upset her. I believe her niece is running the shop this afternoon, so that we can have a good chat. I expect she's told you she doesn't want Mr Watt to know about this burglary whilst he's in hospital?"

"I agree. D'you know exactly what's been stolen?"

"I hope she'll be able to help. After all they've been friends for years. I expect she knows what he has in that old cupboard."

They walked to the lane and the policeman looked across to the meadow. "I understand you're putting up a bit of a fight over this land. Don't want houses and new people, is that it?"

"Oh goodness me, don't say it like that." Maggie felt quite taken aback. "I was a newcomer myself not so long ago, as you've pointed out. No, it's just that it's such an ancient meadow and it would be sad to lose it. Charlie Watt would be heartbroken. We need more houses I'm sure, but I really do think this is the wrong place." Maggie pointed towards the woods. "This wonderful view would be blanked out by large houses. There's no pressing need to develop Little Fordham and it won't be the locals who will benefit, but commuters coming and going."

"The Major will do quite nicely too, thank you very much," PC O' Sheridan added, walking towards his car. "Your husband commutes sometimes, doesn't he?"

Maggie felt her face flush. "What are you trying to say?"

"Keep your eyes and ears open, young lady," he said, ignoring the question. "Call me if there's anything you feel I should know," he said, lowering the window, "I'm told you're quite pally with the Richards family?"

"I'm not sure that pally is the word I'd use, but yes I get on well with Jacky Richards, said Maggie, realising how defensive she sounded. "She's had a rough time."

"So I believe. I'll be in touch," he said, moving off.

Maggie walked slowly back to Nut Tree Cottage. PC O'Sheridan had presumed her reasons for fighting the planning application were selfish. She didn't like the way he'd questioned her friendship with the Richards family either and by the time Robert arrived home her indignation had reached a pitch.

"Now please don't say he was only doing his job, darling, he was actually quite sarcastic."

"Policemen have a difficult job. I'm sure he didn't mean anything," said Robert, hugging her.

PC O'Sheridan got no further with his investigations that afternoon, as Edna was at a loss to know what might have been stolen – she couldn't help despite his insistence that she knew everything about the contents of the cottage.

"No idea what's in his cupboards," she told Dawn Creasey, as they cleaned the cottage ready for Charlie's return. "It's his private business, nothing to do with me. Our policeman gets a bit above himself at times."

"Mustn't forget how good he was when you got beaten up though, Edna. We're lucky to have a good bobby keeping an eye on things," said Dawn.

"I expect he thought you'd know, seeing as you've been good friends since she passed away," said Dawn, surveying the ornaments on the shelf over the range and the photograph of his late wife, Mary. "Here, drink your tea, it's getting cold. What time are you expecting Charlie back?"

"Them two have gone to collect him. I expect they'll get back about four."

Edna picked up a duster and gave the hanging brass horseshoes an extra rub. "I've got him a nice steak and kidney pie for his supper, it'll go well with some of his new potatoes." She finished her tea and rinsed the mugs. "They'll drain. Right we'd better be off. Thanks for helping, I'd never have managed it all."

"Before we go," said Dawn, taking a pair of scissors out of the drawer, "I'll just pick a few flowers for his table."

Edna waited for her before locking the cottage door behind them. They walked down the path, and paused in the lane by the meadow gate.

"It would be a real shame if they put too many houses up," said Dawn, "but you can't stop progress."

"Progress?" said Edna. "Don't talk daft, woman. Come on, I've got a lot to do."

They reached the main road and Edna hurried ahead in the direction of the village green, leaving Dawn to go to the village church and attend to the flower arrangements for the Sunday service.

"Let me know how he is," Dawn called after her, but Edna was already rushing away out of earshot.

The fresh flowers and greenery had already been collected from gardens around the village and some had been bought in the market. Large bunches were standing in the buckets in the back porch. Dawn decided to make a start as the two neighbours who would be helping her were not due at the church for another hour. Pushing open the door and going in to the back room, she wondered why the inner door to the church was ajar. It was always kept shut and the women did the flower arranging in the vestry. The church was dark and silent as she walked in.

"Hello," she called, her voice echoing back to her in the church, mirroring her nerves. She moved down the aisle to turn on the lights, thinking with every hurried step she took about the robbery at Charlie's cottage. "Hello, is there anyone in here?" she called again, hearing the break in her voice.

The church felt different from usual, she was sure she wasn't imagining it and she walked back down the aisle looking left and right, until she came to the front pew. There was a half-eaten sandwich still in its wrapper and an empty beer can discarded on the floor, with some of the contents spilled on the polished wooden seat. Dawn stood still, her legs shaking as if they were going to give way, her heart pounding. The altar cloth was strewn on the floor. The church's precious silverware, the two ancient silver candlesticks and a solid silver salver had gone. Dawn let out a cry that echoed round the church.

—⁓—

Charlie stood in the doorway of his cottage. "All that sitting around's done me no good," he said, clutching at Robert's sleeve.

"I'll put the kettle on," said Maggie.

"Rather have a drop of carrot whisky."

"D'you really think you should, Charlie?" Maggie said, raising her eyebrows and looking with concern at Robert.

"Certainly I should." he said, "and, what's more you can pour three lots out to celebrate me getting out of that darned hospital." He sat down heavily on the armchair by the range. "Nice flowers and I can smell the polish, I guess Edna's been in here tidying up."

"Edna and Dawn have been sorting you out a bit, Charlie."

"I'll tell you this, you two; you needn't think I'm ever going back in that hospital again." He picked up Mary's photograph, "They'll carry me out of here in my coffin and then we'll be together again, won't we my love?"

He swallowed the small glass of carrot whisky down in one gulp while Robert and Maggie sipped theirs slowly, raising their glasses to his future good health.

"I can't tell you how wonderful it is to have you back." Maggie said, "It's been so strange without you."

Robert patted Charlie's arm. "We really missed you. Now, are you quite sure you going to be alright here tonight?"

"After Edna and Dawn Creasey have finished filling me up with food, I'll sleep like a lamb." He took another swig. "My, this is doing me a power of good," he burped, and wiped his mouth with a large coloured handkerchief. "Only trouble is Edna won't let me keep my little Doris in the house. Them two are bringing my dinner at six o'clock, and Edna says she'll not leave till I'm tucked up."

Maggie opened the door of the cottage and looked down the path.

"I'll shut the chickens in later tonight," said Maggie. "But I have to go now. I have to collect the petition for the parish council meeting next week. Robert can stay till Edna gets here, can't you, darling?"

"I most certainly can, as long as Charlie doesn't get me drunk."

"Now then, you're as bad as each other."

"Ah, look, here comes the evening shift – you're early Edna," laughed Robert, standing aside to let Edna and Dawn through the door. "My, something smells good."

"It's a pie and he'd better eat it," said Edna.

"We'll be off then," said Robert. "And leave you to these two good ladies, Charlie. We'll call in tomorrow."

Robert and Maggie exchanged glances with Edna and Dawn.

"He's at the whisky already." Edna said.   "Now you listen to me, Charlie Watt, you can put that bottle away."

Maggie smiled, "Don't be hard on him he's only had one. We're having dinner early as I'm going to collect some more signatures and Robert's meeting Frank Sutton in Waldersby. I'll be back to shut the chickens in later. Cheerio."

—*᎗*—

The following week PC O'Sheridan was given an opportunity to address the parish council about the recent spate of robberies. It appeared that, apart from the church silver and Charlie's belongings, there had been two other burglaries of jewellery and silver in Fordham, several miles away.   A local farmer had reported a van and mower stolen from his yard. The burglar's van hit his sheepdog, which had been left for dead. The village hall was almost full and there was a general sigh of relief on hearing the dog had recovered. Everyone was told to be on their guard and report anything slightly suspicious to the police.

Dawn Creasey's husband raised a laugh muttering, "Edna doesn't miss much and we're all bloody nosy anyway."

"I do hope the councillors will appreciate the strength of local feeling against the proposed meadow development, I've gathered over a hundred signatures," said Maggie, handing the petition to the parish clerk as PC O'Sheridan sat down.

Major Gibson was absent, leaving a jittery Mrs Reed to act as Chairman in his absence.

"Thank you, I'll start the meeting now," she said, nodding at PC O'Sheridan. "So good of you to spare time to speak to us all, and thank you," she smiled at everyone, "for the petition that has just been handed to our clerk. My fellow councillors will debate the planning applications later on in the agenda. We will discuss these matters after the financial report."

"Why can't you discuss it now?" called a voice from the back of the room.

Mrs Reed coughed repeatedly. "I'm so sorry, what would you like to add then? I haven't quite started."

Several people demanded to know why the Major had not attended, before stating their opposition again to the idea of any development.

"Thank you for your very useful contributions," Mrs Reed repeated. "As I said I will start the council meeting now, if you will bear with me. I must ask you not to call out or speak as we go through our agenda. Now, Clerk, if there are no more apologies I will to go through the minutes of the last meeting. Do you all agree that they are a correct record and are you happy for me to sign them?" She peered anxiously at the other members of the council who were looking cold and uncomfortable. They nodded in silence.

The meeting droned on, with more villagers creeping away, while Maggie listened to an endless debate about moles on the green and rabbits invading the cricket pitch, creating havoc on the crease. She perked up when the effect of the speed limit was discussed and became restless again when the tenders for grass cutting the recreation area and village green were chewed over in detail. She was convinced Mrs Reed had planned this, so that most people would have upped and left before the planning application was looked at. At last they got on to planning applications, studying a small extension to a bungalow before finally laying out the plans for the meadow. Maggie smiled wanly, she was beginning to regret having taken on this task for the village and wished she had more courage to express her annoyance at what seemed to her an intentional delay in discussing the Major's plans. Mrs Reed then closed the meeting again to allow two latecomers to make more comments. Some of the older residents called it a 'crying shame' that the Major was not there in person and Dawn Creasey's husband was heard to call out that 'he ought to be present to hear our views'. Maggie was delighted to hear them as the inference from PC O'Sheridan had upset her. She was aware that she was more concerned about Charlie's view across the meadow and how upset he would be to lose it than whether more homes in the village was such a bad thing, but the idea of newcomers had fuelled a debate and here she was representing the opinions of the majority. Better to keep quiet about his view, she decided.

With a final decision to express the Council's concern, and stronger comments about development in the open countryside, the parish councillors were unanimous in their opposition.

"I'm very grateful for this petition, and for all your hard work. It will make our task easier as we put our views to the planning authority," said Mrs Reed.

Maggie got up to leave. "Thank you very much," she said, smiling at the councillors grouped round the trestle table, hugging themselves for warmth.

"You are welcome to stay 'til the end of the meeting if you wish?" Mrs Reed said. "We so rarely have anyone taking an interest and we still have several items to discuss," she added. "It is so encouraging to have seen so many here tonight."

By now the chill of the village hall was penetrating even the warmest clad. In unison, those that had remained got up to leave. The clatter of their voices was heard moving in the direction of the Dog and Duck, as the clerk was ordered to 'feed the meter again'.

Maggie wondered what the planners would finally recommend. Even if it was turned down, the Major could appeal; at least they had got through the first hurdle. The sun was setting, bathing the village in a rosy glow, as she hurried across the green. She ran over what had been said in her head, keen to relate it all to Charlie. Robert was meeting her in the pub later and she could relax and get his views on her becoming the village spokesperson at these meetings. No doubt Charlie would want to know that Doris was tucked up in the kitchen before she shut the chicken house. Also Angela had agreed to try and join them before closing time and she had a feeling her friend had something she wanted to tell her. She needed to hurry.

A TESTING TIME

CHAPTER 26

A TESTING TIME

Jacky sat down in the pub's alcove, next to the log fire. "Here, have a gin and tonic on me," she said, pushing the glass towards Maggie. "I've done more than my stint tonight, and I was s'posed to finish in that kitchen at half past seven. Fat chance, but I'm going soon."

"You show willing and that makes people take advantage of you."

"Well, I enjoy it and the pay's not bad," said, Jacky, pulling a hand mirror out of her bag and reapplying her poppy-red lipstick. "Gawd, what a mess I look," she said, smoothing down her eyebrows with a licked finger-tip. "We've been so busy though. The darts team said the meeting went on a bit?"

"The parish council always does. I've learnt that after just two meetings."

"Why don't you get on it then? You could chivvy them up. D'you have to get elected, or something?"

"There are elections next year. They mentioned it tonight. Who knows, I might be interested. Charlie Watt is always nagging at me to stand."

"There you are then, that's two votes in your favour. I'd better get going," said Jacky, looking around the crowded bar. "I'm glad we've had this chance to have a chat," she added in a whisper, "Len's coming out at the weekend, for good."

"Oh, you must be pleased. I thought you said he wouldn't be released for at least another month."

"I'm pleased and I'm not, if that makes any sense? I've been getting on alright on my own working here, and building up my cake- making business. I've made some more friends," she said, glancing round at the darts team. "Some of them don't trust Len at all, and that rubs off on me. Anyway, he'll probably make me give up this job."

"Oh, Jacky, that's a real shame. I hope not."

Jacky was caught on her way out and persuaded to serve behind the bar, joking with four noisy young men from Waldersby who'd arrived for the match, while some of the residents were cheering on the home team, led by Reg Creasey.

She came over to Maggie again as she collected up stray glasses, "Here's your friend now, I'll get her a drink and then I'm really off. I'd appreciate it if you didn't tell anyone for now."

"Of course, take care. I'll try and pop by before the end of the week."

"Sorry, I didn't get here earlier," Angela said, warming her hands. "I'm so cold."

"You brought the cold air in with you," Maggie said. "Can you throw one of those big logs on?"

"It's really nippy. I was going to jog here, but Tom dropped me off, as James hasn't been to nursery today. All the kids have got a virus, so Tom's gone back to stay with him. He thought we'd like to have a good chat."

"What sort of virus?"

"Tummy ache and a bit of a temperature. He likes his medicine, so he'll be fine."

"Poor little chap," Maggie said, imagining herself caring for a poorly child. "Is he enjoying nursery now?"

"Yes and he's in love with one of the helpers. He told me that he was going to grow up and marry Miss Sproggit."

"Drink up, ladies, you haven't got long," Jeff, the landlord interrupted.

"Sproggit?" Maggie said.

"Poor woman," laughed Angela. "Her name is Mandy Stollit. Unfortunately, all the children have copied James and call her Miss Sproggit. She doesn't seem to mind too much and they all adore her."

"James will capture her heart too, he's such a darling. Talking of love, how are you and Tom? Is Gordon moving away, now that the divorce is going through?"

"No, he's taken that nice big apartment in Waldersby, and has plans for James to stay. Not often, I imagine. He's trying hard though. He was never much good as a father figure was he? Tom and James are much more like father and son."

"I hope you won't mind, Robert told me that he and Frank Sutton had lunch with Gordon yesterday at the golf club. They are trying to get Robert interested, but he really doesn't have the time."

"Why should I mind?"

"I think Robert feels a bit awkward about everything, you know. It's difficult when we've all been friends." Maggie patted her arm, "Don't worry, I'm sure we'll take to Tom, just as much. It's just that you were our first real friends here and we're still very fond of you both. D'you understand how difficult we find it?"

"Of course I do. I'm sad that Gordon and I didn't make a go of it. James will be the winner though with two daddies, one rather posh and one much more down to earth. I'm thankful we don't appear to have caused him any unhappiness."

Maggie pulled her jacket round her shoulders and got up to go to the toilet, "We'd better be going soon."

Jeff rang the bell for last orders, but couldn't be heard above the singing of the darts team from Waldersby, celebrating their victory.

"Pity we didn't have Maggie's Robert with us, then we'd have seen that lot off," said Reg Creasey, as he came towards them with a big smile on his face. "Can I get you both a last drink?"

"Not for me thanks, and Maggie's still drinking, Reg. By the way I must come and see you if you're around at the week-end? I need some decorating if you're not too booked up?"

"I can squeeze you in if it's not too big a job?"

"Just the upstairs bathroom. Remember, we had a leak and Gordon kept saying he'd do it? Of course he never got round to it, and Tom's good at lectures but not much of a handyman. It's retiling mainly."

"I heard you were set up together. Never struck me as a practical sort of chap and I'm not sorry he left our Kate, if you don't mind me saying so. She needs to concentrate on her studies."

"I think Kate's forgiven me."

"You two look serious," said Maggie, as she rejoined them.

"I'm seeing if Reg can do some decorating. Are you going to finish that drink? Reg offered to get us another.

"No thanks, that's kind of you. I'm sorry Robert couldn't make it, we're leaving now."

"Okay, we'll drown our sorrows, ladies, as we lost tonight. You tell Robert that he let the side down," said Reg with a wink.

Angela stood up. "I told Tom I'd jog back, but he won't hear of me out alone at night after what happened. I think I got over it better than he did. By the way he thinks we should consider moving to a bigger village."

"Oh, don't do that, please don't do that."

"It'll mean a lot less fetching and carrying if we do. We haven't begun to look yet."

"I thought you loved it here?"

"I do, you know I do, but Tom suggested it over dinner last night and I've been thinking about it ever since."

"Who'll help me with the fete and jumble sales?"

"Now you're being daft. We're not leaving the country."

"You could buy one of the mansions in the meadow, come to think of it," Maggie said, with a touch of sarcasm.

"Oh, I'm sorry, I forgot. How did the meeting go? Tell all."

"On the way back then. Come in for coffee? I'll drive you down the hill later."

"Okay, thanks. It'll help sober us up and I haven't seen you for days to have a proper chat," said Angela, linking arms. "Last time we talked you were considering going to see a social worker, remember?"

"You're not very observant, are you?" Maggie said, squeezing her friend's arm.

"What's that supposed to mean?"

"You didn't notice, so don't worry."

"Don't be difficult. What didn't I notice?" said Angela.

"You didn't notice me leave my drink?"

"No, I didn't. Should I have? What d'you mean?"

"That I'm sober and could drive you home and that I'm hardly touching any alcohol."

"And so?" Angela paused as realisation filtered through. "You're pregnant? Maggie that's brilliant, marvellous, wonderful news, I'm so pleased for you."

They hurried towards the lane and the cottage, interrupting each other with excitement. "What did Robert say when you told him?"

"I haven't yet. I'll tell him tonight."

Angela squeezed her arm more tightly. "You'll be alright, Maggie. I'm sure you'll be alright."

"I really hope so. I'm praying hard. I don't think I'll be able to cope if I lose this one."

"Don't think that. How long will you need to go on working for?"

"I think Robert might want me to stop fairly soon. He hates me getting up in the early hours when I'm on call."

Maggie hastened her steps as they turned in to the lane. "Come on, I'm frozen. For goodness sake don't let him know I told you first."

"Of course I won't. I'm so chuffed – wowee! Blast!" Angela slipped and lay sprawled on the muddy ground. "These damn potholes, I expect you know each one. You'll have to be very careful, this could have been you," she said, grabbing hold of Maggie's arm and scrambling to her feet.

"I'm sorry, I should have warned you."

"No harm done, apart from these ruined tights. Thank goodness I didn't pull you over."

"Here, use this torch," Maggie said. "And don't let go of me."

As they reached Charlie's gate they stopped and peered at the cottage windows. "Edna's with him. Stay there, I'll just make sure the chickens are shut in," Maggie said, opening the gate.

The lights were shining throughout the cottage and Maggie could see Edna seated at the kitchen table, as she tapped on the window.

Edna motioned to her to keep quiet and pointed up to the bedroom. "He's asleep," she mouthed.

"All's well, all shut up," Maggie said, rejoining Angela. They held on to each other in the darkness and made their way with care, until they reached Nut Tree Cottage.

"Robert's home. I'll tell you all about the parish council meeting when we've warmed up a bit," said Maggie, opening the front door. "Down, Woody, down. I do wish we could stop him jumping up like that, darling," she said, as they walked in to the sitting room. "He gets so boisterous, he'll have me over. Poor Angela fell over in the lane, Rob, just at the top."

"Goodness me, are you that sozzled?" Robert said, eyeing Angela's ruined tights.

"Woody, I know you're pleased to see us." Maggie said, "Calm down now. No, we're both sober, Angela tripped in that big pothole, we really must try and fill some of them in a bit before Edna or Charlie take a tumble."

"I'll try and get some gravel or a bit of hard core at the weekend. Have you both eaten?"

"There's a casserole in the warming oven. I left it for you, just in case you were famished," said Maggie.

"It's far too late for me and I'm really not hungry," said Maggie, filling the kettle. "Who wants coffee?"

"Good idea." Robert said, shooing Angela in to the big armchair by the fire, "Sit you down, Maggie will bring it through. I expect you heard I had lunch with Gordon?"

Maggie fondled Woody's ears as she waited for the kettle, listening to the chatter coming from the sitting room. "Would you like a baby, Woody?" she whispered. The dog's ears pricked, "You'd better not jump all over me, my boy, or there really will be trouble." The dog rolled over on to his back for a rub and tickle, "Soppy thing, you really are better now, aren't you?"

Woody jumped up again, barking loudly, at the sound of a car approaching the cottage.

"Sssh, sssh. Someone's just driven up, Robert," she called. "Don't let Woody out though please."

"Sorry to alarm you all. I thought I'd find you here, Angie. James is asking for you," said Tom at the door.

"Is everything alright?" Angela was already walking to the door.

"Yes, yes. He's been very sick, which has actually made him feel better. He's all tucked up, but he wants his mummy to settle him."

"We're off; must go. Bye you two, I'll phone tomorrow." Angela hurried out to the car. "Forgive me," she called, as they drove off.

"What d'you think's the matter with him?" Robert asked, as they watched the car tail lights disappear up the lane.

"A bug of some sort. All the children in nursery have been going down with it."

By the time their car reached the end of the lane Robert had switched on the television and was engrossed in News Night. "I just want to listen to this, darling, d'you mind? Robin Day is so rude to these poor politicians."

"Poor politicians? It's the only way to get an answer out of them, they're always prevaricating. I'll go and shower, perhaps we can talk later?" she said, deciding that her news could wait a little longer.

"Okay, I'll be up after this," Robert said, not looking up. "Get the bed nice and warm."

"Night 'night Woody," said Maggie, settling the dog in his basket with a treat. "He'll just have to wait to hear about his baby won't he?" she said, closing the kitchen door.

CHAPTER 27

IN SICKNESS AND HEALTH

Maggie put more bread in the toaster – dry, just palatable and the only solution she'd found for the persistent waves of nausea. She hadn't felt this sick with any of the other pregnancies, but she didn't care how bad it got as long as she held on to this baby. Her work colleagues reassured her that the sickness was a good sign and she hoped they were right, having trotted out the same assurances in the course of her work many times.

Robert had already left, as she sat at the kitchen table trying to swallow without retching, reflecting on his reaction the night before. She'd served up one of his favourite meals and Robert had been concerned at her lack of appetite. The sunset was again spectacular as they walked across the meadow and through the woods after dinner; a habit they never tired of. Woody was busy scampering in and out of the undergrowth searching out rabbits and Maggie had waited until they were seated on the fallen log near the badger sett to tell him the good news.

"So you see, darling, I'm coming up to seven or eight weeks, but I'm so scared."

A tear rolled down his cheek, as he hugged her to him. "Maggie, we must just take each day as a blessing and hope and pray that all goes well this time."

"I do feel that we're going to be lucky. Already this pregnancy feels different somehow – I'm nauseous and so tired that I could sleep standing up."

"You shouldn't be out in this cold air. Come on, we'd better get back."

"Don't be daft. I'm not ill, darling and I don't want to be mollycoddled."

He'd held her close as they strolled back and every few steps stopped to kiss her. "I don't think you've any idea how much I love you." He paused and gently stroked away loose strands of hair from her forehead. "I'm not sure that I've enough love for another person, even our baby."

"You will have. I'm always struck by the number of parents that say they never realised it was possible to love their first child so much and when the second one is on the way they don't feel that they'll be able to give their new baby as much. Of course they always do."

Half way across the meadow Woody picked up a scent and streaked off towards the woods again.

"I'm sure Woody knows, because he's being overly protective of me," Maggie said, as they waited for his return. "They say dogs are intuitive and he's hardly left my side."

"His nose will be put out of joint a bit. We'll have to watch him later with the baby; he's so boisterous when he's excited."

"Yes, he'll get used to it, I won't let him be silly. After all, I spend time advising mothers on how to introduce pets to their babies."

They hurried on as Woody reappeared and Maggie said a silent prayer, "Please, please, don't let me lose this baby."

She noticed Robert's eyes had closed briefly and sensed he had been praying, too. Neither of them were regular church goers but maybe He would forgive and indulge them this time?

Charlie stood at his kitchen window watching the couple in the dim light, as they approached the field gate. Something about the way Robert was supporting Maggie struck him as unusual and as they kept stopping he would stoop to kiss her.

"Like a pair of young lovers," he thought.

It was not like them to be so demonstrative. What's the betting that girl's having a baby? That'll be it, Edna said she was looking a bit peaky, he thought to himself and then aloud; "What d'you think, Doris?"

The little hen pecking at crumbs around his feet, clucked contentedly as Charlie scooped her up. Opening the kitchen door, he called out. "You two coming in for a drop of summat? It's just what you need on a cold night."

"Thanks, but no, Charlie. Maggie's tired – they're working her too hard. We're going to have an early night," Robert called back.

"Are you alright, Charlie?" Maggie asked as they neared his gate.

"Doing well, the doctor said when he called today."

Doris squawked and fluttered out of his hold to peck eagerly at the pathway as Charlie moved to open the gate.

"Don't open it, Charlie, we're going straight home. Hold Woody, Robert, or he'll chase her," said Maggie.

"Edna'll be here shortly with my supper," Charlie added. "You get along now and pop in tomorrow if you're passing."

"Good night," they chorused, sauntering back towards the cottage.

"Oh dear," said Maggie, "I hope Charlie didn't mind. We don't usually refuse him."

"I shouldn't think so; he'll be so pleased when you tell him our news."

"But it has to stay a secret for another month at least."

"Whatever we do, we mustn't let Edna suspect anything then," Robert said, closing the front door as Woody squeezed past, heading for the kitchen and his supper. "She'll tell everyone within a ten-mile radius in no time."

Maggie grabbed at Woody, "Now wait, naughty boy, your paws are filthy."

"I'll do him," Robert said, guiding the dog through to the pantry and lifting him into the large butler sink.

Maggie gazed out of the kitchen window as she rinsed the breakfast dishes. Now all that remained was for her to get to the end of this pregnancy, for both their sakes. Robert had been heartened by the news that she felt differently this time and they had talked long in to the night, finding sleep difficult. They had even, laughingly, got round to the sort of nappies they might use when, at last, Robert had succumbed and lay snoring beside her. Neither of them wanted to contemplate losing another baby and were determined to think otherwise. Maggie felt more physically and mentally prepared, as she patted her stomach. 'Just you cling on, little one', she'd whispered before falling asleep.

"Come on, Woody, let's go, it's such a lovely day," Maggie said, pushing the excited dog away from her legs. "We'll visit Jacky shall we?"

Jacky's elderly Alsatian growled at their approach and got awkwardly to its feet, tail half-wagging in recognition of Maggie's voice. She felt sorry for the dog having to spend so much of its life in the cold, outdoors. It looked stiff and arthritic, as it moved to greet them.

"Here's your friend, Woody." The two dogs sniffed at each other, tails wagging. "Your life saver, remember?"

The door opened abruptly, as she stroked the old dog.

"What d'you want?"

Maggie's heart missed a beat, as she turned to see Len, standing in the doorway, naked above the waist, holding a cut throat razor.

"Oh, hello, d'you remember me, Len?"

Half shaven, he pulled a tea towel off his shoulder and patted the soap off his cheek, glowering at her.

"Should I?"

"I'm Maggie Groves, the midwife. I was called out to Jimmy and Tracy."

"Don't need no bloody midwife here, mate, that's for sure," he said, spitting on the ground by her feet.

"No, I know that," she said, smiling in an effort to disarm him. "It's a social call – is Jacky home?"

"She's out shopping, you'll have to come back later," he said, slamming the door in her face.

CHAPTER 28

TO HELL AND BACK

Maggie watched Jacky touch her face gingerly. Her blackened eye and bruised cheek looked so tender and she had a split top lip that would be slow to heal.

"I do wish you'd rung me, Jacky," said Maggie. "You should let the police know about this."

"Just so he can beat me up again? No thanks, he'd probably kill me next time."

Maggie winced at the words and at the obvious pain it caused Jacky to speak through her blood- covered mouth. She had arrived at Nut Tree Cottage with her battered face swathed in a head scarf, terrified that someone might see her.

"Don't worry," Maggie had reassured her then. "Nobody will see you. Edna has taken Charlie to the W.I. coffee morning in the village hall." She'd pushed a mug of tea across the kitchen table. "Can you sip this? I've added more cold milk. Down, down, Woody."

"Don't mind me," said Jacky.

"Tell me everything if you can bear it," said Maggie.

She pictured the scene as Jacky told her story – her drunken husband and his friends, the mess that she had come home to after working all evening at the pub.

"I made some comment about him and his mates having a fry up and leaving it all to me. Len reacted badly and said he'd deal with me later. I knew as soon as I opened my mouth that he wouldn't stand for me nagging him in front of them." She stopped and sipped the tea. "This is helping. After they'd gone he started shouting and swearing, called me names and told me I wasn't going to work in the pub anymore." She winced as the tears welled up and stung her grazed cheeks. "I was scared but I argued back and that's when he hit me across the face, twice. He must have knocked me out because the next thing I knew was when I came round on the kitchen floor and the bastard was asleep on the sofa, snoring." She was sobbing now. "He just left me there, covered in blood. I could have been dead for all he cared."

"I'm so sorry. Has he ever hit you before?" said Maggie, putting her arms around Jacky's trembling shoulders

"When he's drunk. I've managed to get out of his way most times."

"You should report him, you know."

Calmer now, Jacky mopped her tears, "I know what I'm going to do, love. I'm leaving him and he can rot in hell."

"Where will you go?"

"I'll ask my boys, see what they reckon. I came to see you 'cos I can't face going in the pub and handing in my notice. D'you mind doing that for me?"

"Of course not if you really feel you must. I'll run you home after you've had something to eat. I've got some homemade soup that should go down easily."

"I can't go back to my place," Jacky said. "I'll catch the bus and go and stay with my sister for a couple of days. She lives the other side of Waldersby. Len won't dare lay a finger on me while I'm with her and I'll go and get my things when he's out on his clay pigeon shoot next week."

"Here, use this, that'll make it easier," said Maggie, handing her a drinking straw from the pantry. "I'd forgotten I had some. Now listen, you're not going by bus. If it suits your sister, I'll drive you over to her place. I've got to go to the clinic."

The group of pregnant women were chatting among themselves when Maggie arrived ten minutes late. They had been attending classes for over a month now and Maggie knew that friendships were springing up that would last for many years, supporting each other after the birth of their babies far more than the health services were able to. Care for each other and the experience yet to come would ease their journey through motherhood and beyond. Today they were going to learn how to bath a baby and she called them around her as she prepared the towels and bath, before undressing a doll.

During the tea break her thoughts lingered on Jacky and her suffering. Excusing herself from the group she phoned Jacky's sister, who assured her that Jacky was having a good rest and was coping. Reassured, Maggie felt able to concentrate on the second half of her class, the relaxation session, only to find by the end of it that she too was having difficulty in staying awake.

"Are you feeling alright, Maggie?" said one of the women, nudging her awake.

"Oh, goodness, I'm so sorry everyone; too many late nights," she said, slurring her words sleepily.

"Did you have a home delivery last night, Maggie?"

Maggie looked around at all the curious faces, feeling they were a group of mums she could confide in. "Okay, perhaps it would be better if I let you know, you see I'm pregnant too."

The relaxation session ended abruptly as the group sat up to chorus their congratulations.

A nursing colleague popped her head round the door. "Everything all right Maggie? Sounds as if you're having a party."

"We are," said Maggie, wide awake and beaming now.

Maggie kept smiling as she drove homewards, picturing the group of women she'd shared her news with – her mums, their excitement was contagious and she'd managed to push Jacky's problems to the back of her mind, at least for the time being. She thought instead about the meal she was going to put on the table later and about Woody, pining for his walk. But in the grocery store in Waldersby her thoughts turned once more to Jacky and she wondered what it would feel like to be on the receiving end of such violence from someone you once trusted. Feeling sad for her friend she couldn't resist putting a large bar of chocolate in the basket, it always made her feel better. As she turned down the aisle she collided with Robert.

"I saw you! Naughty girl, it's fattening. I spied your car," he said, taking the basket. "How did the class go, darling?"

"I told them, Rob. I had to as I almost fell asleep relaxing the group!"

"I'm counting the weeks; d'you realise we're nearly a third of the way there?" Robert said, sauntering to the till. "I thought I'd pop in and get a few extras, we're a bit low on beer and Edna hasn't got much in stock."

Next morning Maggie received a call from Jacky's sister saying that Len had been making unpleasant phone calls, so they wouldn't be picking up the phone, in case she tried ringing. Jacky was too afraid to go home and wondered if Maggie could collect some personal items from the house. Apparently Len never locked the door and was always out on a Thursday morning.

"I'm damned if you're going anywhere near that house, Maggie. I won't let you go there under any circumstances. Are you crazy? Just imagine what that awful man would do to you if he found you snooping around inside."

Maggie had never seen Robert so angry, but understood his concern. "It's a real mess, Rob. I'll tell her sister that they've really got to involve the police."

"Too right they have. I'm not having you in any sort of danger. What on earth are they thinking of? Damn cheek. You know how unreliable the man is. I'll tell her, if you won't."

"Alright, alright. I'll go and see Jacky and her sister. I'm sure I'd be okay, as Len spends every Thursday morning out shooting. It's quite a ritual for him apparently, but that could change I suppose."

"Don't you dare. I know you, Maggie, but just because you feel sorry for her doesn't mean you should put yourself and our baby at risk. I mean it, I would never forgive myself or you if something happened."

Maggie couldn't stop thinking about Jacky and the problems she faced, as she went on her rounds. Jacky had enjoyed her job in the pub. She had begun to make friends in the village and had experienced a new freedom while Len had been locked away and her talents with cake- making had earned her some money. Now all that had been stolen from her and, somehow, she had to escape and start all over again. It was going to be difficult to get away from Len, but Jacky had to find a way because if his violent drinking bouts continued only God knew where it would end.

Maggie could hear the baby crying before she got anywhere

near the house. The sound carried miles in such a remote spot and the new parents looked distraught as she entered the cottage and picked up their screaming baby. It was as if Maggie had touched a switch and both breathed an audible sigh of relief, as the baby's cries stopped immediately.

"It's always the way. They sense your anxiety I think. Now tell me everything that's happened since my visit yesterday and then we'll run a bath?"

"I expect that was exhausting for you both," Maggie said when the young couple told her how they'd tried endless rocking, singing, winding and patting their baby throughout the night.

As she helped bath him, Maggie tactfully commented on all the layers of clothing he'd had on and a possible cause of his distress. It was important that they were not made to feel guilty in any way and Maggie offered her advice carefully. No amount of books on babycare could cover all the knowledge the new parents needed to absorb. After the bath she held the baby aloft in her weighing scales. To their delight he had started to regain his birth weight and with the baby feeding happily Maggie set off on her next visit. Teaching new parents was one of her favourite parts of the job, but she had to hurry as she still had four more visits to get through before lunchtime. Hopefully, the skills she was developing would come in handy when she too became a mother.

Rounding a bend in the road, she swerved to avoid a pheasant and almost lost control as the car scraped along the bank. The thud as the bird hit the car gave her a shock and she could see the bird flapping helplessly. Halted abruptly she jumped out seconds later to try and help it.

"I'm sorry. You were so beautiful," Her hands shook as she knelt beside it in the road, wondering at the scarlet eye features and exotic plumage. She barely noticed the blood that trickled down her face from a small gash and moved to the side of the road just in time, as another car rounded the bend, hooting urgently. Maggie was relieved to see the familiar face of Dr Southgate.

"Are you trying to get yourself killed? Rather a stupid place to stop, dear," he said, parking beside her. "And that's a nasty cut."

"I know, I couldn't avoid that pheasant. I feel awful, they're so beautiful."

"That bird's a gonner I'm afraid; better off in the oven."

"Poor thing. I couldn't leave it suffering."

"Accidents happen, my dear," he said, patting her arm. "You take it home, it's not too badly mangled." He picked up the now lifeless body. "It'll make a good casserole."

Maggie shook her head, grimacing.

"Well, if you don't fancy it, I'll give it to my wife."

Dr Southgate placed the bird on top of a pair of muddy wellingtons in the boot of his car. "I've had umpteen good dinners over the years, my dear, from road kills. The gamekeeper usually gives me a few brace of pheasant at Christmas, but some are full of lead shot." He slammed the boot down and peered at her forehead. "Now then you need to clean that up, it's only superficial. By the way, you and I must have a chat about this baby of yours. When's your next check up?"

"In a couple of weeks."

"Good. We need to think about the arrangements for the birth. My young partners will want you to go to the hospital and the government is trying to encourage it, but I prefer home births. I'm of the old school I'm afraid and we've never had any problems that I and a capable midwife couldn't deal with. If you ask me, they have far more complications in the hospital and are far too keen to interfere. Home's best in my opinion." He patted her arm. "Thanks for my unexpected supper, take care now. Cheerio."

Maggie studied the side of her car – there were only a few scratches which Robert could deal with. She knew he would be worried about her and the amount of driving her job entailed. She set off again up the winding lane, relieved that it had been nothing more serious.

By the time she had finished her calls she was exhausted and glad to get home and after hearing the story of the dead pheasant Robert offered to take Woody for a run. He was back earlier some days, finishing off work from home. Maggie knew he was becoming anxious about her and the baby, constantly watching over her and would be even more so after the scrape in the lane.

"By the way, Charlie called. He and Edna have a surprise for us. Wouldn't tell me without you here. Said he'll come by in the morning."

"I wonder what it is?"

"Possibly to do with Major Gibson and the meadow, d'you think?"

"Maybe. I must have a little lie- down, Rob. I can't cope with anything else. Did Jacky ring?"

"Not to my knowledge."

By the time Robert and Woody were out the door Maggie was asleep.

—◈—

"Edna and I have decided to settle down together. We're both getting on a bit and Edna worries about me living on my own."

Charlie had asked Robert and Maggie in for a cup of tea early the next day. Edna was all coy looks and avoided eye contact with Maggie, who was overcome with delight and could scarcely control the laughter that bubbled up inside her at the sight of the elderly lovebirds.

"Well, you are a dark horse, Charlie Watt," said Robert "D'you mean to say that you two have been having an affair and we didn't even know?"

"Now, Robert, you know Edna and I haven't been carrying on," said, Charlie, chuckling and looking sheepish. "We're too old for that malarkey. We've known each other for years and it seemed right somehow, didn't it, love?"

Edna? Love? Maggie was unsure how to react, but seeing the look of happiness on Edna's usually stern face she couldn't resist hugging them both.

Robert joined in before he and Charlie settled down to an early round of home brew and Maggie and Edna toasted the betrothal with a cup of tea.

"We've told the vicar but no-one else," said Charlie. "He's given us his blessing and says he'll be more than happy to join us together, but Edna's decided we'll get married in the registry office in Waldersby, seeing as how she and the vicar don't always see eye to eye. Then it'll be back to the Dog and Duck for a knees- up. It'll all be over with before your baby's born."

"With your knees, Charlie? No white wedding then?" said Maggie sipping her tea.

"'Course not," tutted Edna," Now then, Charlie needs you as his best man, Robert."

"I'd be very honoured, dear friend." Robert grinned hugely, as he swallowed another glass. "Here's to the best knees-up we're ever likely to witness."

Maggie's emotions were getting the better of her and she laughed and cried together, clasping Charlie in an awkward embrace. "I love you, Charlie Watt, and Edna had better take jolly good care of you."

"I took jolly good care of my Bert my girl, there's no reason to think I won't do the same with Charlie Watt."

"Oh, I know you'll be a caring wife," sniffed Maggie, trying to embrace Edna. "I'm just a silly, jealous pregnant woman; forgive me, we love you both. I'm so happy for you."

—⁂—

"I've been up to the house with my sister and we've picked up most of my things," said Jacky when Maggie met her in Waldersby the following day.

"Jimmy and Martin came with me, in case their dad turned up and Martin says I can stay with him for a bit. I'm seeing a solicitor about a divorce."

Maggie looked out of the coffee shop window in the market square. She was relieved that Jacky had moved on from talking about the violence her husband had dished out to her over the years, the 'bad crowd' he'd got in with and the burglaries he'd committed.

"That's good, Jacky. Martin's not married is he?"

"No, he and his girlfriend have split up so he's got some room. He never got on with Len either 'cos Len always idolised Jimmy. When this is all sorted he thinks we should go to Spain."

"Spain?"

"Yes. He's packed it in at the factory and wants to get a job in the clubs and he thinks, with my experience in the pub, that we'll both find work."

"That makes sense. Far away from Len too, though you'll miss your granddaughter, won't you?"

"Well, it's easy enough to get there and they'll come out for a holiday. Who knows where it'll all end."

"Your Martin sounds pretty level-headed. I must say I'm feeling much happier about you now. You're looking so much better and your lip is healing nicely," said Maggie, lowering her voice. "I'm being selfish but I'm really sorry you won't be around for my baby."

"So am I, love. But who knows? It may not be that easy to sort out in the end, we'll have to see won't we?"

Maggie agreed, changing the subject to Charlie and Edna.

"Well I'm buggered! 'Scuse my French. You don't mean it? Charlie Watt marrying that old bat? Poor sod."

"Sssh, Edna's alright, she just can't help gossiping and speaking her mind without thinking first. She'll take good care of Charlie; really she will."

"You know your trouble? Always see good in people don't you, love. She's an old cow and always will be," said Jacky, gulping down the rest of her coffee. "I'd better be off now, I've got to see a solicitor. And don't ask me to bake for their wedding will you?" Jacky said, pulling on her coat.

"I had thought of it," Maggie said, kissing Jacky on both cheeks. "I'm meeting Angela later and we're going to plan their 'knees-up! Keep in touch, or you'll have me worrying."

CHAPTER 29

A JOURNEY HALVED

Maggie gazed at her reflection in the long mirror and patted her stomach. She felt very proud of the neat bump protruding over the top of her briefs and was aware of the baby's movements, as she turned from side to side to admire her shape.

'We've made it little one," she murmured aloud, her eyes filling with tears. "Twenty-four weeks, you'll be safe now."

She had been for her routine check up and the calming words of Dr. Southgate had filled her with confidence. He had regaled her with some of the happiest moments in his career and told her proudly of the six babies named after him. "Now don't you worry at all, Maggie. Just take it steady for a few more weeks and all will be well, my dear," he said, giving her a gentle pat on the back.

"How did you get on with the doctor?" Maggie had rushed to pick up the phone, as she entered the cottage; guessing it would be her mother.

"Fine, he's really pleased with me and he's almost as excited as we are about having the baby in the cottage. Don't laugh,

Mummy, I've enrolled Robert and me for the local NCT classes."

"Whatever for, darling? You can do it standing on your head, surely?"

"Robert needs instruction as much as me. Anyway it'll be good for us to meet up with other couples. We can make some new friends."

"I suppose you're right, I'm sure you'll have an easy birth, mine were. You might go over those dates though, you and Eleanor were both two weeks late."

"Really? You never told me that."

"Is the doctor certain, dear? Are you quite sure it's safe to have baby at home? You know there's a lot of talk on the radio about persuading mothers to have their babies in hospital these days? You did say something about a domino the other day. What does that mean?"

"Domino? Domiciliary in and out. I've done a few Domino's with a couple of mums. It's a good idea if they want to deliver in hospital and us to deliver them and bring them straight home. I still prefer to stay in the cottage though, it's our nest."

"Well, you know best, dear."

"My dates are fairly certain, as certain as I can be."

"What does your doctor think about it all? Will he be there?"

"Doctor Southgate's happy we're having a summer baby and at home. He's such a dear and I couldn't be in safer hands. He's assured me he'll come and so has Susan, the midwife who's standing in for me. She's very good. I'll have the A-team, all being well."

"That's alright then. I can't wait to be a granny. Now I must go; it's market day. Keep me posted and I'll ring again next week. Eleanor is looking forward to being an aunty as well. Give Robert a hug from me and tell him to thank Frank for his lovely letter, bye darling, bye bye."

Maggie smiled to herself, it was difficult to contain her happiness. "Come on Woody. Let's take baby for a walk. So now Mum and Frank are pen pals – that is interesting."

—⁂—

Robert squeezed her thighs and Maggie breathed in different levels as he chanted 'Jack and Jill', their chosen nursery rhyme. They'd been attending the NCT classes for over a month and any initial awkwardness at hearing that Maggie herself was a midwife had disappeared in the delight of sharing their worries. Five other couples had enrolled and Maggie knew none of them; she and Robert soon became just another expectant couple, attracting no special attention. Mandy, the teacher taught them to mock the contractions of labour and Robert seemed to enjoy grabbing her wrist in a Chinese burn to simulate pain. Maggie ended up convulsed in giggles when Robert's gentle tummy stroking became too ticklish – she was determined to enjoy being pregnant and everything it entailed.

Now that she had more time to concentrate on herself, Robert and Woody, the days had developed into a familiar pattern of getting up late, taking the dog for a short walk, resting in the afternoon, and after dinner going to bed early while Robert took Woody for a last walk round the woods. Robert had an agreement with Frank Sutton that no overseas trips would be planned until after the birth. Some of the villagers called at the cottage to see how she was getting on, others brought her flowers. She felt accepted and aware of the excitement a new baby was creating in their close-knit community.

But despite her happiness the days were filled with a new concern. Charlie was becoming increasingly forgetful. He had developed a habit of calling on her daily and Edna had had to collect him from the cottage on several occasions.

"He's getting worse you know," Edna said, as she sliced up some ham in the shop. "Worrying me he is, don't like the idea of him going in to a home."

"Goodness me, Edna. Robert and I will always look after him you know, he feels like family to us. What put that idea into your head?"

"He talks rubbish some days and Doreen Creasey told me her dad began his problems like that."

"All old people get a bit forgetful, Edna," said, Maggie, astonished. "What sort of rubbish?"

"He wants me to take him to the tea dances in the town hall, says he needs to get fit. Silly talk at his age, if you ask me."

"I think that's a great idea, I'll run you in if you like," said Maggie, trying to hide her smile.

Edna sniffed, "Thank you, no, we won't be showing ourselves up. What would people think?"

"It'll be different when you're married, Edna. Not long now, you know. I need to check the guest list with you, as Angela and I are popping into the pub later to finalise things."

"I'm a bit busy here now."

"You've only got three weeks to the day." Maggie turned to leave, knowing Edna was best left alone in one of her grumpy moods. As she reached the door she saw PC O'Sheridan approaching across the green.

"Hey, look who's coming, d'you think there's some news of the burglars?"

"Amount of time he spends talking, I don't suppose so."

"Good, I hoped I'd find someone in here, said PC O'Sheridan, pushing his way into the shop. "I'm closing in on our miscreants and just need a little more help concerning the material taken from the church. I need to speak to Mrs Creasey, if you know her whereabouts."

"She's at the hospital today, seeing about her arthritis, so you won't find her in 'til tomorrow and she won't want you calling in the morning because she likes to go to the market," Edna said. "Anyway it wasn't material, it was the silver."

"Just so, Mrs Newbold. I was referring to the missing objects."

"Have you found anything at all yet?" queried Maggie

"That I cannot reveal, young lady. I'll take half a dozen eggs while I'm here, Mrs Newbold."

"Brown or white?"

"Brown, if you have them. Come from Mr Watts I suppose?"

"Yes, and don't you go troubling him."

"That is not my intention, Mrs Newbold. We are continuing our investigations, you can assure him of that."

Edna sniffed again.

"Well, I'll be going." Maggie smiled and opened the shop door. "See you soon, Edna, I'll call in on Charlie on my way home."

"That young lady must be getting near her time?" Maggie heard the policeman say as she left. "Perhaps you'd cut me off a nice bit of cheddar too?"

Despite her disregard for Edna's comments Maggie did feel anxious about Charlie. He was quite rational when chatting to her on his visits. His occasional lapses of memory were not unusual, but she had noticed that he was now forgetting more recent events. She and Robert would have to keep a closer eye on him until Edna moved in. The marriage and joy of the new baby's arrival would give him a lot to occupy his mind.

"The room you've made up as a nursery used to be my cousin's apple store; it was as cold as a fridge. No heating in them days."

Maggie had found Charlie peeling potatoes outside his front door, enjoying the warmth of the sun.

"What's Edna making for your dinner tonight, Charlie?"

"Oxtail stew. One of her best," he said struggling to stand. "Come on in, girl, time for a cup of tea. These old joints are getting worse, I think I'll have a drop of whisky."

"I'm so enjoying this waiting time, Charlie," said Maggie, pouring his tot of whisky and putting the kettle on. "I've never felt fitter, even though I'm getting huge, I'm sure it's a boy."

"Won't matter what it is; you'll love it just the same. I remember my Mary was sure she was having a girl and it wasn't to be. She didn't mind of course and nor will you two, just so long as it's alright and got all the bits it should have."

"Do you ever think of your William, Charlie?"

"Funny thing, but since you've been in the family way I've taken to wondering what he is doing and whether he has any youngsters."

Maggie felt a great sadness as she looked at the old man, wondering how she would feel if her child cut itself off from her; it was unthinkable. Why had William been so cruel? She would make certain that her baby would learn to love Charlie, as much as she did.

"By the way, Angela and I have arranged nearly everything now. The Dog and Duck are being really helpful and I've told them to cater for about thirty. We can use their big room at the back, which is really cosy."

Charlie looked at her, "Well I don't think we'll be needing that now," he said.

"Oh? What d'you mean? You're getting married there aren't you? I've just left the shop and Edna didn't say anything."

"She don't know yet."

"Oh, Charlie. Surely Edna knows everything?"

Charlie looked agitated and poured himself another drop of carrot whisky. "Listen, I can talk to you. Good as a daughter, you are." He sighed and tapped his pipe on the kitchen table. "I'm very fond of the old girl, she's good to me, but I can't stop thinking of my Mary and it would upset her as she and Edna never got on. She didn't like Edna's sharp tongue you see, and she came to me in a dream last night and I could tell she were upset." His eyes shone and a large tear plopped gently on to his shirt front. "Don't know how to tell her. I can't explain it but it's worrying me so, you see I don't want to wed the old girl now."

Maggie picked up the kettle and made herself another cup of tea, stirring it slowly, sitting down close to him. Picking up his large roughened hand, she held it tight, "Charlie, you must do what feels right. We'll all understand if you decide to call it off."

Charlie pulled out a large red handkerchief and mopped his face.

"I know, girl, I know. I mustn't go upsetting you neither, not now you're getting near your time."

Maggie smiled, "Don't you worry about me, I can cope."

She stayed with him while he mulled over the good times he had had with Mary. Stories she had heard a dozen times. An hour later she was back in Nut Tree Cottage, phoning Angela who agreed to call in and have supper with them. She decided it would be better for Charlie and Edna to have their private discussion over the oxtail stew. She didn't feel too unhappy about this turn of events and neither did Robert. In Angela's opinion this had saved Charlie from 'a fate worse than death'.

CHAPTER 30

A WOMAN SCORNED

"It looks as if we're celebrating!" said Robert.

"It does a bit," Angela giggled as she accepted another glass of wine. "Well you know my feelings about Edna."

Maggie pulled a face, sipping her orange juice, "I really feel I could do with a proper drink right now. I know Edna's a bit of a cow as Jacky put it, but she has real feelings for Charlie and to be honest I do think he needs a very close eye kept on him."

"Why? because he's so forgetful?" Angela queried, "Charlie's not the only one. Tom is dreadful, the house is covered in notes to remind him what to do and where to go next. He says he's always been like it. It's so childlike."

"You're happy, aren't you?"

"Blissfully." Angela hooked her arm around Roberts's shoulder, "I love him as much as this chap loves you."

"Okay," said Robert, gently guiding Angela to the settee, "I'll see you home later; don't worry."

Angela looked glad to sit down. "Just what do we need to do?"

"There's not a lot we can do really," said Maggie. "The publican was fine about everything, as he hadn't actually ordered any of the food yet. I'll phone the registrar's office tomorrow; I'm sure this is nothing new for them."

"It will give the village a good story to tell for quite a while," said Robert. "After all, not many people like Edna, do they? We'd better not say too much, they'll all feel sorry for Charlie."

"Come on, let's eat," said Maggie, "I'm almost ready for bed. Woody's starving too, aren't you Woody?"

The dog's tail wagged eagerly as they headed for the kitchen.

―∿―

Charlie had waited until he and Edna had almost finished their dinner before he decided to tell her of his decision. She had been silent for a full five minutes and Charlie wondered if she had understood him.

"Aren't you going to say something, girl?" he asked, laying down his fork and pushing the remains of the meal to one side. "That was a grand bit of oxtail, just like my Mary used to make."

Edna stood up, knocking over the chair. "That's it, that's it. Your Mary, that's what's made you change your mind. I suppose she's been telling you stories."

"My Mary's gone to the Lord, Edna."

"Makes no odds, she can reach you from up there. Never did get on with me, did she."

"Oh, dear. I don't know, I thought we could make a go of it. I'm sorry Edna love, I really am."

"Now you listen to me Charlie Watt. If it's all the same to you we'll carry on as if nothing had happened. I'll continue to look after you like I've always done. Don't you go telling anyone. I'll be the laughing stock of Little Fordham if they know you jilted me," she said, her voice rising.

232

"It's not like that, Edna," Charlie said, grabbing the whisky bottle.

"Oh yes it is Charlie Watt, and you can pour me a good one."

Charlie was flummoxed; Edna never drank his carrot whisky. He poured her a drink and watched in astonishment, as she swallowed it in one gulp.

"I'll be off now," she said, picking up the chair and hurrying to the door.

Charlie sat gazing at Mary's photograph for a long while after Edna had gone, feeling a sense of relief. Was she smiling at him? "You won, my girl," he murmured, pressing the cold photo frame to his mouth.

The next morning Maggie called on him early, "Shall I let the chickens out, Charlie?"

"Yes please, love," Charlie moved stiffly and she guessed he'd slept in the armchair all night.

"And you can bring little Doris back in, it's far too cold for her out there."

"Right 'o, I'm expecting the midwife this morning, Charlie. I'll come back later."

Maggie was due to have a home visit from Susan. She felt a thrill of excitement at the thought of the box of home birth equipment that Susan would be bringing with her, sanitary towels the size of hammocks, soft padding and waxed sheets for the bed, cotton wool, cord ties and powder. She had delivered these boxes herself many times, but was revelling in being on the receiving end in her reversed role. She knew Susan would also want to discuss the things she was going to need and check the layout of the house, as she had promised to treat her exactly the same as everyone else. The coffee and biscuits were ready when she arrived and together they went through the check-list, planning the best position for the bed and marvelling over the small garments bought for the baby.

"No problems," said Susan, taking a urine sample to test. "You know, I'm really enjoying being out of the hospital."

"I knew you would," Maggie said, proffering her arm. "I only ever wanted to be a district midwife. I really don't like all the rush and panic when it gets so busy in the labour ward. I can't imagine how you've managed to do it for so long. What changed your mind?"

"Excellent. On the low side today," Susan said, unwinding the blood pressure cuff. "Talking to you I guess. I really envied the intimacy you shared with your mums and how much they appreciated having their midwife. We don't get that close in the hospital."

"Well, I'm really pleased for you. You'd better be on duty when I go into labour."

"I have every intention of being here. Let's have a little listen in, shall we? "Susan waited as Maggie lay down on the settee. "I love Dr. Southgate; he's a real poppet isn't he? He's definitely planning to be with you." Kneeling down she placed a small trumpet on Maggie's stomach, listening and counting the baby's heartbeats. "Perfect. Is baby active?"

"Very. Usually when I try and have a rest."

"Doctor Southgate was telling me about some of his experiences, doing a forceps delivery on the kitchen table for one woman a few years ago. You'll be as safe as houses with him around, so will I, he's so calm and unflappable." She smiled, "He told me he's going to sit in a corner and let me do all the work though."

"He's been such a support to me," said Maggie, "a real father figure actually."

Susan looked at her watch, "I'd better get going. I've a clinic this afternoon and a new student joining me. Incidentally, I'm sure you don't, but I'll ask anyway. Do you have any objection to one of them attending the birth?"

"No, of course not, they have to learn. They're usually kind and considerate and rather nervous, not hardened like us."

"We're not hard, just efficient and with a bit more knowledge. Okay, Maggie, I'll be off and I'll call again next week. Thanks for the coffee; much appreciated." Susan stopped by the door to pat Woody. "How d'you think this little chap will take it?"

"He'll be fine, he's good with children. 'Bye now, go carefully."

Maggie felt content. It was hard to believe that after all the sad times she was now only weeks away from becoming a mother. The baby moved as she laid a hand on her stomach and she traced the limb that was pushing hard. She pondered over the labour to come, aware of the dangers, but put the negative thoughts to the back of her mind. Stroking her stomach she murmured, "I love you, little one." The baby lurched, as if in reply.

Robert found her asleep on the settee, oblivious to Woody's barking. "Hi, darling, how did it go today? Did your friend come and check you over?"

Maggie took hold of his hand, as he pulled her upright, "Thanks, Rob. I feel like a beached whale. Everything was fine, Susan was pleased with me – us. Remind me to start collecting newspapers."

"Whatever for?"

"Floor covering mainly. And also remind me to get a small hot water bottle to put in the crib."

"I'll be boiling all the water I suppose when the time comes, or is that just in films?"

"No, she'll need to sterilise her instruments and then we'll all need cups of tea. A lot of tea gets drunk."

"Instruments? What do they need those for? It's all supposed to be natural and normal isn't it? I thought that's what we'd been going to classes for? Are you sure we're doing the right thing by staying at home? What if something goes wrong, Maggie? You're getting me worried now."

"Now listen, sit down, darling. We've been over all this. We couldn't be in better hands than Doctor Southgate and Susan. Nothing is going to go wrong. They'll need some instruments to cut baby's cord and so on, the rest is just in case and I might need some stitches. As I said, you and I will need tea, so will they, lots of it. It's going to be wonderful. Now then, give me a hand again and let's have something to eat, I'm starving."

Woody followed her in to the kitchen. Maggie stooped for his bowl with difficulty and patted his head, "Yours is coming, Woody," she said. As the dog gobbled his food down Maggie ladled rice on to hot plates. "Another curry, darling I'm afraid."

"Not to worry, it smells good."

"I've filled the freezer for when baby comes, so that we won't have to think about cooking for at least the first week. This weekend we need to do a big shop."

"What for?"

"Baby's stuff, more nappies, all sorts. Mum's getting the pram, but we've got to choose it."

"Maggie, it's weeks away."

"I know, I'm nesting."

CHAPTER 31

SLOE GIN AND DAMSON EYES

Mud and stones showered the footpath, as the dog pawed at the ground beneath an ancient Oak tree.

"Woody, do come on. What've you found?" said Maggie, yanking the lead, with the dog resisting, intrigued to see he had exposed a shiny metal object.

"It's an old teapot or something," she said, unable to bend over her bump. "Leave it alone, it's supper time, come on."

She made a note of the area they were in before hurrying homeward.

"If you really think it was a valuable horde, darling, you'd better let the police know," Robert said later, when she told him where Woody had dug in the woods. "I'd feel happier if you didn't walk so far, Charlie and I are both worried about you."

"It may be nothing, but I could see that a lot more ground had been dug over and it made me a bit suspicious," said Maggie with a shudder. "I must say I was starting to feel a wee bit scared."

"Well, you're making us all nervous and you've completely ignored what I just said!"

"I haven't. I promise. It is a bit silly of me, I admit."

Next morning PC O'Sheridan showed a keener interest. "D'you think whatever it is could have been buried there recently?" he asked.

"It was a shiny object, but I couldn't be certain what it was." Maggie said, standing at the counter in the police house in Waldersby. "I've no idea at all, but thought I should report it."

"Three burglaries lately and none of them solved, this is certainly worth examining," he said.

"Would you like me to show you the area? I can take you there later today."

Maggie was glad that he at least wanted to investigate and she had to admit she was keen to have another look, so after lunch the trio set off. Maggie recognised the area easily and Woody was eager to start digging again.

"He certainly senses something unusual doesn't he?" she said, as earth spattered her coat once again from Woody's efforts.

"Keep him back a minute," said the policeman, taking a small trowel from his pocket and carefully picking at the earth to expose more of what Woody had uncovered.

"Goodness, that looks interesting." Maggie said, as the dog tugged and whined, anxious to dig again. "That's silver, surely?"

PC O'Sheridan lifted the object aloft, "A chalice I think you'd call it, thankfully it appears undamaged, just a bit tarnished," he said, dabbing at it with a handkerchief. "Yes, indeed, I think we have a result here and there's a lot more stuff to uncover by the looks of it young lady. Whoever buried this lot is going to be back for it sooner rather than later and we want to be ready for them. That's a clever little chap you've got there."

"Yes, and he knows it," Maggie said, patting Woody. "This is very worrying though isn't it? I hope you find everything that's been taken."

"Thanks to that dog of yours we could have a breakthrough. Now I need to get back to my desk and report this. Not a word mind, not a word."

"I've only mentioned it to my husband. We shan't tell anyone else."

"I'm not sure its right to let you wander out here alone with a baby on the way, if you don't mind me saying so," he said gruffly, walking back to the edge of the wood. "Not with these villains about. Now, we'd best get you straight back home."

—⁂—

"Such a pity none of your things have been found yet, Charlie. I'm so pleased we've got the church silver back though, aren't you? Edna can't believe it and the vicar's thrilled."

"Grand little dog our Woody. Tell him to find some Roman coins and make you a rich girl. Trouble is," he said, scratching his balding head, "I can't remember what we had in the cupboard, so no idea what there is to look for. Mary used to tidy it all away. Can't have been that valuable."

"You'll remember it if it's found."

"I haven't looked in there since she passed away."

"Well we can celebrate this find – there's to be a special service next month."

Edna and Dawn Creasey spent hours polishing the silver. Each piece had undergone close scrutiny and finger printing before being released back to the church and now sat gleaming on the altar, apparently none the worse for being buried.

"This is a sad day. I have never felt a church should be locked, or its altar pieces kept hidden. We live in troubled times," said the vicar, gesturing to Maggie to go forward with Woody. "I think a round of applause would be appropriate for Mrs Groves and her dog, Woody, who discovered our precious silver."

Celebrations of the find and the apprehension of miscreants involved continued later that day with PC O'Sheridan at the Dog and Duck, boasting of the part he played, proudly informing everyone in the bar that it was not local lads, but a Cambridge gang who had carried out burglaries in and around the village and Waldersby.

"Opportunists, these boys, so watch out and lock your garages and sheds as well as your house when you go out. I'm warning you, they don't miss a trick. But I can safely say the local crime wave is at an end."

—⁓—

Maggie felt depressed, weepy and irritable. The baby was six days overdue and the frequent enquiries from her mother, sister, Angela, friends from her ante-natal classes, and half the village were getting to her.

"Are you still there?" "Has nothing happened yet?" "Are you sure everything's alright?" "Perhaps you should speak to the doctor or your midwife, dear?"

"I know it's silly, getting cross with Mum. It's just so irritating when everyone keeps asking if I'm still here!"

"Everyone is getting excited, because they care about you," said Robert. "Me too, darling. So any suggestions to get you started? I heard you doling out advice often enough to your mums."

"Well I've walked enough and I don't feel up to sex, nipple twiddling, more hot curry, or borrowing a tractor for a shaky ride, so we'll just have to wait. As I also keep saying, the baby will come when it's ready." Maggie subsided on to the settee somewhere between tears and laughter. "I just wish it was ready now!"

"Hush, now, silly, you'll upset our baby too," he said, sitting down to cradle her in his arms.

"I think you're right," said Maggie, placing a soothing hand on her stomach as the baby began to move.

"Come on, you need an early night." Robert said, laughing. "I'll follow you up after I've cleared up in the study. You must have spent hours sorting out all our bills and bank statements today."

"I had an urge to get all that paperwork filed properly, the desk was in such a mess. Nesting again I suppose."

"Well, that's a good indication isn't it? Have you got the rest of the stuff on those lists?"

"Yes, the bedroom floor is now covered with old newspapers."

"I thought you put them down when labour started?"

"Another urge, darling. I've got the special icepack in the freezer and the other things are ready next to the midwife's box – my little bit of real sponge for sucking on and the like."

—⁂—

Maggie woke at three in the morning. She felt mild tightenings, not unlike her period pains, and went down to the kitchen.

"Sssh, Woody. I think our baby might be coming, isn't that exciting?" she said, roughing up his coat. "Down now, down."

She felt much happier as she made a mug of hot chocolate and filled a small hot water bottle, but the griping in her stomach disappeared, as she settled back to sleep

"I'm not going anywhere now, and I'll bring you breakfast in bed. This could be your last chance to get pampered for quite some time," said Robert, running his fingers through his hair. "You shouldn't have let me sleep in, it's nine o'clock already and

Woody's whining in the kitchen."

"I've only had a show, nothing else is happening, just the odd twinge."

"Well then it could be days yet, according to what I learnt in class, so in that case do you fancy a big breakfast?"

"I'll potter about a bit to see if that gets me going again," said Maggie, trying not to smile at Robert teaching her to suck eggs.

After her breakfast Maggie sauntered around the garden; fed up and tearful once more and it wasn't until late in the afternoon that her labour started again. She began practising the different breathing levels once the contractions became more regular, soothing herself with a warm bath, while Robert hovered nearby, asking what he could do every minute or so. By early evening they were breathing in unison, as Robert massaged her back and Maggie decided it was time to call the midwife.

Maggie had formed a close bond with Susan during her pregnancy and the midwife's presence comforted Robert and enabled them both to relax. She knew Susan was intrigued by their approach to labour and that she had never fully approved of the mind over matter methods that the NCT training was inspired by. She also knew that like many of her colleagues, Susan may be sceptical, but she would not try to discourage either of them. They were coping well, acting as a team. Robert gently doing effleurage-stroking her stomach, massaging her back for several hours and applying the cold pack, until Susan persuaded him that he should have a rest.

"Poor chap, he's exhausted," Susan said as Maggie let him go, concentrating instead on shouting their chosen nursery rhyme, as mountainous waves of pain threatened to overwhelm her.

"I'm losing it, Susan. Help, please don't let me lose control."

"You're doing brilliantly, Maggie, really you are. Believe me you're almost there, your waters are still intact. I'll not touch them, but I'm going to call Robert back."

"How could you fall asleep? You're supposed to be helpi----," Maggie shouted as he re-appeared, aiming a stream of abuse at him.

"Come on, darling, you're doing so well. I'm sorry," he said, pressing the cold pack against her back and ducking smartly, as Maggie yanked it away and hurled it across the room.

"It's too bloody cold," she yelled, pushing his hand away, as he tried to mop her forehead. "Get me the bloody gas now, please," she shouted. "I want to push, I want to push!"

"Okay, don't let me stop you, Maggie," said Susan, after a brief examination. "You've done so well, breathe deeply now. Dr Southgate's on his way."

"This is great stuff, I'll have a jab now," said Maggie, thirty minutes later, drunk on the gas and slurring her words.

"Too late for that Maggie. You've had nearly a whole cylinder of gas, so I think you've probably had quite enough!"

Maggie clutched at the mask, "I need it, don't you dare take it away," she said, clawing at Robert and ignoring the helpless look on his face.

"I could hear you up the lane, my dear," said Doctor Southgate as he came into the room. "I don't think it will be long now before we have this baby, so just ignore me and do what Susan tells you."

Robert and Susan chorused encouragement as Maggie flung the mask aside and started to push. Within an hour of Dr Southgate's arrival she was ready to give birth, having pushed so hard she felt fit to burst. Exhausted and elated she whimpered, "I never imagined it would be like this, Susan," before obeying the final command and smothering an overwhelming urge to scream.

"Good girl, well done, pant just pant, pant," Susan called out as she deftly delivered the baby.

"Born in a caul," she said, gently sweeping away the membrane. "A good sailor don't they say, Doctor?

"So, I'm told." Doctor Southgate said, now standing by her side. "That was a wonderful effort, Maggie," he said, patting her arm, "you've a healthy little baby there."

"It's a boy darling, it's a boy," said Robert, amid tears and laughter.

Dr Southgate smiled benignly. "Well done everyone."

"I can't believe it, Maggie, our baby boy," said Robert, covering her in tears. "You did so well, darling, you were marvellous,you really were."

"I'll just finish and then we can bath and weigh him before I go," said Susan, towelling the baby dry and placing him in Robert's arms. "My guess he's a good eight and a half pounds, what d'you think, Doctor."

"I agree, he's a chubby little fellow."

"He certainly felt that much," Maggie grimaced. "Thanks everyone, my goodness that was tough. Can I hold him properly, Rob. I'll never tell women in labour to 'just relax' in future!"

An hour later, bathed, swaddled and examined, the baby lay in Maggie's arms and gazed unblinking in to her eyes.

Doctor Southgate and Susan both enjoyed the champagne that Robert poured a little too freely and sounded very merry as they left, promising to return in the morning.

"Goodness me, over nine pounds, our very own little dumpling," said Maggie, her voice breaking with the love she felt for the baby in her arms. "Rob, look, he's got damson eyes, he's perfect."

"Caused by imbibing too many sloes darling," he chuckled, lying down beside her. "I think he takes after you; beautiful eyes like his mother."

"Rob, I'm so happy. I wouldn't mind a drop of Charlie's sloe gin right now though. Forgive me for yelling at you?"

"Darling wife, that's a silly question. I think I'm possibly the happiest person in the world at this moment, I'm so proud of you, Maggie," he said, kissing her tenderly and gently stroking the baby's head as he got off the bed. "You know you mean the world to me. Now, I think you need some sleep and I need a drink, strong tea sounds about right." Quietly he left the room and his sleepy family. "I'll crack open another bottle later when Angela arrives, you could have just a tiny drop. Sleep now."

CHAPTER 32

A COUNTRY BUMPKIN

Robert studied the tiny ears of their baby sprawled on his bare chest and marvelled at the perfection of tiny toes and fingers. Maggie had fed him through the night, every time he cried, passing him wearily to daddy to wind. The hiccups amused Robert as the small body lurched and stretched, forming tight fists that clutched at the hair on his chest and made him wince. He gazed at Maggie sleeping at his side and was overcome with love and tenderness. My very own family, he mused, dabbing at the baby's dribbled milky curds and gently manoeuvring to stretch his own limbs.

"Come on, little one, into your crib now." He lowered his son. "Daddy's got to get breakfast, we'd better not wake Mummy," Robert whispered, rocking the cradle.

"I'm awake, I'll have him," Maggie stretched out one arm, "He's hungry, darling."

"Okay, at least you've had a couple of hours since the last feed, but I thought he had to wait a couple more?"

"Strictly speaking, yes, but I rather like the idea of feeding when he wants it and he seems more contented than some of the new babies I've dealt with."

"Dr Southgate said he would call in before surgery. I'll get some coffee on the go."

"Good idea, Susan's coming back early too." Maggie cradled the baby, already nuzzling hopefully at her breast. "It makes sense doesn't it, animals don't sit with a stopwatch. We make life so difficult imposing rules, rather than following our basic instincts."

"I'm sure you're right, darling," Robert said, easing a sticky wet shoulder out of his pyjama top. "Will Susan bath him again when she comes? He's sicked up all over me, so I certainly need one."

"Posseting, not sick – sounds better!. Susan will come in a couple of times today, tomorrow and the next day and then she has a week off and her colleague, Gemma, will be calling. I'm sure she'll make time to bath him again. Daddies have to bath themselves don't they," she chuckled, hugging the baby to her.

"Pity, I thought it was part of the service!" he said, laughing. "I saw Charlie in the lane a moment ago, he'll be anxious to see you both."

"So are we both agreed on his name then?"

"Yes, definitely. I'll let Charlie know all's well when I've got changed."

It was the following day when the new family walked the short distance to Charlie's cottage and gave him the baby to hold. The old man's eyes were brimming with tears as the baby gazed up at him, unblinking. "You're a little cracker, aren't you? So what d'you weigh?"

"Just under nine pounds! Now you know why I was moaning – he was getting so heavy," said Maggie.

"What you calling the little fella then, has he got a name yet?"

"Yes." Maggie and Robert smiled at each other, "Charlie, would you mind if we called him Charlie, after you?"

Charlie pulled a large handkerchief out of his breast pocket, "Here, take him 'fore I drop him." His eyes glinted as he blew noisily. "My giddy aunt, now that's a bit of a shock."

"Are you pleased?" Maggie asked, "We really don't want to upset you."

"Course I'm pleased, just didn't expect it though," Charlie said, rubbing his nose vigorously

"It'll have to be Charlie Senior and Charlie Junior or some such," said Maggie, kissing his cheek, "You don't know how much you mean to us."

"Here's Edna," said Robert, moving from the window to open the cottage door. "She's got some shopping by the looks of things."

"Got your corned beef and a couple of ripe bananas," Edna said, brushing past Robert to plant her basket on the kitchen table. "I thought you'd have visitors today," her voice softened at the sight of the baby. "Well, you're quite a chubby one aren't you?"

"You can have a hold if you like," said Maggie. "Another Charlie for you to spoil!"

"Charlie?" she looked at the old man. "You've named the poor little blighter same as him?"

Robert and Maggie burst out laughing as Charlie Senior pulled a face.

"Trust you, got to have your little dig, haven't you? Well, if Charlie's good enough for me it's good enough for that little mite and I'm honoured to have a namesake, so you'll just have to lump it," he said, blowing his nose vigorously again. "And what's more you can pour us all a drop of my best carrot whisky!"

Maggie suppressed a smile at the shocked surprise on Edna's face at Charlie's robust reply.

"Not for me, I'll take Charlie home for a feed in a minute, "said Maggie, tempted by the thought of returning to her bed. "I'm sure Robert will have my share, won't you darling? I'll be told off as it is for leaving home to go visiting."

"Don't bother for me either, I'll get Maggie back, as she should be resting. I'll pop back later when they're both asleep," said Robert.

News of baby Charlie's arrival was soon common knowledge and Nut Tree Cottage began to resemble a florist shop, with congratulation cards strung from every beam. The postman also delivered parcels daily and the baby acquired a wardrobe of tiny clothes, while Angela brought some meals, and more cakes flowed from Edna and the shop.

"It was touching when everyone delighted in Woody, but this is amazing," Maggie said, a week later after returning from pushing the baby around the village to find the midwife waiting for her. "We feel so lucky, Susan, I can't imagine that anyone would have known or cared if we'd been in London. Dawn Creasey has offered to baby sit at any time and Major Gibson sent a beautiful bouquet!"

"I expect you're right," said Susan. "It's nice to know everyone is interested in you and pleased to have little Charlie in their midst. You'll have to meet up with your NCT group next week and compare progress. Remember this is my last visit, but you can phone me at any time – just because you're one of us doesn't mean you know it all! And the health visitor, Gloria, will call by tomorrow."

"I'll really miss you calling, make sure you drop in if you're passing or need the loo. We're so grateful for everything you've done and you must come to Charlie's christening whenever we decide to have it. I don't know how long it will be before I'm back at work."

"Don't forget to arrange your final check up with Dr Southgate. Incidentally Gloria is dying to know how your NCT training went; she's pregnant and thinking of doing the course."

"What did you really think? I know I'll now be a much better ante natal teacher," Maggie grimaced. "Experiencing a birth should be part of our training!"

"I was impressed. I thought you did really well for a first timer. You lost it a bit at the end, Jack and Jill never quite made it up the hill did they? But he was a big baby, so well done."

"Poor Rob looked so shocked at my swearing," Maggie laughed. "I'm afraid many of my good intentions went out of the window together with the ice pack."

"Dr Southgate said it was a grand performance – I overheard him at the surgery singing your praises."

"He's called three times you know, he wants me to persuade a student of his that home births are a good thing. Apparently, the student is terrified of pregnant women and thinks he will probably pass out when he attends a birth."

Susan repacked her nursing bag and finished her notes. "He wouldn't be the first. Now then, you're in good shape Maggie, promise me you'll keep up your exercises and do try and have a sleep when little Charlie is sleeping."

"I promise. He's a very contented baby and I'm delighted that I've had no problems breast feeding, which was my main concern. Mum's coming next week, she'll probably stay a fortnight as Robert will be in Brussels for a few days."

"Let your mum do things for you, I know you think you must do everything, but she's come to help remember."

"I will. Poor Rob, he really doesn't want to leave us at all."

"He'll see a change in little Charlie even after that short time."

"I know, it's unfortunate but his boss insists that he needs him at a special conference out there. Frank's been so generous to us that Rob doesn't want to upset him. They've never had children, so he has no idea what a wrench it will be."

"Your mum will love looking after you both," said Susan, bending down to stroke Woody who lay beside the crib, making no attempt to move. "How's this little chap taking it?"

"He's glued to the crib and gets agitated if Charlie cries, he's determined not to let him out of his sight."

"I know I don't need to tell you not to leave him alone with the baby if he's so protective." She slung her bag over her shoulder and picked up her coat, "Right, I'm off then. Now remember to ring me if you have any worries at all."

Maggie hugged her, "I promise. Thanks for everything, I'll miss you coming."

As the cottage door closed Maggie picked up the sleeping baby. "Come on, Charlie, I need you with me." Maggie held him close, as instinctively he nuzzled at her breast. She could see a change in his features and fondled the plump swell of his small arms and legs. She studied his face, the flickering eyelids, and the occasional windy smile. "Charlie, I can't ever let you go," she murmured, overcome with emotion and the love she felt for her baby.

The telephone rang incessantly, but there was one call in particular that Maggie was more than happy to receive. It was from Jacky Richards now living in Spain and happily settled with a new boyfriend.

"You must bring your hubby out here for a holiday with the baby."

"That's so kind, Jacky, and we'll think about it. Do you hear anything of Len? He left the village some months ago."

"No, and I never want to, love. The divorce is going through. Martin's looked after me and he's got a job in a posh nightclub and I'm helping out there. That's how I met Colin, his wife left him two years ago and we get on like a house on fire."

"I'm so pleased for you, Jacky, after everything you've been through. Make sure you come and see us and little Charlie, if you come back here at all."

"The little one might be at school by the time I get to see him. You take care now and I'll ring you in a week or two to catch up."

Maggie watched as Robert moved toys and baby clothes from one side of the spare room to another, telling him all about the conversation she'd had with Jacky earlier.

"Angela will help," she said, as he piled up the heap of presents for the new baby. "She's bringing fish and chips round later."

"Good. I need to get some work stuff sorted out and this room is not fit for your mother to sleep in. Shall I bring Charlie in from the garden?"

"No, it's warm and Woody will bark when he wakes. Mum always stuck us under a tree in all weathers! Incidentally Edna actually asked if she could take him out in the pram."

"What did you say?"

"I said she could. We need that sort of help and I know she'll take good care of him, she's quite taken with our little one. She and Dawn have also said that they will look after him when and if, I decide to go back to work."

Robert looked up in surprise, "Really? I thought we'd already decided against you going back to work until Charlie went to playgroup, and then only part time?"

"I might get called in to do the odd shift. I'm planning to start my classes again in a couple of months anyway, and they can cover then if you're away."

"You do amaze me. I didn't think you would let Edna anywhere near our little one."

"I think we misunderstand Edna at times, so I'm quite happy to let her help."

"Okay, it's up to you, she'll be fine I'm sure."

Maggie gazed out of the window at the pram, the umbilical cord had been severed but the attachment she felt for this tiny baby was overwhelming, "Oh, Rob, do stop, I need a cuddle."

With his arms around her she let the tears fall, "I cannot describe how happy I feel, we are so lucky. We've waited so long for Charlie."

"Now we have him, darling," he said, his voice breaking with emotion, "and I have you too."

CHAPTER 33

TO HAVE AND TO HOLD

Maggie and her mother stood admiring the flowers, bunting and balloons decorating the village hall to celebrate the christening of little Charlie. The church ceremony had taken place during morning service.

"I'm so glad you two moved here," said Elizabeth, switching on the big tea urn. "I can't think of a nicer, kinder group of people, darling. Fancy Edna and Mrs Creasey organising all this. Mrs Creasey seems to think the world of you and little Charlie."

"Yes, it's like one big family really. It's hard to describe the love and attention we've received since the little one was born."

"I wanted to say how smart you both looked, darling, that's such a pretty hat. Pity we couldn't get your christening gown on Charlie though, you and Eleanor looked adorable in it when you were babies, his fat little legs do look more suited to his sailor suit."

"He'd have looked silly, Mum, in a lacy gown! James looks cute in his outfit too, doesn't he? Angela and I went up to the London and couldn't resist buying them both in Harrods' sale."

"I'd have joined you if I lived nearer." She lowered her voice. "Goodness me, Angela's so big, she must be getting very uncomfortable now, and the last weeks drag so."

"She is. She planned to get pregnant the moment she and Tom got married, and she did. Some women are so lucky aren't they?"

"You finally made it, darling. What a struggle it was. Shall I milk these cups?" she said, arranging them on a small trolley.

"Yes, good idea," Maggie said, adding plates of sandwiches, "I can't believe Charlie is nearly a year old, can you? We're hoping we can have another baby of course but not just yet, we're so enjoying him."

Maggie could hardly believe herself how quickly the days and months had passed since the birth of Charlie. He chatted and toddled now, a happy little boy.

"Time flies, dear. Can it really be five years since your father passed away? It astonishes me to think of it."

"Yes, it seems incredible. I do wish Dad could have met everyone here, and most of all his grandson. You mentioned the Creaseys, Dawn is always offering to look after Charlie, and Kate babysits for us whenever she's at home."

"That's wonderful, such a help. I'll only put milk in half the cups. Some will want black coffee, although I should think the oldies will prefer tea," said Elizabeth, gazing round the hall. "Do many things go on here?"

"Lots, there's an art group starting up, which I want to join. I've offered to be on the committee in Angela's place. Last week we had a meeting to toss around some ideas for a mother and toddler group, Scottish dancing, keep fit classes and even judo and karate for the children. We'll need to do some fundraising, perhaps another jumble sale or bingo night! I suppose I can't persuade you to move down here?"

"Oh, no, darling. I couldn't leave your father."

"Eh? Mum, he's in the cemetery!" Maggie said, almost dropping the plate she was carrying.

"I know, but I do like to spruce up the grave occasionally, and I feel he's still around me in the house. You'll understand one day, dear. Besides Eleanor isn't properly settled yet; by the way she's so glad you asked her to be a godparent, she's thinking of changing her job again you know and no doubt her boyfriend. She's so contrary, I really think he's the right one for her, such a nice lad. There, d'you think thirty cups will be enough?" Elizabeth said, pushing the trolley into place by the table now laden with food.

"There are mugs in the bottom cupboard if we run out."

"I have to say I thought the service was lovely today and the vicar is rather sweet isn't he, even though he nearly drowned Charlie. Shall I slice some of the christening cake up ready?"

"Good idea, and we could make up some more of those cheese and pineapple sticks. Don't let the vicar hear you say that," said Maggie. "I don't think I'd call him sweet either!" she chuckled. "He can be very stern at times."

"How is young James coping with the idea of a new baby?"

"Absolutely loving it I think, he adores our Charlie."

"Does he see anything of his father?"

"Not much, Gordon's pretty hopeless with him. He speaks to James on the phone occasionally and has taken him on a few outings, but that's about all."

"Here they come, there's our nice Frank, I must say 'hello' and ask him if he enjoyed the theatre. He began telling me about a show he'd been to the other day. He really has been incredibly good to you two," she said, hastily whipping off her apron and washing her hands.

Maggie smiled to herself as she watched her mother flirting

mildly with Frank Sutton. It was becoming obvious that despite him being married the pair were rather fond of each other. Little Charlie was being pushed round the hall by two of the village children and Angela was warning them about bumping in to the guests. It was very special having her friends and family together, she reflected. Maggie felt that she now knew everyone in this small village; her relationship with many of them had developed as she took walks with Charlie and Woody, meeting and greeting them as they passed. The village functions, the fete, jumble sales and other activities brought them closer and her role as a nurse and midwife had given her a special place in the community – just as Charlie Watt had foreseen when they first arrived.

"I'd forgotten how bloody uncomfortable these last weeks could be, Maggie. This one never stops kicking and I'm so tired. It's alright though, Susan checked me over yesterday," Angela said, helping herself to a cup of tea and flopping heavily onto the bench. "What's up?"

"Happy, that's all. You look fantastic, pregnancy suits you, only a few more weeks and it'll all be over. I'm glad you're having a home birth – Susan's really keen on this water birth idea. My one regret is that I'm not your 'deliverer' this time."

"I just hope you can be there as extra support if I need it? What d'you really think of water births? I'm told the baby will like it and I'll have a lot less pain."

"It's an amazing idea, but I'm not sure that I would want it. I'll see how you get on first. I suppose without all the usual handling, glaring lights etc it really must be so much kinder to them and less of a shock."

"Added to which I have chosen my mood music and I'll have candles burning. If all goes well it will be quite an experience.

James was nearly tugged into the world with forceps, wasn't he? Thankfully you were there to protect me then, but this is going to be a very different experience. Fingers crossed."

"Have you hired the pool yet?"

"No, Tom's going to pick one up next week so that we can do a test run, see how long it takes to fill – we don't want to be in a panic at the last minute."

"Oh, look at my mother – what an outrageous flirt - I love it." Maggie chuckled, watching Elizabeth as Frank put his arm round her. "She and Frank get on so well, don't they? Even though I keep reminding her he's married. I think Mum gets quite lonely at times, she needs another man."

"Good luck to her. She's an attractive woman, Maggie."

"It's all quite harmless. Right, let's think about you. I'll pop round tomorrow and we'll go over the breathing, so you'll have less to think about. James was a week early, wasn't he? So this one might decide not to wait."

"Hopefully it won't be any earlier." Angela said, "Oh, could you get James for me, he looks as if he needs to go outside to play, I told him not to run around now everyone's holding their drinks, he's a bit over excited."

"Okay, we'd better stop chatting and get the last of this food on the tables. I've a couple of battenburgs and some chocolate swiss roll to slice up."

"Dawn and Kate are doing a good job, the sandwiches and sausage rolls have virtually all gone."

"I was telling Mum how good James is with little Charlie. I know he'll love his new baby."

"We feel happy about him, he chatters a lot about his new brother or sister. I'm determined that he won't feel pushed out."

Maggie shooed James out to play with his older friends and manoeuvred little Charlie, asleep in his pushchair, into a space between Charlie Watt and Edna.

"Could you keep an eye on Charlie, Edna, please? I must just nip to the loo."

"I will, the other one won't, he's been asleep for the past half hour," she said glancing at Charlie Watt snoring beside her. "He'll be tipping off that chair if I don't watch him."

Maggie nodded; the old man spent a lot of time sleeping and she was beginning to feel concerned, not just for the time he slept but for his memory lapses and lack of energy. Once so keen to look after his vegetables or take a walk to the shop, he couldn't seem to summon up the energy for either activity these days.

"Leave me be, girl," he'd told her when she tried to encourage him on several occasions in the past few weeks to walk to the village green with her, pushing little Charlie's pram. And asking him to go and see a doctor only made him agitated. So Maggie had asked Dr Southgate if he would be able to call, unannounced, and he had agreed to do so the following week.

Two hours later several of the villagers and some of the guests were drifting away. Robert's younger brother, Chris, who had arrived the night before to play the part of a godparent was staying for a few days. Maggie noticed that he'd spent most of the time talking to Tom Farrow, it was good to see that they had a lot in common. Maggie looked around the room at those who were left; the party had been a success; Eleanor was now a tipsy, giggly godmother. Robert's Aunt Jenny was the only family member who hadn't made it for the christening, as she was recovering from a hip fracture, but she had promised to see them later in the year and Ben, Robert's older brother, had also agreed to fly back to the UK at Christmas.

Yes, it was what families were all about and her family was sure to expand, hopefully growing and thriving as relationships developed, thought Maggie, as she crossed the hall to join her mother and Frank Sutton.

"Darling, Frank's just told me he has a business meeting in Carlisle next month and I've invited him to stay, isn't that fun?"

Maggie wondered whether her mother's coquettishness was due to an excess of champagne. She had noticed her dabbing on rather more perfume than usual in the Ladies earlier.

"You can show Frank the sights up north, Mum."

"Now then, are you leading my boss astray?" laughed, Robert, joining them to fill up their glasses.

"Don't be silly dear, I wouldn't dream of such a thing," Elizabeth said.

"I wouldn't mind if you did," said Frank, holding out his glass. "It's not bad champagne this, Robert."

Goodness me, thought Maggie, her mother was actually fluttering her eyelashes!

"Rob, can you wheel our Charlie back home in a minute? I need to help Edna as Charlie will be a bit tottery, he's slept for the last hour and couldn't even finish his tea."

"Shall I collect up the crockery?" said Elizabeth.

"Please. Dawn's offered to wash up."

"I'll go when I've finished this," said Frank. "Elizabeth, perhaps we can have lunch in Waldersby before you go back?"

"Thank you, that would be nice."

Maggie noticed how pleased her mother looked, waving to Frank as he was leaving.

"Mum, you two seem to be hitting it off rather well, don't forget he's a married man."

"Don't be silly, Maggie, I think I'm old enough to make friends without upsetting a marriage, especially an unhappy one. Now then, I think your Charlie Watt has had enough dear, and I don't mean tea."

"What's that supposed to mean?"

"He's tired, frail and getting very forgetful. I think he feels ready to go."

"Mum, I know Charlie's ready for bed but I thought you meant something else. Don't say it like that."

"That's right dear, he needs his bed."

Maggie knew that Charlie was weary and deep down she had been worried about his increasing frailty. Her mother's comment made her fearful. She would spend some extra time with him over the next few days, keep a closer eye on him. Our little toddler will liven him up she decided, as she hurried across the hall to help Edna.

—m—

Charlie tried to busy himself in the garden, ignoring the cold as he pottered around his vegetable patch, wondering where he'd put his trowel. Funny how so many things seemed to be missing these days. His tool box was half empty and Maggie had found his garden shears next to the hedge in the lane. Luckily they were still in one piece, despite cars running up and down.

"You must be careful, Charlie," she kept telling him.

Feeling chilled he ambled back to his cottage and sat by the warm range. Mary, his wife smiled at him from the mantelpiece.

"Making us both a cuppa, are you dear?" Charlie said, speaking to the framed photograph. The wall clock chimed three o'clock, as he fell asleep.

Dr Southgate found him later that afternoon. Charlie had passed away shortly before his arrival.

"A very nice way to go, Maggie dear," Dr Southgate said, endeavouring to lessen the shock. "He didn't die alone you know. Doris, if that's what you call that little hen, was nestled on his lap."

An unstoppable flow of tears trickled onto little Charlie's head, as Maggie hugged him to her.

"We should have been there," she told Robert.

"Darling, Edna keeps saying the same thing. We weren't there with him, but I know that Charlie knew how much we all loved him and like the doctor said, he didn't die alone or in pain, he had his precious Doris on his lap. You know what?"

"What?"

"I think Elizabeth saw this coming, she's quite intuitive isn't she."

Maggie's sobs increased as Robert held her tightly.

"We've got our little Charlie, he was the grandchild Charlie Watt never had and that gave him the greatest joy," he said, trying to console her. "So, if you don't mind I think we should raise a small glass of sloe gin, even if you are breastfeeding, to the best Grandad our little boy could have wished for. It's not disrespectful, I know Charlie would approve. Remember darling, that's how he came in to our lives."

Holding two small glasses aloft they drank a toast, "To Charlie, our dearest friend."

EPILOGUE

Maggie grieved for many months following Charlie Watt's death. His son, who had had no contact with him when alive, appeared to sort out the cottage and belongings. Maggie and Robert found it difficult to be civil and were even more distressed when he arranged for all the household effects to be sold off, or sent up North. Edna did not hold back and told him exactly what she thought of the way he had neglected his father. Maggie managed to keep the photograph of Mary, which she found discarded and Charlie's cap and two large yellow handkerchiefs became her most treasured possessions.

Angela safely delivered her baby girl, Rosie, in a birthing pool witnessed by Maggie. Maggie was offered her own case load on the district and returned to full time midwifery, juggling child care with her shifts. Robert was promoted to senior director of the company, as Frank Sutton planned retirement. The friendship between Frank and Elizabeth continued apace.

Charlie's cottage was put up for sale and Robert and Maggie were delighted when Angela and Tom decided to buy and renovate it. James attended a playgroup and was soon to go to primary school in the next village. Gordon retained the barn and relationships between them all remained amicable.

The community support for the village hall increased and the activities that Maggie hoped for began to take place. Dawn and Edna were in charge of the over-sixties group and organised whist drives and excursions. Maggie came to rely on them for babysitting, which enabled her to return to full-time midwifery.

Charlie Watt was buried in the local churchyard, a favourite picnic spot for little Charlie who often pointed upwards to the clouds above and "G'andad in the sky." A comforting thought to overcome the sadness which prevailed for so long in Maggie's heart.

HAUNTEI.
TOD.

Andrew Green

S.B. Publications

To Norah Bridget, my dear wife, with my thanks for her help, support and general encouragement.

First published in 1997 by S.B. Publications,
c/o 19 Grove Road, Seaford, East Sussex BN25 1TP

©1997 Andrew Green

ISBN 1 85770 121 6

Designed and typeset by CGB Lewes
Printed by Island Press Ltd
3 Cradle Hill Industrial Estate, Seaford, East Sussex BN25 3JE

ANDREW GREEN, BSc, MPhil, FETC, has been a member of the Society for Psychical Research since 1972, having written a number of books and several hundred articles on ghosts and hauntings, edited three recent works on phenomena, appeared in numerous television programmes on the paranormal and has been appointed as a consultant to the Ghost Club.

In 1993 he featured in a Dutch TV film, *De Stoel,* investigating Glynde Place with the owner Viscount Hampden. In 1996 he was commissioned to examine alleged phenomena in the Royal Albert Hall. The exploits there resulted in his inclusion in the BBC's Television Review of the Year.

His activities have been featured nationally and internationally. The *Sunday Telegraph* termed him Britain's Spectre Inspector, and he participated in two American and two German film productions in the same year, as well as appearing on Italian and Australian television. He was also interviewed on Radio Mexico, Radio Eire and Radio Riviera.

Andrew has been tutoring adult courses in the south east for some twenty five years and continues to provide individual lectures on hauntings.

His attraction to the paranormal began in 1944 when he took a photograph of an empty house in which police records showed twenty suicides and a murder had occurred between 1883 and 1934.

The resultant print showed the image of a girl of about twelve sitting in one of the upstairs windows. One of three young victims was Anne Hinchfield, a twelve year old girl who fell or was pushed, from the top of the seventy foot high building in 1887. On researching the incident Andrew established what he believes is the formula for apparitions, as well as their cause.

By the same author

Our Haunted Kingdom (Wolfe)
Ghost Hunting: A Practical Guide (Garnstone)
Ghosts of the South East (David and Charles)
Phantom Ladies (Bailey Brothers and Swinfen)
The Ghostly Army (MacDonald Educational)
Ghosts of Tunbridge Wells (Hadlow)
Mysteries of Surrey (Napier Publications)
Mysteries of London (Napier Publications)
Mysteries of Sussex (Napier Publications)
Haunted Houses (Shire Publications)
Haunted Inns and Taverns (Shire Publications)

INTRODUCTION

IN spite of attempts by sceptics and hard line scientists, ghosts, phantoms, apparitions, call them what you will, continue to be seen by normal and apparently rational individuals often reluctant to reveal their experiences. A recent survey confirmed that more than ten million people in Britain had witnessed, or been aware of, an inexplicable presence, none of which were reported as being harmful or evil although some were occasionally described as being potentially frightening.

Unfortunately there have been numerous attempts to sensationalise some incidents and to fictionalise small and often insignificant cases out of all recognition. One of the main reasons for the continuing, nay increasing, interest in aspects of hauntings, is the proliferation of media features, often regrettably of poor quality, offset by the ghost walks organised by enthusiastic guides in towns such as Hastings, Horsham, Battle and Worthing, all of which add interest, if not knowledge, to the subject.

One television producer told me: 'If people want ghosts, then ghosts we will let them have – regardless.' And this was from a company intent on producing educational material of high quality.

The problem is, and often will be, to establish whether a witness is describing a factual occurrence; an hallucination; a case of blatant imagination perhaps for publicity purposes, or a genuine incident of spontaneous phenomena.

One of the earliest reports of a ghostly haunting must surely be that found in an Egyptian text which describes a high priest of Amun being haunted by a former chief treasurer to King Rehotep who lived in 1700BC. The ghost had drawn attention to the deterioration of his tomb, the location of which had in fact been mislaid, and as a result of the spectral appearance, the tomb was re-discovered and renovated.

Since then the ghost population of the world has exploded. Britain, some believe, is the most haunted country of all. It certainly does contain a marvellous variety of spectres ranging from a vast collection of monks in grey, in black – in Robertsbridge there is one in a red habit; women in white, scarlet and purple; cats, dogs, a number of horses; and there is even a report of a ghostly badger.

In Sussex there is a the wealth of hauntings. It is a county crowded with castles, old manor houses and ancient inns. It had some notorious gangs of smugglers and in earlier days almost every village had its resident witch. It should also be remembered that the remains of the earliest European, Boxgrove Man, was discovered in 1993 only a few miles from Chichester. He has been dated as living in 500,000BC, but so far as is known, fails to haunt.

This selection of ghostly incidents is listed in alphabetical order of the towns and villages in which they were reported to have occurred over the last twenty five years or so. The accounts detail what was seen, where and by whom, and in some cases pose the question: Why?

Poltergeist hauntings, although strictly unrelated to genuine apparitions, are included.

Andrew Green
Mountfield
1997

ALFRISTON

The Smugglers Inn

OPPOSITE the Market Cross is the 600 year old Smugglers Inn. This attractive old pub, originally the Market Cross Inn, was owned in the eighteenth century by a smuggler named Stanton Collins.

One of the intriguing aspects of the building is that it has at least twenty one rooms with forty eight doors, six staircases – and a ghost. In 1994, shortly before being filmed for a Dutch television documentary film, *De Stoel*, Maureen Ney, the owner, and her daughter, had seen the ghost of a woman in what appeared to be a long gown which looked 'quite modern', standing at the bottom of the stairs adjoining the bar.

Carly, a fourteen year old friend, told me that she well remembered the occasion when she saw a figure in white. She was certainly not frightened by it. 'I thought it was a friend of the family, until it vanished,' she said. No one has identified the phantom. Could she perhaps be associated with another room, as yet undiscovered, as suggested by Mrs Ney.

Deans Place Hotel

THE owner of Magpies, a bookshop in the village, reminded me of the phantom dog which used to haunt Deans Place Hotel further down the road. Until recently it had not been seen for several decades, neither had the blue lady reported in the 1970s by the teenage daughter of a leading photographer.

She was coming down from her bedroom one morning and as she passed a large wooden trunk on the landing she was brushed aside by the figure of a young woman in a long blue gown. She described this rude guest to a member of the staff and asked who she was, only to be told there was no one who looked like that staying at the hotel.

Perhaps the girl had seen the ghostly victim of a horrifying murder who had been cut up and put in the settle on the landing. She has been seen by several people, but they have not been frightened by her. The young witness agreed that the face of the ghost was calm and pleasant, but there was 'something peculiar about her'.

Her appearances were thought to have ceased but a few years ago an American visitor asked about the lady in blue he had seen in an upstairs corridor. He had also seen the phantom dog in the hotel car park.

AMBERLEY

Amberley Castle Hotel

IT is not surprising to find a resident ghost at this luxury hotel for it was originally a bishop's palace and has a 900 year history. The owners, Martin and Joy Cummings, knew of the stories concerning the haunting when they purchased the building in 1988, but they are a little disappointed at not having seen the phantom for themselves.

The apparition is not that of Queen Elizabeth I, who did stay here during the latter half of her reign, but of a fourteen year old girl who has been seen and heard by the workmen still completing the restoration and conversion of the property. It is believed that the little ghost is Emily, a serving girl in the palace kitchens, who was seduced by one of the bishops some time in the fourteenth century. The cause of her death is not known, perhaps it was as a result of the sexual encounter or maybe she died of marsh fever which was prevalent in the district at the time.

The site of the old palace kitchens is just outside the main wall on the north side and it is here that the phantom figure has been seen, not just by the staff and workmen but quite a number of visitors who have asked about the young girl.

'She appears to be such a sad little soul,' said one visitor, 'I just thought she was perhaps a orphan, or someone in distress or something, until she slowly faded away, just a few yards in front of me.'

ARDINGLY

Oak Inn, Street Lane

Norman Parker and Mrs Sherlock moved in to this fourteenth century tavern in August 1996. According to Mrs Sherlock's son, Keith, they have so far seen nothing unusual themselves but a couple of customers have reported seeing the ghost of a young girl. Odd physical phenomena, however, has caused some trouble.

'One of the taps on the wine dispenser was forced open during the night and we found over five litres of wine on the floor,' said Keith. 'But just as annoying is the switching on and off of the hand driers in the toilets.'

The apparition – which had long dark hair and wore a grey cloak – was seen at about 6pm coming from the rear of the building and walking towards the inglenook, where she sat down and just slowly faded away.

Within the last ten years an elderly couple, sitting on the bench beside the fireplace, turned to the woman serving behind the bar to inquire about her unusual companion who, they said, 'seemed to be ignoring her'.

The barmaid, somewhat apprehensively, assured the customers that she was the only person behind the bar – there was no one else there. It took a few seconds for the witnesses to be convinced and then one remarked: 'Oh, she has just vanished .'

Was this, I wonder, another example of a ghost of the living ?

ARLINGTON

Woodhorne Manor
THIS fourteenth century thatched manor house, reputed to have been the haunt of smugglers, had at least one tunnel leading to the church. For safety reasons it has now been blocked up.

A former owner, Mrs Christine Williams, witnessed the ghostly phenomena that is detailed by Joan Forman in *The Haunted South*. It consisted of the sound of 'voices arguing loudly in an upstairs room, like two drunken men having a diabolical row.'

What frightened Mrs Williams was that the voices seemed to be coming from a non-existent room over the stream which adjoins the property. On making inquiries she was told that a previous owner had experienced the same disturbing phenomena and her sister had also heard the sound of raised voices when she was alone in the house.

Quite recently noises of raucous parties have been heard coming from the now empty house.

ARUNDEL

St Nicholas Church
WHEN a solicitor took a photograph of the interior of the parish church of St Nicholas in the 1940s he was puzzled, on receiving the print, to see on it 'a shadowy robed figure, possibly that of a priest, standing in front of the altar'. What mystified him was that, apart from himself, there was no one else in the building when he was taking the photograph.

Some years later visitors reported seeing the phantom of a woman in the bell tower. She is thought to be one of the nuns from the convent of the Poor Clares.

One of the most recent hauntings was in December 1995 when a bell-ringer going up the stairs in the tower found himself following an unknown companion, who had disappeared by the time he reached the bell chamber. 'Not only did I feel that someone was ahead of me. I could hear, quite clearly, their footsteps, just in front. It really was a bit weird,' he said.

The interior of St Nicholas church is divided by a brick wall constructed as a result of a legal dispute involving the Roman Catholic Duke of Norfolk, the Church of England rector, then the Rev G Arbuthnot, and a group of nuns who had been allowed to use what is now established as the Fitzalan Chapel.

Shortly after the funeral of the ninth Duke, late in the 1970s, one of the churchwardens, Howard Frith, glanced into the chapel and saw a white haired woman in a long blue gown, kneeling at the altar. He assumed that she was a member of the family and quietly left the building.

Outsider he met one of the gardeners and described what he had seen. 'That's impossible,' said the gardener. 'That part of the chapel is locked and I have the key in my pocket'. He produced it and both men hurried back to see if the door was indeed locked. It was – and the chapel was empty.

Another weird incident occurred in 1983 when a Mrs Wilkinson and her family visited the chapel. She suddenly felt a strange rapport with the marble effigy of a woman in Elizabethan dress on a tomb in one of the side aisles. She said she was 'strangely but very strongly drawn' towards the sculpture, but her husband felt so cold and had such a strong feeling of antagonism from it, that he had to leave.

Three years later two friends of the.Wilkinsons admitted that they too found that particular area of the chapel 'definitely uncomfortable, even aggressive' and had left in a hurry.

Norfolk Arms Hotel

DURING the 1980s, this hotel in the High Street was slightly affected by poltergeist activity. Pots and pan started sliding off shelves in the kitchen and the radio was switched on and off by an unseen hand.

However, what was not an example of psychokinetic energy was the incident witnessed by Hazel Sampson who had been working in the tap room in the afternoon. She told the *Worthing Herald* that she had turned round to see 'the figure of a man, naked to the waist, leap from the kitchen window into the back yard of the premises.'

What was odd is that the window was not fitted until the 1950s, so the tragedy must relate to comparatively recent times. A face was seen at the window shortly afterwards, but there was no one in the yard .

According to rumour, one of the hotel bedrooms was the scene of a murder in the 1800s, but the only incidents that have affected that area are the sounds of an invisible chain being dragged on the ground. 'Like that of a dog trying to get out of a kennel' said Bill Beere, the Town Crier of Arundel, who has researched the haunting.

Arundel Castle

THE 'Blue Man', continues to haunt Arundel Castle. He wears the clothes of the period of Charles II and he frequents the library. He was seen quite recently by one of the custodians, who told me that there was nothing scary about the ghost. 'I was intrigued and wished that he had stayed longer. He was only there for about a minute and then vanished,' he said.

The library is also haunted by St Philip Howard's little black dog. Philip, Earl of Arundel, was attainted in the reign of Elizabeth I and sentenced to death for failing to renounce the Roman Catholic faith. The sentence was never carried out and he spent eleven years in the Tower, accompanied by his dog, until he died on a Sunday in 1595 and was beatified as the Blessed Philip Howard. In 1970 he was canonised as a saint by Pope Paul VI.

Several of the guides at the castle have been asked, always by children: 'Whose is the little dog in the library?' No adult has yet reported seeing it.

BALCOMBE

Rail Tunnel

A HAUNTING which occurred at the southern entrance to the rail tunnel on the line to Three Bridges during the Second World War is described by Leslie Fairweather in his book on Balcombe published in 1981.

After a number of bombs had exploded in the area, a soldier on patrol decided he would be safer if he took shelter in the tunnel. He had only been there a few minutes when a group of three men in old style uniforms approached. When he challenged them they slowly changed into three misty columns and faded away.

Later the sentry discovered that during the First World War three soldiers, perhaps sheltering as he had been, but from the weather rather than enemy bombs, were killed at the same spot by a train travelling from the north.

In 1995 the old soldiers were seen again. A group of youngsters reported that they had been seen 'three blokes in funny old fashioned uniforms' standing in the tunnel entrance. When they went to investigate, the figures faded into the brickwork of the archway.

BATTLE

Abbey

SURELY one of the most famous haunted buildings in Sussex is the abbey built on the site of the battle of 1066 by William of Normandy? Although the town itself is host to a number of ghosts few only are factually associated with events of the eleventh century.

As far as the abbey ruins are concerned, one of the most recent incidents was that reported in June 1996. Stewart Dunkley from Zimbabwe took a photograph of the side of one of the buildings, using an automatic camera to exclude risks of a double exposure. The resultant print shows a strong beam of light beside a chimney stack.

'If you look closely at it you can make out the face of a man. It is most mysterious,' said one of the custodians.

In February of the same year, in the open ruins of the Rere Dorter, adjoining the fishponds, and the huge Common House, one of the falconers demonstrating hunting techniques with birds of prey, was astounded to see the figure of a monk in a black habit walk towards part of the Guest House and vanish into thin air. The man's wife, also a witness, was said to be 'a little affected by her experience'.

A few years earlier James Minahane of St Leonards visited the abbey with his mother on a hot sunny day in August and, to quote from his letter, 'noticed a walk bordered by yew trees along the high boundary wall and went down it to see where it led, whilst my mother stood outside it on the lawn. I remember feeling a chill when halfway down the path, which surprised me as it was so warm and sunny a day. The walk had a dead end, so I returned along it back to where my relative was standing, wearing an astonished expression. She asked me what had become of the other people who had been walking the path with me, but I had to reply that I had been alone.'

What his mother had witnessed was what a number of visitors had reported over the years – two monks, one dressed in an off white or butter coloured habit, and the other in black. Their cowls were not visible, but the men were said to be benign in appearance and looked as if they were in their thirties.

One of them was short and heavy with long ginger hair and the monk in the black habit had dark hair and a paler complexion. Both were wearing sandals.

There was nothing hazy about them – they seemed to be arguing about something and waving their arms as if to emphasise various points in their discussion. On reaching the end of the path they just vanished.

Neither Mr Minahane nor his mother have had any psychic experiences before or since and were certainly not anticipating such an event, so they were fascinated and intrigued enough to carry out some research.

They found the path was shown on one old map of the area as the Monks Walk, but on another as the Ghosts Walk. The monk in black was in the habit of Benedictines, an order vowed to silence. His companion might have been a Cistercian.

The Monks' or Ghosts' Walk in the grounds of Battle Abbey. *Photo: Graham Buckley.*

13

The first Cistercian abbey in this country was founded at Robertsbridge in 1250 by an Abbot from Battle, Robert de St Martin. The monks wore habits of rough sheepskin or lambs wool, which would appear off white in colour.

In January 1982, one of the maintenance men working for the Ministry of Public Works, was crouching down doing some repair work on an archway in part of the long Guest House. He called, without looking, to his companion to ask for a bolster – a four inch wide chisel. Receiving no response, he looked round to find kneeling beside him the figure of a monk in black who 'just slowly faded away in front of my eyes'. His colleague, Frank, was outside on the terrace having a smoke.

A few years later one of the custodians was checking the empty building and on reaching the same archway, twice heard the sound of a man's voice calling: 'Let me out'. He spent some time searching the premises and is still mystified, having discovered no cause for the appeal.

In 1979 Marcus Granger from Eastbourne saw the figure of a woman in a long red gown of the Elizabethan period. 'The material looked to me like velvet', he said.

The woman had appeared in the top western corner of the huge Common House, where at least two other ghostly figures have been seen fairly recently. One was that of a farrier wearing a leather apron and the other, witnessed by a fourteen year old Canadian boy on his first visit to England in 1972, was that of a Norman knight.

A haunted triangle.

ONE afternoon in 1988 in a cottage in Mount Street, at the north end of the town, Joyce Pain was quietly reading in her front room when suddenly the figure of a young golden-haired girl glided through the front bay window. It stood for a while looking at Joyce's friend who was dozing in an armchair opposite her. Joyce was astounded, but the child was emitting a feeling of such tender warmth and love that she simply wanted to cuddle her.

'I couldn't tell what she was dressed in, but got the impression she had on a simple little dress of about the 1920s', she said. After a few seconds, the mysterious child, who appeared to be about six years old, turned towards Joyce, gave a heart warming smile of great affection and just faded away.

A few months later Kathy O'Brien, then the owner of the Bayeux

Restaurant at the entrance to Mount Street car park, was woken at three in the morning by her five year old daughter at her bedside asking for a glass of water.

'Immediately behind my daughter was the figure of another little girl, about six years of age, with beautiful golden hair. She was just looking at me with such warmth and an attractive smile that all I wanted to do was to give her a cuddle,' she said.

'I blinked several times, but she just smiled even more. I was about to get out of bed when my daughter said: "Please Mummy, can I have some water?" and with that, the mysterious little visitor faded away'.

What established a triangle of

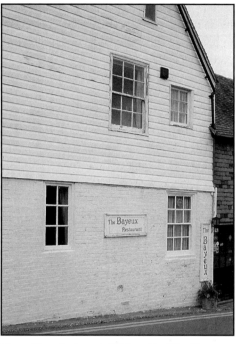

Two sides of a haunted triangle – The Bayeux Restaurant and, below, the Bayeux Cottage Cafe. *Photos: Tom Perrott.*

hauntings was to learn that the Bayeux Cottage Cafe, a few yards from Joyce's home, had also been visited on several occasions by the small golden haired ghost. Some years earlier, when the building was a private house, the owner's wife had seen the girl standing in front of a grand piano. They had both seen her going up and sometimes down the stairs. One afternoon the girl actually touched the owner as he was about to walk down the stairs and he nearly fell. The elderly couple fully agreed that their phantom caller was charming and full of love.

In the 1920s the house, which later became the Bayeux Restaurant, was the home of the Hoad family – highly respected butchers. Originally there were twenty one but due to infant and other deaths, the final adult total was seventeen, all of them with sparkling golden hair and it was said, ' the most charming and loveable dispositions'.

Before it became a restaurant another elderly couple owned the house. They told the solicitor handling the sale that they were convinced the building contained two ghosts, but neither were ever seen.

One presence was that of someone standing at a bricked up window on the ground floor where, they were told, farmworkers would be paid out. The other was more relevant. It was the sound of someone young and sprightly, running along the upstairs corridor.

'We were always happy when we heard it, even though the sound sometimes woke us up,' they said. 'We think it was a little girl and we are sorry that she never made an appearance.'

St Mary's church

WITHIN the last twenty five years has come a report of the haunting of St Mary's Church in Battle. A former Dean of Battle, the Very Reverend A T Naylor, who was tragically killed in a motor accident a short time ago, told the Reverend G Mackenzie of Pulborough that one Sunday morning, after celebrating Holy Communion, he was puzzled when some members of the congregation referred to 'the new curate who had helped with the chalice'.

They had seen the figure of the young man enter the sanctuary and leave through a side door, before the actual offering of the sacrament. Although an effort had been made at that time to obtain the services of a replacement curate, none had been forthcoming, so who the mysterious stranger was no one has been able to establish.

On another occasion Mrs Naylor had seen the phantom of a monk in the vicarage garden.

The organist, Mrs Jackie Spriggs said that when practising in the Lady Chapel in the evenings, she often feels as if she is being watched, 'but it's a pleasant experience, certainly nothing frightening.'

Old Charlie

SOME years ago, Mr Alexander, organiser of the Battle Festival, saw at the junction of Netherfield Hill and London Road, the ghost of his elderly gardener, 'Old Charlie', just two hours after the old man had gassed himself in his bungalow nearby.

'There was no doubt that the figure I saw was that of Charlie standing at the corner with his bicycle. I had known him for over twenty years and would certainly not have mistaken him for someone else.' he said.

In 1995 a teacher from a local school was returning home from the council offices in Watch Oak. As he approached the junction with Netherfield Hill he noticed an old man coming towards him on the other side of the road. 'There was something peculiar about him,' he said. 'He was wearing an old brown mackintosh that I would associate with the 1930s, and had a glazed expression on his face – like a zombie. When he passed me I turned round, but he just wasn't there. He had vanished, but there was nowhere he could have gone. Anyway I don't believe in ghosts.'

BEXHILL

Police Station

THERE are not many present day police stations that are genuinely haunted, but according to at least two reliable witnesses – one a member of the cleaning staff and the other a retired police officer – this one contains the ghost of an unseen walker.

On several occasions he, or she, has been heard shuffling along one of the corridors into the photocopying room, usually when it is empty. However, a WPC was there by herself one afternoon and said she certainly did not like the atmosphere that was engendered by the mystery visitor.

Associated with the sounds was a figure of a little man with dark hair

Bodiam Castle. *Photo: Graham Buckley*

parted in the centre and wearing an Edwardian suit. He was seen by Lilly, one of the cleaning staff, in what was then the witnesses room and later became the CID office.

It has been suggested that the apparition could be a former court official, perhaps the coroner who was suddenly taken ill and died near the office some time ago.

BODIAM

A REAL fairy tale castle, and certainly one of the most photographed, is the manor house Sir Edward Dalyngrigge was given permission to fortify in 1385 against possible attack by the French marauders who had twice raided the Rother valley.

However, the castle never had to face an attacker and by the eighteenth century it was derelict and would have been demolished had not East Sussex MP, John Fuller of Brightling, bought it before a builder did so. It was saved a second time in 1916 when it was bought and restored by another politician, Lord Curzon. When he died in 1925 he left the castle to the nation and it is administered by the National Trust.

There is little information available regarding the two ghosts that are supposed to reside at Bodiam. The phantom of a woman in red has been reported more than once, watching from one of the towers on moonlight nights, but who she is and why she watches and for whom remains a mystery as does the identity of a young boy who has been seen running towards the main gateway.

He vanishes halfway across the bridge, suggesting that maybe he fell into the moat and was drowned. His clothes resemble those of the days of Dickens, according to one custodian who saw him shortly before locking up the museum sector one evening in 1994.

BOLNEY

London Road

ONE evening some five years ago, three motorists travelling south towards Brighton on the busy A23 decided to pull in to the Queen's Head. As they started to slow down to turn into the car park, a woman in a grey dress suddenly appeared in front of their vehicle.

The driver slammed on his brakes, but it was too late and all the passengers as well as the driver, felt the sickening thud as the car hit the pedestrian. It skidded across the road, crashing into the barriers and coming to a stop only yards from their destination.

A couple of witnesses to the accident said that they saw a woman appear out of the blue and in their opinion the crash was caused by her sudden arrival on the scene. The problem was where had she got to? In spite of an intensive search of the area by the police, the two witnesses and the three motorists, she was never found.

Further north on the same road, between Handcross and Crawley, shortly before the junction with the M23, a youngish woman in a red coat is occasionally seen by the roadside. When a motorist stops to offer her a lift, she is nowhere to be seen.

BRIGHTLING

ONLY a few years ago a man named Collins, thought to be associated with drug dealing, was found brutally murdered and his body dumped, with that of his black Labrador, in the woods only yards from where the aerial ropeway from the gypsum mines crosses the road, north of Darvell reservoir. The crime has never been solved.

One evening in 1976 a member of a local youth club was walking home when, near the site, he saw the figure of a tall man dressed all in black walking a few feet in front of him.

'There was something peculiar about the man, especially the way he walked. I didn't like it', he said. 'He turned towards the verge and vanished.' In February 1996 the figure was seen again by a couple taking an evening stroll in exactly the same area and about the same time.

In his *Sussex Ghosts and Legends* Tony Wales tells of a case of phenomena in a cottage in the village which eventually burnt down and the occupants, an elderly couple, were forced to live in a nearby hut.

The site of the cottage is thought to be where a woman called Barbara Allen fell or was pushed into the well in the garden many years ago. A servant girl, maybe Barbara, confessed to talking to a witch who told her that many calamities would befall her employers, but she would be torn to pieces by the Devil if she revealed this information to anyone.

In October 1995, an elderly woman in black wearing clothing resembling Edwardian widow's weeds was seen walking towards the site of the cottage before vanishing. The witness, a farm labourer who had been working late, was relieved to learn that he was not the only person to have seen the mysterious female.

BRIGHTON

Royal Pavilion

THERE has been extensive restoration work at the Royal Pavilion since the arson attack on the Music Room and a number of those engaged in it have reported hearing the sounds of footsteps coming from the tunnel which leads to the Druids Head Inn.

So numerous were the reports that investigations were carried out in the empty passages, but no explanation for the sounds could be found. On two occasions the vague figure of a large woman in a dress, shawl and bonnet was seen by the searchers. She faded away when one of the team called out to her.

Was she perhaps Martha Gunn, the 'queen of the dippers' who looked after the fashionable ladies when they wished to indulge in a little sea bathing.? Martha, who died in 1815, was a great favourite of the Prince Regent. Another of the Prince's favourites, and later his wife, was Maria Fitzherbert. She has also been suggested as a possible candidate.

There have been several sightings of a lady in grey at the Dome – the former stables of the Pavilion – and her appearances are accompanied by the sound of footsteps.

Members of the maintenance staff including stewards, electricians and security officers, have also reported seeing the figures of a soldier in a red jacket and a coachman walking about in the building.

Regency Hotel, Regency Square

ALTHOUGH in their ten years of ownership the proprietors have not seen the ghost themsleves they accept that this small private hotel is haunted, 'mainly in the rooms on the first floor'.

The hotel dog and a cat flatly refuse to go up the stairs and often sit at the bottom of the flight looking at an invisible something or someone on the landing above. In the past few years the ghost has been reported by occupants of the Regency Suite. It is of a young woman who rushes towards a window and then, as she reaches the wall, vanishes.

The girl is believed to have been a cripple who was somehow affected by the gas lighting, or the fear if it, and jumped through the window to her death, leaving behind her clogs which are on display in the bar.

Hotel staff have also seen the figure of an older woman in the room and believed it to be the landlady of the small lodging house that occupied the site in Victorian times.

Stag Inn, Kemp Town

THIS 300 year old former coaching inn used to be haunted by the ghost of a tall man wearing a large apron and two black arm bands. The apparition was seen on a number of occasions by customers and successive licensees up until 1982.

Since then Albert, as he became known, seems.to have deserted the place, but as in many other haunted pubs, beer keg taps are often found to have been turned off or on by some unseen hand. Staff say 'it's all down to Albert.'

Druid`s Head, Market Street

NEAR to the Town Hall is this former fisherman's inn which was granted a licence in 1855. Before that it was a meeting place for smugglers and it is believed that there are two sealed tunnels in the cellars, one leading to the beach and the other to the Royal Pavilion.

Derek Woods became the licensee in 1975 and was interested to learn that the three daughters of his predecessor had all seen the ghost, but were unable to provide much detail.

The phantom figure that.he saw 'just for a fleeting instant' three years later was hooded, like a monk or a nun 'and it flitted under the stairway in the main bar.' He never saw it again.

However, one of the barmaids told John Rackham, a local researcher, that she had seen the ghostly figure of a woman in a red dress in the same area of the pub. 'She just moved towards the stairs and vanished. It was so quick. I didn't have time to think about it,' she said.

Regency Tavern, Russell Square

A FEW years ago several poltergeist incidents occurred here. Furniture was moved about, a few glasses over the bar were seen to be swinging about by themselves and some of the electrical equipment acted up.

Nothing was found to account for the occurences and, as in the majority of such cases, after a time the phenomena stopped of its own accord.

Recently a couple of staff members have reported seeing the phantom of what they described as 'a tall and rather whispy woman'. Once she was seen to walk straight through one of the temporary barmen.

Battle of Waterloo, Rock Place

TOM and Peggy Butler, tenants here in 1978, never saw the pub ghosts although a number of their customers did. But Tom admitted that one occasions he felt the presence of an unseen entity.

In the autumn of 1996 a decorator working in the extension said he saw the figure of a tall man wearing an old fashioned coachman's cloak 'walk, or rather glide, straight through the front door.' A phantom matching that description was also seen on two occasions in the gents, where it vanished.

There is a belief that the ghost is of the coachman who was driving a nineteenth century mayor of Brighton and his daughter to an evening function when they were waylaid by a ruthless highwayman who shot and killed both men. Neither the young girl nor the killer were ever seen again.

Theatre Royal

THE phantom of a grey lady makes not infrequent appearances, usually in the dressing room area, although she does occasionally haunt other parts of the theatre.

She has not been positively identified but the majority of witnesses and researchers seem to agree that it is probably the apparition of Sarah Bernhardt. Why this great French actress should choose to haunt this particular Brighton theatre no one has been able to decide. She made the first of a number of appearances here in June 1894 when she was touring with Sardou's *Fedora* and *La Tosca* .

Early one afternoon a cleaner working in a corridor in the front part of the building saw the ghostly figure brush past her and vanish into a blank wall. It was soon discovered that in the wall was a bricked–up doorway which led to the original paybox used by patrons for the cheaper seats in the gods.

The wife of the actor, Gerald Flood, came face to face with the apparition when she was the wardrobe mistress to the company presenting Alan Ayckbourn's *Relatively Speaking* at the theatre. She was in the laundry room when she heard the sound of a door banging and when it seemed no one was going to shut it she went down the corridor to do so herself. On reaching the door she felt an inexplicable force pushing it from the other side.

She pulled the door open and was met by the figure of a woman of about fifty five years of age wearing a long grey full skirted dress and with a sort of grey veiling on her head. 'I noticed some silver hair hanging beneath it in a fringe,' she said. 'On reaching the end of the corridor, the figure just faded away.'

The Lanes

THE cluster of narrow alleyways and twittens packed with antique shops, boutiques and restaurants that are the Lanes of Brighton today is a great attraction to visitors to the town and, it seems, to the occasional ghost.

A nun in a grey habit makes spasmodic appearances. The rather vague figure has been seen near the old Friends Meeting House. She then disappears on reaching the bricked up archway.

A legend has grown up to account for this haunting. It says that the woman had a love affair with one of the soldiers guarding the Priory of St Barholomew and eloped with him but was caught and bricked up within the walls of the building.

It is more likely to be that the fervent young woman was so determinedly committed to the religious life that she chose to be confined in a small cell to intensify her supplication and eventually died there.

Preston Manor and St. Peter's Church

THERE is some magnificent furniture and many unusual works of art on show in this charming Georgian house, pictured above, owned by the borough council. Also on occasional display is the ghostly form of a woman in

Preston Manor

white who has been seen in the grounds and in the nearby Church of St Peter by visitors and a couple of security officers.

The ghost appears so like a normal human being that she was once mistaken for a member of a party visiting the museum and on another occasion as one of a group of tennis players. It is not until she vanishes when approached that people realise she is an apparition. She appears by her style of dress to be someone who lived in the Middle Ages.

A few years ago, after being interviewed on film at Preston Manor for a Southern Television feature about my book, *Ghosts in the South East,* I was told by the then curator that the room in which we were had been filming was often said by visitors to have an unpleasant atmosphere. One of them had suggested that this could be due to 'the shameful activities of Lady Ellen Stamford who lived there until 1932.'

A disturbing sensation has sometimes ben experienced in a corner of a front bedroom, the cause of which has never been explained. It seems to emanate from a triangular wardrobe or cupboard with holes in the top of the door. David Beevers, the present curator, says that some visitors still report having a feeling of unease when in that area.

The ghostly woman in white was seen by two or three members of the church choir not very long ago. She emerged from the south side of the building before disappearing.

On a Sunday evening a few days later a couple strolling through the graveyard were met apparently by the same phantom who walked beside them for a few feet before 'slowly fading into a nearby terracotta tombstone,' which could very well have provided a clue as to her identity had they noted the inscription on it.

BURWASH

Bateman's

For many years both the National Trust and the staff at Bateman's were reluctant to admit that the charming old house was in anyway haunted, other than by 'a feeling of calm and peace'.

It was the home of the famous author and poet, Rudyard Kipling, from 1902 until his death in 1936. When his widow, Caroline, died four years later she left it to the nation on condition that it would be open to the public and Kipling's study would be kept just as it was.

In 1975, during a visit arranged by the prestigious Ghost Club, John Harvey glanced into Kipling's study and saw the figure of of the poet standing looking out of the window. John was about to greet the former owner – 'even though I was flabbergasted' – when another member of ths party approached the doorway and the figure faded away.

A number of other visitors to the house and some of the guides now admit that they have seen the famous man in his study, usually just looking out of the window towards the delightful garden. Others, perhaps less sensitive, speak of the strong sense of activity and energy in the immediate area.

A former custodian was told by a local couple that one summer's evening they had seen the ghost of Caroline Kipling tending some of the flowers in the garden.

CHICHESTER

Willow Cottage

THIS attractive sixteenth century house owned by Sheila and Peter Darvill has, as one would expect, a long and mixed history and seven or eight rooms of varying sizes available for overnight accommodation.

Mrs Darvill learned when they moved in that one of the rooms was known locally as the brewery for at one time the property was a coaching inn and brewed its own ale. There was also said to be a smugglers' tunnel which led to the nearby creek, but perhaps of greater interest, the building had at one time been used as a whore house. 'But not any more,' I was assured.

In 1996 two overnight guests returning at about 11pm, glanced up at their bedroom, a converted attic, and were embarrassed to see that they had left the light on. The curtains were wide open and they noticed the figure of a tall woman in black with long dark hair, standing in front of the wash-hand basin. They said it was definitely not the owner, Mrs Darvill.

On entering the house they asked about the person in their room and this so puzzled Sheila Darvill that she went outside with her guests to see if they could possibly have mistaken one of the dark oak beams on the ceiling for the strange figure. They all looked up at the lighted window but there was no tall woman to be seen.

Friends and members of the family have heard the sound of footsteps coming to the front entrance, and on several occasions a series of loud bangs on the door. They described them as 'three loud raps, as if by an angry or impatient caller', but there was never anyone there.

Mrs Darvill said her son nearly always suffers nightmares if he sleeps in the attic room 'but guests don't seem to have this trouble thankfully'. The tall woman has never been seen since, but she did see the figure of a tall blonde haired man pass the front window and one night woke to find the tall thin shape of a man standing beside her bed.

'I thought at first it was my husband returning from a visit to the bathroom, but he was sleeping soundly beside me.' she said.

One evening Sheila's mother glanced up the stairway and saw an elderly woman holding on to the banisters on her way towards the landing. Her granddaughter, who was standing close to her, was unable to see the figure, but felt its presence. At no time have the Darvills felt any fright or nervousness about their unknown guests. They fully accept that they must have lived there at one time. However the family dog is not so philosophical for he sometimes stubbornly refuses to go up the stairs and is reluctant even to approach them.

'We are assured by guests that the place is really homely and friendly, which merely confirms what we already know,' said Sheila.

CHIDDINGLY

Footpath near Stream Farm

THE path joining the road on the right just south of Stream Farm was a former smuggler's route and once a group of free traders were ambushed at Stream Mill, a few yards to the south east, by a number of Customs and Excise officers.

In the resultant fight a number of the smugglers were killed. Two, badly wounded, managed to escape and make their way towards one of the farm buildings where they collapsed and one died.

Recently some newcomers to the area, walking their dogs, were puzzled to see a ragged individual stumbling along and apparently walk right through one of the houses.

'We thought he was a drunk at first, then we saw him vanish,' said one of them. 'It was weird'.

CRAWLEY

George Hotel

CRAWLEY High Street was originally part of the main London to Brighton road and it was spanned by the inn sign of the seventeenth century coaching inn, the George Hotel. Here the Prince Regent and his entourage would stop for refreshment and a change of horses on their way to and from the Royal Pavilion. The road was also used by smugglers transporting their contraband from the coast to London.

Although the hotel's ghost has only been seen as a faint shape a number of visitors have admitted to feeling rather uneasy when approaching a small cubby hole on the first floor now used as a telephone switchboard control room.

Other phenomena experienced includes the malfunctioning of corridor lights which go on and off by themselves. The problems are believed to be caused by the invisible ghost of a former night porter.

According to the housekeeper, Sarah Jordan, shortly after the inn was opened in 1615, the night porter, Mark Hewton, who would insist on delivering wine to residents at night whether they wanted it or not, was found dead in his room opposite what used to be bedroom No. 7. It is now used as a functions room.

It appears that a guest had, for some reason, put poison into a bottle of wine. It was later taken away and what was left in the bottle was drunk by the unfortunate man.

One or two former members of the staff commented on the rather unpleasant feelings that they had in the locality, but Sarah feels that the hotel is really a warm and friendly place.

Hog's Head, High Street.

JOAN Conlon, the new licensee of this fifteenth century inn, formerly known as the Brewery Shades, is convinced that it is haunted. 'My cleaning lady told me that she has more than once found ash from a man's pipe and the smell of pipe tobacco in the Ladies,' she told me. 'A couple of customers have also told me that they have seen the ghostly figures of a woman in grey with a young child, in one of the upstairs rooms.'

A former manager told Joan that when he lived there he came in one afternoon and found his bed blazing. The cause of the fire was never found, but it was in that room where the ghosts appear.

The phenomenon Joan did not appreciate was the ringing of the front door bell at six in the morning, which occurred shortly after she took over the pub. There was no one there and the bell itself was jammed or suffering from a weird malfunction, because it took some time to stop the ringing and it then became totally erratic, ringing off and on.

CUCKFIELD

Ockenden Manor Hotel

A MEDIEVAL manor house with fourteen bedrooms, secret passages and tunnels, a priest's hole in a chimney adjoining an original hidden chapel and set in some five acres of grounds, must surely be a haunted.

I was interested to learn from Wendy, a member of the staff, that a number of guests and some of her colleagues, have seen a phantom grey lady in one of the corridors, and also in the Elizabethan bedroom.

The young ghost is believed to be a chambermaid who was killed when one of the tunnels leading to the King's Head Inn in South Street collapsed in the nineteenth century. She is known to have used that route to meet her lover, but one evening, after the manor 'shook as if affected by an earthquake' her crushed and mangled body was discovered in the rubble beneath the building.

A mysterious feeling has also been reported, on a number of occasions, in the area of priest's hole, but it is in the Elizabethan bedroom that visitors are most affected. Wendy told me that several sensitive or psychic people have actually asked to be moved to a different room because of their feelings there. Why the ghost should affect that particular part of the building is not known.

Cuckfield Park

PEOPLE travelling from Cuckfield to Ansty on the B2036 are likely to be affected by the ghost of Mrs Anne Sergison who died in 1848 at the age of eighty five. When alive she was known as 'Wicked Dame Sergison' and may well have been an example of a living phantom because some eighteen years before she died there were reports of her haunting the avenue to the house. Apparently she objected to her daughter's marriage and was seen as a ghost at the wedding reception in 1890.

The new owner of the house has reported seeing a shadowy figure in the corridors and guests have commented on the feeling of a presence on the main stairway. On a couple of occasions the vague shape of a woman has been seen in the same locality.

EASTBOURNE

Beachy Head

A CHALET on the top of Beachy Head, once used as a small museum and history centre and latterly as a facility for the Samaritans, has been demolished. Perhaps it was thought that its existence provoked more suicides than it stopped as the number of deaths every year from this 600 feet high cliff top do not decline.

Photo: Sussex Express

In 1979 an eleven year old Dutch boy was among the dozens to throw themselves on to the rocks, strengthening the mythical tale of a mysterious black monk beckoning victims to their death.

One of the suicides in the 1850s is thought to be the ghost that is still seen walking along the cliff edge before she suddenly vanishes. The figure has been described by some witnesses, who have also seen her near the site of an old building belonging to Bullockdown Farm, as a youngish woman in an old fashioned grey dress. She was seen by three evening walkers towards the end of 1978, and there have been some more recent sightings.

There is nothing frightening about her,' witnesses say, 'it is what she does that is scary.'

Another ghost that used to frequent the cliffs, but is hardly seen these days, is that of a farmer's wife carrying a small baby in her arms. She would stand only a few feet from the crumbling edge of the cliff before she taking three steps forward and disappearing.

Devonshire Park Theatre

A MYSTERIOUS violinist used to haunt this theatre. Whether the vague figure seen by doorman Steven Gausden in 1980 was that of the phantom it is impossible to say, as the shape of the ghost was too indistinct.

Steven, then newly appointed and unaware of the earlier hauntings, was locking up one evening when he saw a dark figure that seemed to be shuffling between the orchestra rail and the front stalls.

Naturally he assumed that someone had accidentally been locked in and was trying to find the exit so he called out, offering help, but the figure failed to respond. When the shape reached the end of the stalls, it disappeared although the exit door there was locked.

'The house lights were not on, so I couldn't make out a face,' Steven said later, 'but as the phantom passed across in front of the brass rail in the orchestra pit, the reflection was blotted out for a second. It really was quite weird.'

When he reported the incident the following day to Roger Neil, the theatre manager, Steven learned about the ghostly violinist who had been seen fairly regularly up to 1968.

The last person to see the apparition, and give a full description of it, was Geoff Standfield, the theatre electrician.

All Saints Hospital, Meads

SOME two hundred years ago this hospital housed a nursing order of nuns, the members of which, as well as carrying out their normal religious duties, ran a small hospital there. Over the years it has developed into a geriatric clinic and residential care home and is no longer run by the religious sisters.

In September 1975, a senior cook on the permanent staff turned round while preparing the evening meal and saw a figure standing just behind her. It was that of a middle-aged nun in a grey habit and just as she was about to greet the stranger, the cook was startled by the ghost vanishing 'like a small cloud of steam'.

Up to that time reports younger members of the staff had made about the appearance of the nun had been dismissed as imagination. Many now fully accept that one of the nursing nuns still inhabits her former home – maybe to provide some spiritual comfort for the residents.

Willingdon

ON the roundabout at the junction of main A22 with Kings Drive and the Willingdon Road there have been instances of phantom-victim-of-car-crash sightings.

A number of people were killed in a multiple collision which occurred early one evening in 1923 and on and off since then the sudden appearance of a tall woman in a grey dress of the 1920 period has been reported.

She is believed to have been one of the party of golfers who were involved in the fatal accident. She has been seen so often that she herself seems to be the cause of car accidents, although few, thankfully, have been fatal.

One motorist who has seen and reported her on two occasions is John Martin of Hailsham. 'I nearly had a heart attack when I first saw her suddenly appear in front of my car. I was convinced that I had hit her and killed her,' he said.

'The second occasion was more than a year later, by which time I had completely forgotten the earlier incident. Exactly the same thing happened and it was only when I got out of the car did I find that there was no one there. I know of a number of other motorists who have suffered from the same shock of crashing into someone who isn't there.'

Chaseley, Bolsover Road,

THIS large house built in 1893 for a local solicitor, is now a residential care centre for physically handicapped patients suffering mainly from spinal injuries.

In charge of the home is the matron, Jane Lewis. I had the pleasure of meeting her in November 1996 and spoke to a number of permanent and temporary residents, all of whom had experienced, in some form or other, the haunting that affects Chaseley.

Douglas White, a Dunkirk veteran and former engineer, assured me that a few days after his arrival in August, he turned round to see the figure of a woman sitting in the chair beside his bed. 'She appeared to be about forty years old', he said. 'But it was a bit difficult to see her face clearly for she was wearing a veil. Her clothing was Victorian or maybe Edwardian and she just sat there for some time before fading.'

A member of the staff reported seeing the figure of an eleven year old child running along a corridor leading from the central staircase, and the sounds have also been heard by others on more than one occasion. The child appears in a Victorian dress.

Bernard Power told me that when he was with Sam, another resident, in the recreation room, he saw two women in the bar. 'One was quite tall and wearing a shawl and the other was shorter and much younger,' he said. 'Their clothes were rather old fashioned, but before we had time to inquire who they were, they just faded away '.

The snooker room in the basement is where Derek Glyde saw the grey lady. 'It was more like a column of grey mist in the shape of a woman,' he said. 'Before I could contact anyone else – the wheelchair wouldn't move quickly enough – the apparition, or whatever it was, had vanished. Maybe it was just smoke, but if so, where did it come from?'

I think it can be safely assumed that the ghostly figures are associated with the previous owners, are completely harmless and merely add a touch of interest and mystery to the warm and friendly atmosphere that has been created, not just by the staff but also the residents themselves.

One of the major candidates for the ghostly visits would probably be a former owner of Chaseley, Mrs Helen Hornby Lewis, who died in 1930. She made a number of charitable gifts to the town including the Helen Garden between Holywell Retreat and Holywell.

Jane Lewis pointed out a particular narrow corridor with a small staircase leading to the flats over the main building which is affected, she said, not by sounds but an intense feeling of cold and, at times, 'a peculiarly cold breeze from absolutely nowhere.'

EAST LAVANT

Royal Oak Inn, High Street

SMUGGLERS on their way to and from Chichester were regular customers at this old inn in the eighteenth century. Whether the sound of footsteps heard coming from an empty upstairs room is connected with them in any way is uncertain for it was not until the 1950s that an apparition associated with the noises was actually seen and described as the figure was of a slim man of average height with a very scruffy beard.

When the house was known as Fanny Glover's, locals firmly believed that the ghost was that of someone who died there mysteriously about a hundred years ago and was then seen fairly regularly in the back bedroom.

ERIDGE

Eridge Park Estate

BETWEEN the A26 at Eridge Green and the A267 at Frant is the Eridge Park, the Sussex estate of the Nevills, Lords Abergavenny, from Tudor times. The original 1573 hunting lodge was remodelled in 1810 and demolished and replaced by the present Eridge Castle in 1938.

As far as is known, no ghost haunts the house, but one of the barns a few yards of the main building does contain, at times, a pitiful little phantom in the shape of an eighteen year old parlourmaid.

Having succumbed to the wiles of a member of the family and expecting a child, she hung herself from a beam in the store. Unmarried serving wenches who became pregnant were not always tolerated in Victorian times. Often they were given only two choices. 'Run away or do away'.

The vague shape of the suicide was reported in September 1990 by one of the younger estate workers who had been carrying out some maintenance work in the area.

He described seeing 'a mist in the shape of a young woman slowly drift away from the main doorway of the barn towards the centre cross beam, where it vanished. I thought it was steam, then got frightened for it might have been smoke, but when it just faded away, I couldn't make it out at all. One of my mates told me later of the girl who hung herself there. He had seen her too.'

ETCHINGHAM

King John's Lodge, Sheepstreet Lane

THE king who gave his name to this stone built lodge was not John of England but King John of France who lived here in exile after his capture at the Battle of Poitiers in 1356.

Its present owners, Mr and Mrs R A Cunningham, offer comfortable accommodation to visitors to the area and have a ghost as well as a tennis court and swimming pool in their charming garden.

Steve Ollive, who has worked there as a gardener for most of his life, told me that he had seen the figure of a man on two occasions entering the corridor of hedges on the east side of the grounds, but failing to emerge at the end near the house.

'He appears rather as a late Victorian country gentleman,' he told me. 'He walks quite quickly, and quite silently and he vanishes at the end of the hedgerow. There's nothing to worry about. He looks quite normal.'

FIRLE

Firle Place

THIS magnificent house has been the home of the Gage family since the 1400s and contains a marvellous collection of Old Masters, some fine English furniture and, it seems, a ghost.

She is thought to be connected with General Sir Thomas Gage who was Commander-in-Chief of the British forces in America at the outbreak of the American War of Independence. Some believe that the phantom is that of his wife, Margaret Kemble, who matches the description provided by the occasional witness who sees her as 'a tall woman in grey with an impressive bearing and demeanour.'

Ram Inn

WHEN George and Mary Hafflett left in 1985 after completing a seventy seven year stint at this village inn they took with them, as a souvenir, the original brass cash till that was able to give change for a sovereign. They left behind the 'limping lady' ghost, for in 1994 a Dutch television crew filming a documentary, were told about the mysterious sounds frequently heard in a room above the bar.

According to the present owner, it was here, 'probably in the late Victorian period,' a young woman who worked as a basket maker in the village was found dead. She had been given the use of the attic room by a sympathetic landlord who was aware of the problems suffered by the young woman born with a deformed and badly twisted leg.

Many visitors, as well as members of the staff, have heard the sounds of the limping footsteps moving up the narrow stairway and into the tiny room that was her home.

HASTINGS AND ST LEONARDS

A21 Hastings to London road.

SOMETIME in the autumn of 1987 a motorist travelling south from London towards Hastings noticed a young woman wearing a blouse, jacket and pleated skirt standing at the edge of the road at the junction with Paygate Road from Sedlescombe. Assuming that she was waiting for a lift, he slowed down and she moved towards his car. He pulled in to the side and asked her where she wanted to go. He was given the rather vague destination of 'Alexandra Park' and the girl got into the back seat.

As his passenger did not replied to his questions and comments he slowed and looked behind him, when he was near Claremont School, to see if she was all right.There was no one in the back seat. He pulled in to the school entrance, had a thorough look inside the car and even walked back a few yards in the hope of finding some clue as to the whereabouts of his erstwhile companion. There was no sign of her.

The motorist feels that it is of some relevance that a few days later Sussex suffered one of the worst storms ever recorded in the county and thousands of trees were destroyed, dozens of cars damaged and some lives were lost.

One of the victims of the hurricane was a young woman who had been waiting for a relative to pick her up at Sedlescombe junction and take her to a friend's house opposite Alexandra Park in Hastings. Was this a case of a ghost of the future, some weird example of premonition, or simply too vivid an imagination?

Hastings Castle

THERE have been constant tales of a phantom nun, or a woman wearing a brown cloak with a hood, being seen on the West Hill below the castle built by William of Normandy in 1066.

In 1976 the widow of a former custodian claimed that after seeing the figure of the ghostly woman, she had been able to identify the phantom as Agnes Silby, a lover of a fourteenth century dean of the king's free chapel inside the castle walls.

On other occasions the figure has been seen carrying what looks like a baby in her arms. On reaching the south facing wall of the castle she and the child disappear. Some say that the apparition is that of a local woman who, in Victorian times, was deserted by her fisherman lover and she is disposing of the illegitimate child that resulted from the affair, as well as of herself.

A photograph taken by a visitor in 1979 showed the vague figure of a woman bending down and apparently looking for something within a few feet of the wall or perhaps searching for buried treasure or even digging a grave.

Old Town

MRS Thurlow visited Hastings from Kent on a hot summer's day in 1985 and was sitting on a wall in the Old Town waiting for her friend, who had gone to the Tourist Office in the Stade, when her attention was suddenly attracted to tall, slim woman wearing a full length black dress and a black shawl who seemed to be looking for someone.

'I thought she was a fisherman's wife or perhaps a widow, for her clothing reminded me of Victorian widow's weeds,' she said. 'I glanced away to see if my friend was returning but on turning back was surprised to see that the woman had gone. She looked so out of place in the summer sunshine, and I was puzzled as to where she could have gone.'

This is not the only occasion that a figure in widow's weeds has been seen in that part of the Old Town, but it is certainly one of the best of the reports, especially as it is from a visitor new to the area.

King's Head, Courthouse Street

SQUEEZED between the cluster of old properties in Courthouse Street in the Old Town, is another example of a haunted inn. What is unusual about this one, is that the ghost is only seen in or near the ladies' lavatory.

The apparition is that of a young scullery maid and she was seen, according to James, who is on the pub's permanent staff, as recently as June 1996 by a customer who, visibly shaken by her experience, wanted to know the identity 'of the poor little soul in a mobcap who looked so scared and frightened and vanished when I got near her.'

The only information available to account for her presence in that locality is that some 200 years ago the kitchen staff lived in what became the cellar of the pub. Later a section was divided off and toilet facilities installed.

It seems likely, according to old records, that the ghostly scullery maid was the one who was so soundly beaten by her employer that she died from the wounds, having just managed to crawl back to her bed before collapsing.

Stag Inn, All Saints Street

A CUSTOMER who was in sombre mood when he went in for a quiet drink one evening in 1988 was, a few minutes later, shaken from his melancholia by the presence of a figure of a middle aged man wearing what he thought was a costume of highwayman Dick Turpin.

His first idea was that the man was dressed up as he was taking part in the Hastings Festival – until he remembered it was not on at the time. Then, to his amazement, the figure reached a doorway to the private quarters and 'just faded through it'.

No one else admitted to seeing the figure on that occasion but reports of the appearance of such an apparition at the pub have been made over a number of years.

Queensway, St Leonards

A COUPLE driving up Queensway towards the Ridge one evening in 1995 were approaching Napier Road when they were forced to brake hard to avoid hitting a horse and rider that suddenly crossed in front of them, making no sound.

They reported the incident to the police and gave the detail that the horse was wearing an ornamental form of trapping bearing a coat of arms on which the principal charge was a raven. Obviously they knew about heraldry.

The couple had stopped the car and got out and examined the earth on either side of the road but found no signs of any hoofprints. It was because of this that they felt that the police should be informed. They were surprised to be told: 'Yes, we know of two or three identical experiences near that spot, but we can't explain them.'

A raven forms a major part of the coat of arms of the Corbett family who came to England with William of Normandy and there is a Corbett mentioned in the Knights Rolls of the Battle of Hastings. It was along the Ridge that the Norman army marched on October 14, 1066 to meet the forces of Harold of England near the Senlac stream.

There was a suggestion that the horse and rider came from a nearby gypsy encampment, but that hardly explains the silence and the absence of hoofprints.

Royal Victoria Hotel, St Leonards

NOT long ago a chambermaid asked one of the senior staff about a dog that was running about in the corridor near the housekeeper's room and was surprised to learn that what she had seen was a phantom animal.

Many years ago there had been a serious fire and the assistant manager and his dog had both died in the flames, and both used to haunt the hotel.

The apparition of the man, wearing a grey suit, appeared through the wall of one of the bedrooms in the part of the hotel rebuilt after the fire some years ago.

Nowadays, it seems, it is only his dog that frequents the corridor. There is, however, another unusual phenomenon. Often in the early hours of the

Royal Victoria Hotel, St Leonards.

morning the empty lift, which has been found to be in perfect working order, will descend to the reception area without being summoned.

The room in which the manager and his dog died was later reduced in size to accommodate the lift, which was installed several months after the fire.

St. Helen's Hospital

THIS former workhouse, with its hospital radio station which operated from the original cells for miscreants in the basement, has been replaced by the new Conquest Hospital on the Ridge. This raises the question – what has happened to the hospital's ghost?

Adrian Barnett, DJ and presenter of Hospital Radio Hastings, had often been a little apprehensive on hearing heavy footsteps coming along the empty corridor that led to his studio. 'But there was never anyone there,' he told of the *Hastings Observer* in December 1989. 'And anyway the studio was locked from the inside so no one could get in'

Some members of the nursing staff admitted that they felt a little uneasy when approaching the studio, and there have been reports of the sighting of an elderly man in a sort of blue uniform, perhaps that of an old fashioned warder.

85 De Cham Road, Bohemia

THIS former coach house built between 1873 and 1899, now a private house, has been reported as housing a number of ghosts. In the early months of 1996 the ghostly figure of a man wearing leather gaiters, a check jacket, a neckerchief and a cap, was seen on the first floor landing and was mistaken for an unexpected visitor – that is until the figure faded away in front of the witness.

Other phantom visitors are the children who have been seen in the garden. One appeared to be about six years old and wore a Victorian type dress. She vanished as mysteriously as she appeared.

White Rock Pavilion

FEW people realise or recall that this entertainments centre was built in 1927 on the site of a hospital which had its own mortuary. The ghost of the theatre is, in the main, poltergeist phenomena, although an apparition of a tall elderly man wearing a faded raincoat was seen in 1985 by Marion

Hartley who was then in charge of the bars.

The ghostly figure was sitting in a chair in the far corner of the bar lounge. 'There was no way in which he could have got in without the keys and I was still holding them, having just opened up for the evening,' said Marion. 'The alarm system was still switched on and when I turned round to ask the man who he was and how had he got in – he had vanished'.

During the farewell party organised for Marion and her husband a little while later, she and a number of friends were shocked when a glass tumbler from the back of a cabinet suddenly 'flew out in an arc and smashed at my feet.'

There had been earlier incidents. In 1972 Barry Hopkins, a singer appearing in a variety show at the theatre, went to his dressing room before the performance. It was in complete darkness and he took a few moments to get his bearings.

Suddenly he was aware of a presence standing beside him, and the room became freezing cold. He ran out, stumbling through the auditorium and colliding with a fellow artist who was appalled at his frightened appearance and white face. 'It was the unexpectedness of it all that caused the illogical panic' he said. 'Normally I wouldn't have been scared.'

HERSTMONCEUX

THE village and castle of Herstmonceux gets its name from the Saxon Herst or Hurste, a clearing or village in a wood, and the Norman Monceux. Idmea de Herste, a member of a noble family, married Ingelram de Monceux and the manor thus became known as the Herste of the Monceux.

The last male de Monceux died in 1330, but his sister, Maud, married Sir John Fiennes who was, it was claimed, descended from Charlemagne. The family prospered and in 1384 Sir Roger, who by then owned Hever Castle in Kent, applied to the king to 'embattle his manor of Hurst Monceux in Sussex'.

The resultant castle was probably constructed on the site of the original manor house and is thought to be the oldest brick building of any consequence in England. Possiby Sir Roger chose this building material because he had seen brick chateaux during his military service in France and copied the method of construction with bricks actually made on site.

By 1693, Thomas Lennard, Lord Dacre, the last descendant of families to inherit Herstmonceux, was in such financial and personal trouble – he had married the illegitimate daughter of Charles II when she was merely thirteen, while he was barely twenty – that he had to ask permission to sell the family home to pay off his debts. His wife had left him to live in France.

In 1708 the estate was purchased by George Naylor, a London solicitor. who married a daughter of Lord Pelham. He and his wife moved into the north west section of the castle, leaving their only daughter, Grace, to the eastern apartments.

A legend grew up about the girl being starved to death by a governess. Hence her ghost, that of a grey lady, still walking the corridors in the east wing. Actually Grace died in 1727, at the age of twenty one, and is buried in the nearby church. Her father died three years later.

Dr Francis Hare became the next owner and it is likely that it is that it is his wife, Bethia, a sufferer from mental instability, who is the female ghost that used to be seen wandering the estate in a white nightgown. She was often joined by a white doe.

The grey lady has not been seen for many years, unless it was she who was the phantom who caused a bit of a panic at the east gate entrance in March 1980 when Mr R H Tucker, one of the astronomers when the Royal Observatory was at the castle, organised a dance for a local folk dance group.

At about 10.15pm Mrs Daisy Guy and Mrs Marjorie Haylor, both from Eastbourne, were leaving the castle by car and had to wait for the automatic security barrier to open. Daisy suddenly saw what she described as 'a woman in a long light grey dress with a flowing skirt,' cross the drive from behind a tree and pass through two cars in the front of the queue'.

The figure continued to glide across the grass and disappeared on reaching the beech hedge which borders the grounds. 'What's going on? Who's that woman?' Mrs Haylor asked of her companion, for she too saw the figure, as indeed did the occupants of the two other cars.

Mr Tucker knew of the haunting of the east gate by the ghost of a man in a long overcoat of old fashioned style, but was so impressed by the report of Mrs Guy and Mrs Haylor that he recorded an interview with them on the following day.

Members of the Walt Disney Adventures team at Herstmonceux Castle
Photo: Tom Perrott,

The road where the grey lady was seen after the dance in 1980

A better known haunting is that of the Headless Drummer and it was for this reason that I organised a night's vigil in April 1996 for two editorial members of *Walt Disney Adventures*. Regretfully they heard and saw nothing while they were encamped in the Drummers' Room and were a little peeved to be told the following morning by a member of the staff, Andrea Edwards, that she had heard the drumming the previous evening when working on the ground floor beneath the haunted room.

The affected area is shown on an early eighteenth century plan of the castle and it is thought that the sound, originally concocted by smugglers to frighten away the Customs officers or inquisitive villagers, was linked to the invented tale of a headless drummer walking the battlements.

However Horace Walpole, in a letter dated 1752 describing his visit to the castle, wrote: 'they showed us a dismal chamber which they called the Drummers Hall, took its name from intrigues of Tartare or Tart, a French gardener who alarmed the family by beating after the manner of a drum to frighten the inmates, no doubt to conceal the operations of the smugglers who frequented the Hall and whose friend the gardener was.'

An iron chest was discovered in 1738 and on striking it the sound resembled that of a kettle drum. But although the drum and the drummer have long gone, the sound lingers on.

Giving some credence to the haunting however, is the report in the *Victoria Times Colonist* of December 7, 1994. It detailed problems suffered by a film crew with CBC Newsworld and added: 'Pascal Leblond, a cameraman, agreed that the cause of the trouble was the fun loving ghost at Herstmonceux.'

The group had been attempting to shoot opening scenes with the castle as a background for *The Queens Forum on Social Policy,* a general discussion programme organised for the new owners of the castle, the Queens University of Kingston, Ontario. When the presenter, Alison Smith, who was also the programme's moderator, started her lines, a high keening drumming noise disrupted the proceedings. The source was never identified. It was only when the film crew admitted to believing that the castle was haunted that the phenomena mysteriously ceased, allowing the crew to finish their work, but several hours from the planned schedule had been lost due to the mysterious drumming.

Another legendary haunting of the castle is by the ghost of Thomas, the third Lord Dacre, who is said to be seen galloping across the fields on a black horse. He was executed at Tyburn in 1541 for killing a keeper when illegally hunting deer in the park of his neighbour, Sir Nicholas Pelham.

Millers House, Windmill Hill

The owner of this 200 year old house, Mrs M A Gerdes, was asked by the electrician who was doing some work for her shortly after she moved in, if she had seen the ghost.

She had not and still has not, but a cousin from Yorkshire on a visit in 1993 asked about an unusual woman that he had seen on the stairs. 'She was in her late fifties, with short grey hair and dressed in the style of the late eighteenth or early nineteenth century,' he said 'She had a Paisley top with a stand-up collar and a separate skirt.'

Originally the witness had assumed that the visitor was perhaps a neighbour who had just popped in from next door. 'That was until she just vanished in front of me,' he said.

From the electrician, a Mr Relf, I learned that the figure he had seen was certainly that of an elderly person. 'I couldn't see much detail, I don't know whether it was of a man or a woman,' he said. 'He or she was sitting on one of the treads halfway up the stairs and it was a couple of minutes, I suppose, before it just faded away.'

Millers House, Windmill Hill, Herstmonceux

Windmill Hill Stores

LATE one November evening in 1995 June Burchmore was going to get something from the back of the shop and glanced up the stairs to see a black shape on the landing. 'It didn't seem to have a clear outline' she said. 'It was a bit muzzy, but I feel that the shape was certainly that of a human.' As she looked at it the apparition faded away.

Earlier the same week Jane had told her husband, Bryan, that she had seen the outline of a woman in a purple cloak going through a wall in the corridor on the first floor at about eight o'clock at night.

One or two of the Burchmore's regular customers say they have 'sensed something' in the part of the shop where the woman has appeared.

HOLLINGTON

Wishing Tree Inn

IN April 1991 Lillian Penn told me that she always found the cellars rather creepy, and said she often felt as if someone was watching her when she was changing the barrels. Dee Harmer, who then had been at the pub for nearly three years, had also experienced the feeling of being watched and on more than one occasion, being touched on her shoulder by an unseen hand.

'I think the lady in black has come back,' I was told, but who she is or was, no one seems to know. Some four years earlier, Edie, the cleaner, had seen the figure of a lady in grey twice – once in the licensee's flat at about ten in the morning and on the second occasion at lunch time in the cellar when 'she seemed to smile at me.'

There are also reports of visitors' dogs being affected by something that scares them when they are near the kitchen. Customers have hear footsteps coming from an empty room upstairs and in 1976, when in the kitchen preparing an evening meal, the then licensee's wife suddenly felt what she described as 'an unseen something' brush past her and she heard the rustle of a woman's dress.

Quite recently an aged lady in an early Victorian dress was seen pushing an antique perambulator across the road outside the pub. The young couple who saw her when driving past in the early hours so narrowly missed hitting her that they stopped the car to remonstrate with the jaywalker, only to find that the woman and the pram were nowhere to be seen.

HOOE

Red Lion

FROM this former smugglers' inn, when it belonged to James Blackman, a member of the Groombridge gang, convoys of contraband were moved up country to Ashdown Forest. And outside the inn were six lime trees to indicate to the free traders that this was a safe house.

Today the licensee is Keith Barton, a member of the family who have been at the Red Lion for generations. Although he has seen and heard nothing untoward, he believes that the old place may well be haunted.

A few years ago a customer rushed across from the bar to stop a man wearing a long old fashioned greatcoat from walking into the Ladies. 'Sorry, matey, you can't go in there' he said, putting his arm up to restrain the stranger, but as he did so the figure 'just vanished'.

During the summer of 1995, Keith was asked by two women customers if he knew the place was haunted.

The tobacco shredding machine kept in the attic of the inn in smuggling days

'I believe so,' he replied, 'why do you ask?'

'We are professional mediums,' was the reply. 'We noticed the figure of a man who looks like a farmer, sitting over there in the corner. He is wearing a long buff coloured greatcoat, but it is rather old fashioned. Oh! He's gone.'

Was he, I wonder, the same ghost that was seen some years earlier?

HORSHAM

A24 at Southwater

AN example of the increasing acceptance of ghosts and hauntings by local authorities is the promotion of the three hour Haunted Horsham on Halloween walks organised by West Sussex County Council.

However, it does not include the details of the phantom hitchhiker sometimes offered a lift from a layby near the junction of the B2230 with the A24, just north of Southwater.

Motorists who have stopped to pick up the teenage girl are given an address further south. Those who pull in to the wayside cafe a few miles further on to take a break are a little disappointed when their passenger refuses to join them.

On returning to the car the drivers find that the girl has vanished. Some, after waiting a few minutes for her to reappear and feeling that the parents might be concerned regarding her whereabouts, have been known to telephone the number given by the hitchhiker, only to be told that the daughter of the house was killed while hitch-hiking outside a Horsham cafe some five years earlier.

The Causeway

LEADING to the parish church is an attractive tree-lined road known as The Causeway, with a very old house situated on the north corner. A figure of what appears to be a monk has sometimes been seen, usually in the evenings, walking from the road to the churchyard before vanishing on reaching the wall.

No one knows who he is or what is the cause of his haunting. One idea is that he was buried in the wrong place or rather with the wrong faith.

HOVE

Museum and Art Gallery, 19 New Church Road.

IN April 1996 I was called upon, as a consultant, to investigate an alleged haunting at the Royal Albert Hall, an event that attracted a major part of the international media, which rather limited any attempt at a serious research.

However, during my eighteen hour visit, I recorded a mysterious and rather sudden rise in temperature from 72° Fahrenheit to 83° degrees F. It occurred in what had been known as the Garden Room on the top floor behind the organ. The area at the time was full of cables, stanchions and general clutter as an old staircase was being removed to be replaced by a lift.

It was in this locality that footsteps had been heard and an attendant had felt an unseen someone tap her on her shoulder. Because of the state of the site and the fact that under normal conditions one would expect a drop in temperature, to see the thermometer registering a nine degree increase was quite puzzling.

I had never known this type of occurrence before but in Judy Middleton's *Ghosts of Sussex* there is an account of a similar temperature rise occurring at Booker Hall in 1985.

In January of that year, according to the book, a group of psychic researchers went to investigate reports of inexplicable footsteps being heard moving about upstairs when the building was closed to the public. A door was also heard to close, followed by the footsteps walking down the corridor behind a counter in the entrance hall.

Not only did the investigators arrive with sound and atmospheric recording apparatus, but also an ozone sniffer. Every time the thermometer was placed next to a large ecclesiastical embroidery it registered two degrees warmer than the rest of the room.

This work of art, consisting of separate panels and strips in coloured silks and metal thread on linen, is mounted on velvet and dated *c* 1550. Above the portrayal of Christ, the most prominent feature of the cloth, is the figure of God and below the cross, St. John supports the Virgin Mary.

Immediately the sniffer was brought close to the portion showing the cross, it started to bleep and it was here that the temperature rose, despite the embroidery being enclosed in a heavy frame.

Hangleton Manor Inn

THE attractive frontage of this sixteenth century inn, said to be the oldest domestic secular building in the district, is today somewhat obscured by the proximity of the surrounding properties.

The legend to account for the occasional appearance of a young woman in a brown dress of a material that resembles silk is that she is a serving wench who was seduced by the lord of the manor, gave birth and threw the child out of an attic window.

It is unlikely a serving wench would be dressed in silk so the anonymous youngster is known as Lady Jane by the staff. Her infrequent appearances are associated with weird rappings issuing from behind the wood panelling in one of the larger ground floor rooms. There have been recent reports of doors opening and closing inexplicably.

ICKLESHAM

NEAR to the junction with the main road and Laurel Lane and nearly opposite the Robin Hood pub, partly hidden by the roadside hedge, is a small pond, which say local residents, 'emits a feeling of great dread, or even evil'.

The phantom figure of a young soldier has been seen gliding across the road from the pond, towards Laurel Lane. On reaching it, witnesses claim, he just fades away.

The uniform has been described as that of the First World War although the ghost, for some unknown reason, is associated with the report of an aircraft that crashed in the vicinity in the 1940s.

ISFIELD

Lavender Line

THIS small station was opened in 1858 and closed exactly 111 years later, to become completely derelict. However, in 1983 the building and a small length of rail track was purchased as part of a private venture, and the resultant Lavender Line was opened.

It continues to provide interest to visitors and railway enthusiasts with a railway museum and, as an added attraction, the figure of a lady in a white gown has been seen on a number of occasions, standing forlornly on the station platform.

'She appears mostly during the summer months, especially during early evenings,' I was told by Lee Blake, who has investigated the haunting on behalf of a local research group,

The clothing of the phantom, who disappears after a couple of minutes, is in the style of the early 1900s, which rather confirms the belief that the ghost is of a woman who is waiting for her sweetheart to return from the wars. He never arrives.

What is slightly unusual about the haunting is that the ghost also walks through what used to be the original ticket office, which is now the buffet, and has been seen there by several members of the volunteer staff, as well as the occasional visitor.

On reaching the platform the figure stands there for a moment or two before moving forward and vanishing, suggesting that she committed suicide by throwing herself under a train.

But there is another more mystifying ghost that inhabits the station. A man in an old style uniform has been seen in the evenings at the other end of the platform, in the area known as the lobby.

It was originally the train shed. One researcher, when approaching the site, felt as if he were being pushed back and suffered a very unpleasant constriction on his throat.

Is this mysterious figure in any way associated with the forlorn female one wonders ?

JOHNS CROSS

ONE afternoon in 1983 a couple were driving towards Hastings on the A21 and approaching Vinehall School, when from the entrance drive came an elderly man of average height carrying a sack over his shoulder. 'His clothing appeared a bit tatty and as he reached the middle of the road 'he suddenly stopped and just vanished,' they said.

The driver of the car pulled up and both got out to see where the man had gone, slightly concerned that they might have hit him, but there was no sign of him. This was not an isolated report, for the sack carrying walker has been reported on a number of occasions. His identity remains unknown.

LEWES

HM Prison

IN 1980 I included a report of the haunting of Lewes prison in my book *Ghosts of Today* but I was surprised to learn in 1996 that the apparition is still around and had been seen by two of the warders earlier in the year.

The phantom is a woman in Victorian type clothing who is seen moving slowly along one of the corridors. She is thought to be the ghost of a relative or close friend of one of the inmates who, during a visit to the prison, dropped dead at seeing the conditions under which the prisoners were kept.

That was in the bad old days of the 1800s.

LEWES

4/5 North Street

TONY RICHARDS leased this former corn merchant and nurseryman's premises late in 1995 and opened it as a flea market. Initially there was a series of weird coincidences. Lights were found to be switched on after he or his wife, Sue, had turned them off when they closed for the night; sounds of stamping and walking feet were heard; and voices mimicking those of Tony, Sue, and their colleague, Danny.

One evening Tony was in the office on the first floor, bending over to examine a television set, when he heard Danny behind him call out: 'Haven't you finished yet?'

But Danny at the time was in Brighton – some ten miles away.

Steps have been heard running up and down the stairs into the office and the radio has been switched off by the invisible runner. Once, when Sue was in the kitchen, the voice called out 'where are you?'.

Tony was downstairs and the only other occupant of the shop was reading a book and certainly not talking or calling out.

Even the Richards' eleven year old son has been fooled by the voice which has copied his mother's and called for him to come downstairs. When he reached the ground floor Sue was surprised to see him. She had not uttered a word and certainly had no intention of calling him away from his video game.

One day last October Tony was in the room adjoining the office and about to walk to the stairs leading down to the front door, when he saw the clearly defined shadow of a boy of about four years of age passing over the floor. His own shadow was travelling in the opposite direction.

'It was so clear,' he told me. 'I feel that I would be able to recognise the boy if I met him.'

Although some customers have heard the mysterious footsteps, so far no one else has seen the silhouetted shadow. It could be the ghost of a little boy of nine who was killed when a bomb fell in front of the shop on January 20, 1943. He was the only casualty and was tossed across the road by the blast, and into the building itself.

Recently the sound of breaking glass was heard at about 10.30pm but nothing was found to account for it. The family's pet rabbit has, on two occasions been found locked out of his hutch, but moving around quite contentedly in his run.

LOXWOOD

Main road and Drungewick Manor

THIS village was at one time the home of the unusual Cokelers sect. Occasionally, at a certain spot on the main road near Spy Lane, motorists have reported seeing a figure resembling a monk.

This apparition, perhaps associated with the monastery which was once at Drungewick Manor, normally stands beside the road, but has been seen to walk into the path of oncoming traffic, where it vanishes, having caused drivers to brake hard, swear and curse at the disappearing phantom.

The Cokelers, also known as the Society of Dependents, was formed in 1850 and members owned and managed co-operative shops in Warnham, Northchapel and here at Loxwood. Their life style was quite strict. They had totally to reject the use of tobacco and alcohol, the delights of television and radio and even flowers and music.

The phantom, perhaps mistaken for a monk, may well be a former member of the sect. The women, who always dressed in black with straw and velvet bonnets, shawls and long skirts, would sometimes accompany their men, who would also be wearing sombre clothing. Some of them, it is believed, may well have been dressed in monkish habit.

MIDHURST

Cowdray House and Park

THE legend of the curse of Cowdray is well known. The ruins of the once magnificent house are, it is said, the result of a disastrous fire in 1793 caused by the curse placed by the Abbot of Battle on Sir Anthony Browne who was granted the abbey by Henry VIII following the Dissolution of the Monasteries. Although it took more than 250 years to come into full effect it finally succeeded, and the family died out.

A ghost of a woman in a long white dress, believed to be the phantom of Lady Montague, is still seen in the Lady's Walk on summer evenings. She was the wife of the fifth Viscount Montague, who had a heated argument with the family chaplain in the confessional and shot him.

The murderer fled back to the house to hide, it was believed, in a priest's hole in the Keeper's Lodge. His wife, although horrified by his ghastly crime, would visit him in the evenings and they would walk together in the grounds until it was time for him to return to what became his dungeon for fifteen years.

Why it is only her apparition that is seen and not that of the her husband remains a bit of a mystery.

The last sighting of her was during an all night party near the ruins in 1994. A young couple, who had left the main group of revellers, saw a wraith slowly approaching them. Then, to their surprise, she vanished from the path along which she was walking.

NINFIELD

DURING the 1980s I was told by the director of a firm of building contractors in Rye, of an unusual incident in a house his company had been called upon to renovate and modernise. One of the young apprentices was doing some carpentry work in the dining room and an older man was plastering the wall at the end of the room.

The apprentice accidentally dropped a chisel and when he bent down to pick it up from the floor, saw a pair of trousered legs on the other side of the bench. They were not those of the plasterer and when he straightened up he was shocked to find no one there.

The lad bent down again and saw that the legs had not moved. The trousers were shabby and he noticed they were tied at the waist with a piece of old cord. He stood up again and this time saw the vague shape of a man's headless torso facing him.

The lad was so upset that he shrieked out to his companion who, on turning round, also saw 'a misty shape of a torso' which faded as he ran towards the boy. Both witnesses were so upset by their experience that they were allowed to go home. The young apprentice refused to work in the house again and he was allocated to another site.

In *Sussex Ghosts and Legends* Tony Wales tells of two brothers who were hedge cutting in the churchyard and had a sudden and furiously violent quarrel about a lover that they shared.

The elder threatened that he would cut off his younger brother's head unless he stopped seeing the girl and getting no satisfactory reply he did just that – cut off the boy's head with a sickle.

He was later hanged for murder, for the killing had been witnessed by a couple of villagers. Both brothers were buried in the same grave.

NORTHIAM

Hayes Arms Inn

LAST autumn Pamela and Stephen Broadhurst took over as joint managers of this fifteenth century hotel and soon heard of the haunting. One of the most recent witnesses was the daughter of the owner, who saw a ghostly figure in one of the bedrooms.

Her description of the spectre was exactly the same as that given by Jean Anderson, a former owner, who in 1980 she saw a young woman of about thirty, wearing a white hat and a grey gown, standing in the middle of the room. 'She was holding something in her right hand, but I couldn't see exactly what it was.' she said.

Although the haunting has always been sudden and totally unexpected, no one has ever been frightened by her as, they say, she always seems to be such a friendly person. Research suggests that the ghost, who is seen for only about thirty seconds before she vanishes, is that of Molly Beale, a baker's daughter who was found murdered in one of the bedrooms. From the style of her clothing she lived in the Edwardian era.

When there was a spinning wheel in an alcove adjoining the main bar, the figure of an old woman was seen, on more than one occasion, bending over the machine as if examining it. Some believed that she was Molly's mother and rumours at the time implied that there was some connection between her appearance and that of her daughter.

Crown and Thistle

WHEN Mrs Marsh and her family took over this fourteenth century pub, they did not realise that they had taken over a resident ghost as well. Her daughter, Hayley, has seen the phantom of a woman aged about forty and wearing a long dark dress and a funny old bonnet, walk through the side of the building.

Brian, a relief manager, also saw the apparition in November 1995.

'She was standing for a few seconds by my bed. She didn't worry me, just surprised me,' he said later.

Mrs Marsh herself saw the figure of a man in a doublet and hose, with a feather in his hat, walking quite purposefully along one of the upstairs corridors. 'I'm not really bothered about it though,' she said, 'for I gather we are not the only witnesses, and so far no one has been frightened. Why should they be?'

Northiam Parish Church

WHEN practicing in the church a few years ago the former organist, Mr. Holdstock, was surprised to hear the sudden noise of men's voices in the vestry, for he knew the room to be empty, the door locked and the key safely in his pocket.

A member of the parochial church council also experienced the same phenomenon and one of the helpers providing flowers for a special occasion in August last year actually unlocked the vestry door when she heard the voices to see if there was anyone in there.

The vestry was empty, but as Mr Holdstock had done, she also said she could smell the scent Arum lilies although there were none in the church at the time.

PEASMARSH

Horse and Cart Inn

INCIDENTS of poltergeist activity are more frequently experienced in pubs and houses to which the owners have just moved and they are often described as hauntings.

When one considers the traumas and tensions suffered in moving house, it is not surprising that one hears reports from the newly arrived about the weird movement of glasses, or the smashing of ashtrays, the switching on and off of electrical equipment and taps of beer barrels caused by some unseen power or energy.

What is slightly unusual is to learn of sexual harassment by a ghost, as described by members of the staff in this sixteenth century inn.

Cilla Gurden, who took over the license of the Horse and Cart more than twelve years ago, was reaching for the handle of a pump to serve a regular customer with his usual pint of the best when some 'saucy devil' suddenly pinched her – at least that is what she thought. She turned round to find the customers smiling and giggling. 'It was Harry,' they assured her, a name they gave the ghost they say is 'rather cheeky'.

Cilla Gurden. *Photo: Jack Pleasant.*

Maria Wall, one of the bar staff, was 'attacked' in a similar fashion, and earlier on the power was cut off from the vacuum cleaner while she was cleaning the carpet. 'That must have been Harry, for there was no one else around at the time,' she said.

Yet another victim was Linda Piggott, who suffered the same bottom pinching indignity as Cilla. The culprit, if there is one, is presumed to be the ghost of a man interested only in female spheropygians, an eighteenth century word for 'full and rounded buttocks', but he has so far remained invisible.

'We just wish he would keep his hands to himself,' said Cilla, 'but we would never call in an exorcist, for he is rather fun to have around.'

PEVENSEY

Castle

A FEMALE figure used to be seen gliding along the top of the outer walls of Pevensey Castle, originally constructed in the third century by the Romans as a defence against Saxon raiders.

Some believed that the ghost was that of Lady Pelham, a supporter of Lord Bolingbroke, once the owner of the castle. Her appearance one

evening so scared a group of four local lads who had been larking about there, that they reported the incident to the custodian. He was impressed with their account to such a degree that he made an official entry in the records.

She was also seen one afternoon in September 1984 when by a group of twelve young visitors to the castle. They were puzzled by the appearance of a woman in medieval dress standing at the bottom of Castle Hill and were even more dumbstruck when she vanished as they approached her.

In 1993 a group of archaeologists based near the south wall were annoyed to find that the refrigerator in their storage hut was not working. To repair the unit it was necessary to gain access to the main fuse box which was in a room in the north east tower. This took some time for the container was behind an iron gate, also securely locked. A security man from Eastbourne had to be called to sort out the problem. The incident was really of little importance, except that the team was puzzled as to who had been cut off the power and how anyone had gained access to the fuse box.

They were even more puzzled when on two consecutive mornings they found footprints in the dew covered grass, in the centre of the ruins, leading from the chapel site to the outer south wall where the ghostly figure used to be seen. But there were no footprints leading to the chapel.

The mystery was partly forgotten until the 1994 digging season started and exactly the same puzzling events occurred.

Bag End Cottage

Backing on to the Mint House is a nineteenth century cottage, home of a local author, but also another phantom. Robert Stevens told me that one day in July 1995, at about 2am, his mother, who had been lying awake because of the uncomfortably hot weather, felt her dog jump up on to the bed. She turned over to push the animal away and suddenly realised that a tall broad-shouldered man of about forty years of age, with fair hair was standing in the middle of the room staring at something on the floor.

The only clothing that she could see he had on was a pale coloured loose shirt, for below the waist was just a black shadow. The figure remained visible for only a few seconds before disappearing. Mrs Stevens described the incident as: 'Very interesting and not at all frightening'.

The Church of St Mary the Virgin. Westham

AFTER the publication of Michael Stone's sighting in 1978 of the ghost of a man in a modern day suit, it was not foreseen that another witness would tell of an identical incident in 1995. But that is what happened.

Charles Brownlow of Worthing, on a visit in September, the same month that Michael had seen the apparition, decided to have a look at this Norman church. He opened the gate for another visitor coming towards him.

'I said "Hello" but as I did so the man vanished. He just wasn't there any more,' he said. 'He was about my height, five feet ten, and wearing the sort of suit I would associate with a business executive, or dare I say it, a funeral director.'

Is this another case of a 'living' ghost?

The Old Mint House

WHAT is now an eighteen room antique shop was originally a Norman mint, dating from 1342, although considerably changed by 'Merry Andrew' Borde, physician to Henry VIII.

St Mary's church, Westham and, below, the haunted room at the Mint House.

Next to the Oak Room on the ground floor a double murder was committed, it is claimed, in 1586. Thomas Dight, a London merchant, returned unexpectedly one evening to find his mistress in bed with a stranger. In a fit of intense hatred and jealous rage, he grabbed the woman, had her tongue cut out and threw her manacled body into the minting chamber.

The distraught lover was suspended from the ceiling over a large fire, in front of the terrified woman, until he eventually expired.

The ghost of the young woman still makes her presence felt and quite recently heard by members of the staff. One assured me that he 'really did feel that the young lady was with him in the room.'

Earlier, another twenty year old custodian saw the ghostly figure when dusting some artefacts in the haunted room.

POLING

ONCE this hamlet, reached only from the A27 between Worthing and Arundel, contained a subordinate house, or preceptory, of the Knights Templars. The occupants were only interested in maintaining their estates and general farming, which perhaps explains the peaceful nature of the haunting.

The phenomena is of choral singing but with organ accompaniment, which is unusual, for the ghostly voices are chanting a Latin psalm of a period long before the organ was invented.

The haunting, if that is what it can be termed, has been reported more than once within the last decade.

PORTSLADE

Foredown Tower, Foredown Road

THE water tower standing at the northern end of the former site of the Hangleton Isolation Hospital was converted into a Countryside Centre by Hove Borough Council in 1991, after it had been derelict for more than thirty years.

The entrance hall and adjoining office was, for a short period when part of the Hove Sanatorium, used as a mortuary which may have some connection with the haunting.

Early in 1992 one or two members of the staff reported that they felt that they were being watched by someone or something unseen, and inexplicable sounds would be heard. The security alarm would go off for no reason and for which no explanation could be found.

In April of that year footsteps were heard walking up and down an area of the first floor, but despite a thorough search by the police, nothing was discovered to account for them. A former member of the staff said that one afternoon she was about to walk through the hall and was astonished to see a figure standing by the working modelling of a camera obscura, which was not switched on at the time,

The lower half of the phantom was clearly seen to be wearing a pair of rather grubby greenish brown tweed trousers which looked like everyday working clothes of the Edwardian period. The top half of the figure was somewhat obscured by 'a sort of mist but appeared to have on a longish coat or jacket.'

I got in touch with one of the custodians in October 1996 and he told me that he personally had experienced nothing at all but had heard rumours that an earlier staff member had indeed witnessed what was thought to be a ghost.

'But it has gone away now, at least we think so', he said.

POYNINGS

A FEW yards from the graveyard adjoining the church is a large pond where something mysterious happened in 1993.

A couple of tourists on their way to explore the Devil's Dyke, took the bridle path from the end of Dyke Lane and, glancing down towards the pond, they noticed a young boy running backwards and forwards at the water's edge. He seemed in great distress and then he appeared to leap into the water but the watchers heard no sound of a splash and saw no ripples on the surface.

The witnesses managed to get down to the pond's edge but there was nothing untoward to be seen. They went back to the Post Office, where they had previously bought some stamps, and described what they had seen.

They were told that in September 1883 three local lads had been bathing in the pond and two had got out of their depth. Their companion ran to the church, where evensong was in progress, but no one in the congregation took notice of his pleas.

It appeared that he was in such a state of panic that he was unable to tell them exactly what was the trouble and how urgent was the need for a rescue party..

In desperation he ran back to the pool and, although he could not swim, jumped into the water in a desperate attempt to save his friends. But he was unable to rescue them.

Both the older boys were drowned and it was only because a farm worker saw the brave rescue attempt that the third boy was pulled from the pond, only to die from shock shortly afterwards.

PYECOMBE

London Road

AT the junction of the A281, West Road and the A23 London Road at Dale Hill is, according to various reports, one of the most haunted sites in the south east. One afternoon in 1976 Patrick Geary and his wife were driving south towards Brighton, when they both saw a woman in a pale fawn mackintosh suddenly appear to run across the road to the central reservation, between the dual carriageways, and on reaching it, vanish.

They drove on for a few yards and pulled in to see what had occurred, but like so many mystified motorists before them, they were completely unable to find any sign of the pedestrian.

Some other drivers have been convinced that they have actually hit the woman and carried out more detailed, but equally unsuccessful, searches.

Only a few yards further north on the A281, the ghost of a young girl with blonde hair has been seen in the early evening, staggering towards Wayfield Farm. She disappears when anyone stops to help her. It is thought that she is the phantom of a motor cycle crash victim from the 1960s.

RIPE

ONE evening, shortly after the Great Storm of 1987, Ingrid Johnson was driving along Ripe Lane towards the village when her car stopped suddenly and all the lights went out. She tried to restart the engine, but failing to do so, decided to wait for a few minutes and try again.

While waiting she glanced across the road towards the hedgerow and a farm gate and saw the figure of a man in the uniform of a German airman, sitting on the top rung. She continued to look at him, thinking that there must be some filming going on in the area, when he simply faded and disappeared..

Ingrid was intrigued enough to get out of her car to look for the airman only to realise that even the gate had vanished and in its place was a thick hedge. On returning to her car she was delighted to find that the engine started at the first turn of the ignition key and she drove home without further incident.

Later, discussing the sighting with friends, she learned that others had also seen the phantom pilot and it was assumed that he is the ghost of the pilot of the German plane which crashed in the field during the Second World War.

ROBERTSBRIDGE

London Hastings Road, A21

THERE are not many policemen who are willing to admit to seeing ghosts, although it is known that a number have done so. Perhaps it is the official attitude, or what they assume to be the official attitude, that stops them being open minded on the subject.

Or maybe it is simply the personal feelings of the witness involved, such as that of one police sergeant who was transferred to Oxford shortly after his experience here in 1977.

He had been sitting in his panda car outside the George Hotel in the High Street one night, idly waiting for something, anything to happen, when someone he recognised came swaying out of the pub, got onto his bicycle and proceeded in an erratic and potentially dangerous manner up the hill towards Poppinghole Lane.

The officer, noting that 'Fred', as we shall call him, had failed to fit any lights to his machine and was developing a really crazy attitude to his pedalling, decided to follow him until he reached the junction with the lane and then pull over in front of him, and 'at least to caution the stupid old fool, and warn him off.'

Within a few feet of the layby the sergeant pulled out in front of the cyclist and parked. He got quickly out of his car to stop the drunken man, but found that 'Fred' and his machine were nowhere to be seen. 'They had just vanished and really there is nowhere for them to have gone,' he said.

It was only when he reported the incident at Battle police station that he recalled that only a few years earlier 'Fred' had been killed at the junction of the A21, when he was involved in an accident with a large lorry and decapitated.

The sergeant refused to accept that he had seen a phantom. 'I don't believe in ghosts or apparitions, so it couldn't have been one, could it,' he said to me later.

Seven Stars Inn

THIS village on the river Rother came into being as a result of the building of the first Cistercian Abbey at Salehurst, some of the ruins of which were incorporated into a private house in Victorian times.

The abbey, founded either by Robert de St. Martin or a relative, Alvred de St Martin, received its charter in 1198 and is closely associated with the thirteenth century timber framed building originally known as Androwes but now the Seven Stars Inn.

For decades it has mysteriously been linked with a legendary ghost of a red monk, but claims that the building is connected by an underground tunnel with the ruined abbey in the parish of Salehurst, more than a mile away, are extremely doubtful. However, in living memory two villagers did explore what they described as 'a sort of a tunnel leading from the cellars of the pub in an easterly direction.' They had to give up their explorations after a few minutes because of the bad air.

The original entrance can now no longer be detected, but the poltergeist phenomena, which has been going on from at least 1970, is still occasionally observable.

When I got in touch with the pub in July 1996, Mark, one of the bar staff, told me that only a few days earlier a blackboard used as a menu had moved from a shelf and tapped him on the shoulder. 'And no, it didn't just fall, it moved,' he said.

Earlier Jason Chaston had reported that gas taps on the barrels had been turned off three times in one week `by themselves.' Jane Syrett, another young member of the staff, had been a little concerned when a jelly that had been on a shelf in the larder adjoining the kitchen, flew across the room and landed on the floor beside her.

'It must have travelled about seven feet, all by itself,' she said

The Red Monk of Robertsbridge as he appears in effigy at the Seven Stars.
Photo:Tom Perrott

In 1980, when Mrs McCarthy was in residence, what must have been among the most impressive incidents occurred. She had sent her son to her sister's home in St Albans for the weekend, hoping to ease the tension that had developed because of forthcoming school examinations.

When she collected the sheets from his bed for washing on the Saturday she was greatly annoyed to find a large hole in the bottom sheet.

'It was about eighteen inches in diameter, and looked as if it had been cut, badly, with scissors,' she said.

After speaking to her son on the telephone she was convinced that he was not responsible for the damage so she bought two new pairs of sheets,

The Seven Stars Inn, Robertsbridge

which she just tossed on the bed and locked the room, intending to deal with them the next day.

One can imagine her feelings on finding that exactly the same damage had been inflicted on the new sheets. The holes had been cut right through the tough plastic wrapping. The second replacements were, thankfully, not touched.

Mrs Christine Pierce suffered, among other things, the destruction of twenty eight cups when she was working in the kitchen. She had been washing up and could only stand and watch as some unseen force gently pushed fourteen cups along a shelf until they fell to the floor and smashed. The same thing happened the following evening.

The most bizarre incident of which she told me was when she was preparing to leave to open a new restaurant in Bexhill. 'I was just packing up some things in my son's bedroom, and picked up two new pairs of sheets to find that there were holes right through both of them. They were about eighteen inches round. . . it was weird,' she said.

Mrs McCarthy had said nothing of her experiences to Christine. 'It might have put her off buying the place,' she told me later.

Early in 1996 the new owner, Colin MacGregor, held a house warming party which included among the guests a couple of police officers from London. Because it was late by the time the party finished they bedded down in the main sitting room upstairs, above the bar. They were woken by the sound of banging and saw two drawers of a Victorian dressing table on the landing rapidly opening and closing on their of their own accord. They hid under the blankets.

One of the bedrooms affected by poltergeist activity

The phenomena continues and the claim is that Seven Stars is one of the oldest haunted pubs in the country. No one will argue with that.

Even when Guy Lyon Playfair was taking a photograph of Mrs Pierce in the kitchen for one of his books, a loaf of bread travelled from one side of the kitchen to the other, a distance of about fourteen feet, and hit his right foot. Poltergeist incidents can affect anyone.

RUSPER

Star Inn

THE ghost who frequents this pub near the Surrey/Sussex border is in no way frightening for it appears only as a shadowy figure sitting on a stool in the main bar. It was last reported in 1988, when a visitor who noticed 'a sort of undefined shape,' asked the manager about it. He was disappointed to be told: 'Sorry sir. We don't know, but others have seen it recently.'

There have been other small poltergeist manifestations – lights switching themselves on and off and beer taps acting up, usually at the busiest time in the evenings.

RYE

Mermaid Inn

MANY thousands of visitors come to this historic former smugglers' inn which television crews used as a base during the making of the BBC tv film of Stella Gibbons' *Cold Comfort Farm* in 1994.

Much has been written about the ghostly duel witnessed when, for a time from 1913, the Mermaid was run as a private club by Mrs May Aldington, the mother of novelist Richard Aldington. It became an hotel again after the Second World War and in 1993 Bob Pinwell and Judith Blincow bought it and since then other manifestations have been reported.

A doctor and his wife were so shaken by seeing a woman in grey at the foot of their bed that they ran downstairs in the middle of the night and waited in the lounge until daybreak – too scared to return to their room.

The proprietors' daughter, Georgie Pinwell, said when she was staying in that room she felt someone sit on the side of her bed next to her .'But there was no one there,' she said. Chambermaid Kate Davis said her usual polite good morning a woman guest she passed in the corridor. On receiving no response she turned to see that the guest, or ghost, had vanished.

Bob and Judith have got to know the rooms most affected by the resident phantoms. In Room 10, for example, a bank manager and his wife woke to find man walking through their bathroom wall and straight across the bedroom. On reaching the wall near the bed, the figure faded away.

A woman in a light greyish gown has been seen sitting in a chair by the fireplace of Room 1 and often guests find that clothes they have left on that chair appear to be soaking wet in the morning. Another female phantom visits Room 5 and in Room 18 a man in old fashioned clothes is occasionally found sitting on the bed

Some members of the staff have witnessed phenomenal incidents, including a rocking chair that moved and had its cushion squeezed flat as if someone fairly large was sitting on it.

Lamb House

A SHORT walk away, in West Street, is the house where James Lamb entertained King George I when he was a shipwrecked off Rye in 1725.

An old woman in Victorian clothing has been seen sitting in a corner chair in the hall by the front door. A number of visitors to the house, now administered by the National Trust, have wondered who she is and why she disappears so suddenly. A former tenant of Lamb House, the author Rumer Godden, has implied that she may be Mrs Paddington, Henry James's cook.

Tourist Information Office, The Strand

AN example of possible poltergeist phenomena has recently occurred in the tourist information centre. According to Joanna Arkley, the assistant manager, the model of murderer John Breeds' skeleton in an iron gibbet was found to have been lifted and turned round to face the reception desk.

The next morning the exhibit, which was too heavy for any one person to move, had been returned to its normal position.

Ghostly walkers

MERMAID STREET has more than its fair share of female phantoms. Two women in long gowns and one in a blue dress and a wimple have been seen crossing the road near Jeakes House. Another walks straight through a wall of a bedroom on the upper floor of a house nearby.

The ghost of a little boy in a white gown, 'rather like a kimono', used to visit the owner of the first house in Watchbell Street and was reported to be still around in 1981.

The Old Tuck Shoppe in Market Street is another haunted establishment. Several of the staff have reported seeing a lady in grey walking down the stairs that lead from the attic to the first floor.

On a number of occasions pedestrians taking the short cut from Cinque Ports Street through Needles Passage to the Mint have heard footsteps coming towards them and have stood aside to let the walker pass. But they see no one – yet they continue to hear the footsteps until they fade away at the end of the twitten.

Three different walkers in the Gibbet's Marsh area have seen a shepherd in an old smock coming across the field towards the river, always between the hours of midnight and 3am. One witness was walking his dog, another returning from a club, and the third, in January 1993, was walking to work.

Fletchers House

SAM JONES, who lives in Fletchers House in Lion Street, the birthplace of playwright John Fletcher, a contemporary of Shakespeare, was climbing the stairs at the end of his shift in the restaurant below when glanced up to the third floor and saw 'a sort of a.shadow'.

Thinking it was his sister, he continued to climb the stairs and on the landing he saw a 'rather Victorian looking' figure of an old man dressed in top hat and tails.

'I thought that he was a diner who had got lost looking for the toilets,' he said. 'But then he moved into our private bathroom and when I followed I found there was no one there. The old chap had simply vanished.'

Up to that time Mr Jones had been inclined to dismiss stories of ghosts, even the one seen by a former owner, Mrs Betty Howard in 1951. The phantom she saw was that of a young man in an Edwardian suit standing in more or less the same part of the building.

The Union Inn, East Street

WITHIN the last five years the Union Inn has joined the list of haunted inns. A golden haired young girl in a white dress.had been seen walking silently through the restaurant towards the kitchen before vanishing. A

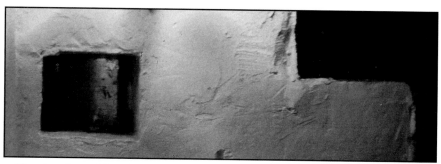
The glass fronted hole in a wall of the restaurant in which some bones were found.
Photo: Tom Perrott

number of staff say that they have, in fact, stood aside to let her pass, only to realise that she was 'not solid'.

An investigation was carried out by members of a scientifically orientated society in 1994 during which the cellars were examined partly in order to establish the source of an unusual smell. A reporter accompanying the group was slightly concerned when the kitchen door suddenly opened and closed with a loud bang ,for no reason and without any human aid.

Behind a glass fronted hole in a wall in the restaurant are some bones that were found in that particular spot by a builder when a central heating system was being installed. Their small size leads one to think they may be those of a child. But why anyone should want to bury the remains of a child in a wall is something of a mystery – or are they, perhaps, the bones of the little girl ghost?

White Vine Hotel

ANOTHER case of poltergeist activity occurred at this hotel in the High Street in November 1995. The owner, Mrs Geraldine Bromley, was told by a couple of overnight guests that they had felt the presence of someone in their room. 'But it was really quite pleasant,' they said.

Later, when changing the linen in the bedroom, Mrs Bromley put two pillow cases on the bed but when she turned to pick up a sheet, one of the cases had been carefully returned to the back of a chair.

'But the kitchen is the most haunted area in the hotel,' she said. 'In one week alone we found carrots in with the onions, five plastic container lids in the flour sack and sugar put in with the potatoes. Now a mixing bowl has vanished'.

The haunted path beside the church at Salehurst.
Photo: Graham Buckley

SALEHURST

Church Lane

ON the south side of St Mary's church is a narrow lane leading to the bridge over the river Rother, the dismantled railway line and eventually to Fair Lane and the ruins of Robertsbridge Abbey.

Over the years a number of people have reported experiencing what they describe as 'a mysterious and totally inexplicable sensation which seems to cause shivers and shudders', at one point only a few yards from the bridge.

The vicar, the Reverend John Lambourne, suggested that this was the spot where an old mail coach had crashed and caused the death of some passengers although today it is hard to believe that coaches could ever have used the narrow path.

Nevertheless ten members of a group of fifteen adult students exploring the neighbourhood in September 1995, had experienced the sensation and certainly believed that a terrible tragedy must have occurred there.

Someone who used to live in a house nearby told me that he had experienced a feeling of intense horror when he was in his back garden early one morning.

SEAFORD

Corsica Hall

WHAT was once the home of Francis, fifth Lord Napier, is now a county council adult education centre. It was here, in May 1772, one of Lord Napier's sons, a little boy, accidentally shot his father's domestic chaplain, the Reverend Mr Loudon. For years afterwards the house had the reputation of being evil and unlucky and no tenant could be found for it.

The ghost of a young boy wandering in a ground floor corridor near the kitchens has been reported not just by members of the staff but also by the occasional adult student.

The wraith has been described as 'an adolescent lad, wearing clothes of the eighteenth century, and looking really miserable.' Partly associated with the apparition is the intense feeling of cold experienced at one particular spot in the corridor. The temperature change has been reported more often than the visual haunting.

SHOREHAM

Adur Civic Centre, Ham Road

THERE are probably far more cases of poltergeist of poltergeist phenomena than the popular press would like to admit. In the reception area of this centre the sound of a bell has been heard and on occasions a 'figure in green' has been seen.

The sound of the bell from the sloop, *HMS Shoreham*, is heard as a single chime, always between six and seven in the evening. It is only quite recently that the apparition has been seen moving rapidly towards the coffee machine on the first floor.

The unknown ghost, named 'Charlie' by the cleaning staff, is fully accepted as being quite friendly but no reason has been found for his bell ringing exploits.

The Coastway Hospital Radio staff, who have seen the figure when leaving their tiny studio, claim that it disappears just before reaching the end of the corridor.

Assistant security superintendent Rod Patterson told the *Adur Herald* that he had heard the noise several times but he could offer no explanation for it, or the appearance of 'Charlie'.

The building was originally a Music Hall offering entertainment to troops in the First World War and then became a cinema. Now that a varieties of courses and clases are held there perhaps the ghost is hinting that bell ringing should be include in the syllabus.

What seems to be a positive identification of the ghost is the one offered by Kenneth May of Rock Close. He firmly believes that the phantom in green overalls is that of a former caretaker of the Coliseum Cinema which replaced the old Music Hall building.

The picture house later became a factory producing hydraulic pumps and Mr May recalls the occasion when an odd job man came running down the stairs from the canteen one evening shouting that he had just seen a ghost.

'I believe that ghost was the same as the apparition of 'Charlie', a maintenance man who was accidentally electrocuted when working in the Coliseum,' he said.

SLINDON

THIS village, close to the race course of Fontwell Park and only a few miles from Goodwood, is haunted by a ghostly horse. Several times in the last couple of decades riders from stables near the racetrack, taking an early morning canter in the woods, have seen a riderless white horse galloping towards and then to vanish when only a few yards away.

The occasional rambler in the wooded countryside has also been startled by the phantom creature. 'We were stunned ,' one witness said. 'We had no warning at all. It was completely silent. No sound of hoof beats or anything.'

Sometimes riders find that their own steeds will stop suddenly at a particular spot and refuse to move on. Although no one has yet established any real cause for the appearance of the phantom animal, there has been the suggestion that it relates to an incident when one of the stable lads was struck by an overhanging branch and killed when on an early morning ride. His horse, a white stallion, galloped back to the stables, thus raising the alarm and the eventual discovery of the young rider's body.

STORRINGTON

The White Horse, The Square

HERE, in one of the rooms at the top of the building, is something unseen that occasionally touches guests and members of the staff on their shoulder and at the same time causing the room to 'feel like a fridge.'

Unaccountable footsteps have also been reported by visitors, both in the room and in the corridor outside. Strange shuffling noises have also been heard in the same locality, for which no explanation has yet been found.

Although Sir Arnold Bax lived in the White Horse from 1940 to 1952, no one has even suggested that the phenomena is due to his death, although a letter addressed to his executors arrived in 1977 and was put temporarily in his old room.

On being collected the following morning the envelope, it was said, 'appeared to have been dragged through the dirt and was covered in some sort of mud', although the room had remained locked.

TANGMERE

Military Aviation Museum

ON this former Battle of Britain airfield there are many reminders of this country's supremacy in the air including machines such as a rare Swift biplane, a record breaking Meteor and some intriguing working exhibits. The museum also houses, it is thought, a ghostly presence which unfortunately has never been seen.

A number of visitors have expressed a feeling of unease at a certain spot in the Battle of Britain Hall and in March 1996 a woman found it impossible to persuade her dog to pass through it. 'The animal crouched on the floor, growling and apparently badly frightened and simply refused to move,' I was told.

It was in the same area that others have expressed a feeling of intense cold, that so far no one has been able to explain.

Here also, when it was a fully operational airfield, eighteen members of the Women's Auxiliary Air Force were killed one afternoon when a bomb hit their shelter during a particularly heavy daylight raid. There have been a number of reports of visitors hearing women screaming.

UPPER DICKER

Michelham Priory

THE Augustinian canons who founded this priory in the thirteenth century were removed by Henry VIII in 1536 and the church, the site of which can still be seen, demolished.

Some years ago the ghost of a former resident was seen in the fourteenth century gatehouse and more recently a phantom lady in grey, leading a small dog, appeared at the entrance kiosk. It was not allowed to approach any nearer because of the animal. On turning away, she suddenly vanished like a puff of smoke. This incident so upset an elderly couple waiting on the bridge to buy tickets that one of them needed first aid.

It was in 1969 that the figure was identified as that of a member of the Sackville family. Even though they owned the priory they visited it only occasionally. During one such visit the mother of the last of a branch of the family was horrified when her child fell into the moat and was drowned.

Another youngster, Robert Child, was strangled when his clothing became entangled in the nearby millwheel. Some believe that the incidents are the same, but the watermill is some distance from the kiosk entrance.

Other phantoms have been reported in the Tudor room, but one of the most recent incidents of phenomena occurred in 1990 when the resident manager was checking the building before closing it for the night.

A BBC film crew had been shooting a sequence for a classic serial and a member of the staff was astonished to see a wig that had been carefully, but temporarily, hung on the back of a chair, 'suddenly leap off and fly across the room.' A couple of the camera crew witnessed the incident.

Shortly after the crew left, the manager went upstairs and noticed that the door to a small room used as a store was ajar. He glanced inside and was astounded to see the window slowly opening completely by itself.

'As far as I know that window had not been opened for decades. It was rusted solid. Yet there it was, slowly and silently opening. It really was very weird,' he said. 'I was able to close it and fasten it again but only with some difficulty.'

It was not very many years ago that a Rhenish stoneware jar, known as a Bellarmine, was found when new drains were being dug right up against the main entrance to the house. It bore the moulded mask of a bearded man, as do all such jars, but inside were the mummified remains of a heart – perhaps animal, perhaps human – stuck with numerous rusting pins.

Bellarmine jars were made from the fifteenth century onwards and are named after the Italian cardinal and theologian, St Robert Francis Bellarmine, who died in 1621. He held high office at the Vatican and was much praised for his tolerance and learning. He was canonised in 1930.

WANNOCK

Filching Manor

MANY splendid examples of the great motoring marques of the past are on show at the Foulkes-Halbard Motor Museum at Filching Manor, between Wannock and Jevington. The collection, which includes the world record breaking Bluebird K3, originally driven by Sir Malcolm Campbell, and seven of the veteran cars that took part in the 1996 London to Brighton Centenary Run, has been put together by Paul Foulkes-Halbard, originally

Filching Manor.
Photo: Paul Foulkes-Halbard.

an artist by profession.

He told me that there are at least two tunnels beneath the house, which was built in 1450. One is currently being excavated. The other, it is believed, used to lead to the Eight Bells at Jevington.

It is only in recent years that ghostly incidents have been noted. In October 1996 the strong smell of tobacco was sensed not just by the owner, but a number of visitors. Mellow pipe smoke was noticed in hot summer evenings in part of the main dining room although smoking, for obvious safety reasons, is not permitted anywhere in the museum.

A month previously a hooded monk was seen walking down the road which passes the entrance and he nearly caused approaching cars to collide in an effort to avoid hitting him. The phantom was reported by a woman visitor to the museum. She had assumed that he was a real, solid individual until he faded away into the hedgerow.

The mystery monk may have some connection with the ruins of a twelfth century Premonstratensian abbey two and a half miles away, near Otteham Court.

Another weird experience at the manor was the sound of a clanging bucket heard in the empty undercroft. The sound was accompanied by a woman's voice but unfortunately the words were indistinguishable.

Dogs are affected by something invisible to the human eye when they are near a small alcove leading from the dining room and a strong feeling of discomfort and unease has been experienced by a number of visitors when nearing the hangar housing motorcycles and a collection of bicycles.

WESTMESTON

St Martin's Church

SOUTH of Ditchling the B2116 road passes Blackdog Hill on the right. Here, many years ago, a headless dog was seen roaming the fields. The phantom animal was said to be the wraith of a creature that had been disturbing pheasants and had been shot by a gamekeeper.

At the crossroads in the village of Westmeston the figure of a nun has been seen walking from the church and passing through the wall of a nearby cottage.

There have also been reports of 'a weird and rather unpleasant smell' that emanates from a hill overlooking Downsview and the surrounding farmland. It nearly always occurs towards the end of May each year and is often accompanied by the sound of moaning which has been associated with victims of the Battle of Lewes.

WINCHELSEA

Strand Hill

A FEW years ago, when I was single and before I moved into Sussex, I decided to have a touring holiday in the county. On reaching Winchelsea for the first time, I was struck by its charm and intrigued by the appearance of the partially ruined Church of St Thomas, and parked in the road beside it, which leads eventually into Strand Hill. It was about 4.30pm and having examined the ancient walls and the interesting little museum opposite, I

The ruins of the church at Winchelsea.

returned to my car intending to drive straight back to the George Hotel in Rye, where I was staying.

I was about to drive off, but braked on hearing the sound of horses hooves approaching from the right. They came nearer and passed the end of the road I was on, only to fade away to nothing. Puzzled I jumped out of the car but could see no animals, nor people for that matter, and spent some minutes looking for the cause of the noise. On returning to the hotel, I mentioned the incident to the manageress only to be greeted with a smile.

'So you have heard it too,' she said. 'Often visitors who have been to Winchelsea say that they have heard the sound of those phantom horses. There are two of them, you know. They are thought to be the ghosts of the mounts of a couple of highwaymen, or were they smugglers, who were caught and eventually hung for their crimes. There's nothing to worry about. They cause no trouble.'

I was able to trace a couple of other witnesses to the sounds and now wonder for how much longer they will be heard.

WORTHING

Connaught Theatre, Union Place.

FEW people have seen the grey lady who haunts one of the dressing rooms and the site of a former art gallery here, but one evening in 1974, after a matinee, one of the actors was walking along a corridor behind the scenes, and happened to glance into number one dressing room and was puzzled to see the figure of a youngish woman in a long grey gown sitting in front of the mirror applying make up.

Realising that it was unusual, as everyone else in the cast had gone home and the building was practically empty, he turned back only to find there was nobody in the room.

A few days later one of the early morning cleaners saw the same lady in grey go past and greeted her with a 'Good morning'. As there was no response she turned round and was 'rather shaken' to find that the corridor was empty.

At about the same time Angelica Clayton, a young student, saw a grey lady with a white face and something on her head vanish into the wall. The figure was passing a rail of clothes, but seemed to be above the top layer and was wearing a costume of the Elizabethan period.

'I realised later that she was probably walking on a different floor level,' she said.

One of the latest sightings occurred in 1987 when Joseph Hall, a trainee, went to get something from beneath the stage but on returning by way of the spiral staircase suddenly realised that he was facing 'a ghost, a phantom, an apparition, whatever. She was wearing a Victorian sort of dress, but I am afraid I didn't stay long enough to study much more detail.'

The stage manager agreed that there is something at the bottom of the stairway that causes people to shiver, especially at night.

Field Place House, The Boulevard

THIS eighteenth century country house was originally the home of the Cooke family for some 300 years, and still retains much of the original oak panelling and carved fire surrounds. The Cookes were followed by the Westbrooke-Richardsons and then in the late 1800s the Henty family took possession.

Field Place, Worthing

In 1956 Worthing Borough Council bought the property which now offers accommodation for various functions.

The current manager, Nigel Henty, a relative of the earlier owners, was not really surprised to learn that a couple from High Salvington had, like a number of other visitors, seen a ghost that perhaps resembles one of his early relatives.

In August 1996 Laurence Craig-Brown and his eleven year old son James saw the figure of an elderly woman in a black flowing dress walk down a corridor, turn and disappear through a wall. They noticed that the apparition strongly resembled the unknown woman portrayed in an old portrait hanging just inside the entrance to the building.

The woman in the painting is wearing reasonably modern glasses. 'So it's not really a very old ghost,' said one of the witnesses, 'but still no one seems to know who she is'.

Research continues and may one day her identity may be revealed and even the reason why she haunts the place.

MGM House, Heene Road

ON September 27, 1996, this building was officially opened by the Heritage Secretary, Virginia Bottomley, and she unveiled a special plaque to commemorate the occasion.

The connection between heritage and this sparkling new £1.5 million headquarters is presumably that it has inherited the site of the old Corporation Baths which were demolished in 1971.

However, the entirely new office block has also inherited some of the ghostly incidents that were reported as occurring in the earlier building. Admittedly the occurrences are more likely to be incidents of poltergeist phenomena, but who knows? Perhaps the presence of Mrs Bottomley produced so much tension and stress that someone was nervous enough to energise the psychokinetic force needed.

In the basement, which houses the filing department, staff have heard mysterious and inexplicable sounds, and two of them have reported feeling someone's hands on their shoulders.

Another staff member was convinced that she heard her name being called, although the office was empty at the time.

In common with such weird incidents, the computer had been malfunctioning, with the screen inexplicably showing the date of January 1 1904, for which no one can find any significance.

BIBLIOGRAPHY

A History of Herstmonceux Castle by David Calvert and Roger Martin. International Study Centre, Queen's University, Canada 1994.

A Short History of the Parish of Salehurst by Leonard Hodson 1914.

Britain's Haunted Heritage by J A Brooks. Jarrold 1990.

Ghostly Tales and Hauntings of East Sussex by R Stevens Bassett. GLX Publishing 1993.

Ghosts of Sussex by Judy Middleton. Countryside Books 1988/96.

Haunted Churches of England by Graham J McEwan. Hale 1989.

In Search of Ghosts by Ian Wilson. Headline 1995.

Phantoms of the Isles by Simon Marsden. Webb and Bower 1990.

Secret Sussex by Hardiman Scott. Batchworth 1949.

Sussex Ghosts and Legends by Tony Wales. Countryside Books 1992.

The East Sussex Village Book by Rupert Taylor. Countryside Books 1986.

The Haunted Pub Guide by Guy Lyon Playfair. Harrap 1983.

Theatre Ghosts by Roy Harley Lewis. David and Charles 1988.

Weekend Haunts by Robin Mead. Impact Books 1994.

West Sussex Ghostly Tales and Hauntings by R Stevens Bassett. GLX Publishing 1993.

Windmill Hill by Daryl Burchmore. Windmill Hill Stores 1994.

Newspapers and magazines

Adur Outlook.

Brighton and Hove Gazette

Evening Argus.

Psychic News.

Rye and Battle Observer.

Rye Memories,Volume 24 edited by Jo Kirkham. Thomas Peacocke Community College.

Shoreham Herald.

Worthing Herald.

ACKNOWLEDGEMENTS

MY thanks for help and assistance in compiling this collection are due to the following kind people:

Gillie Arnell of Herstmonceux, David Beevers of Preston Manor, Nick Battershill of Shoreham, Bob Brown of Lancing, Daryl Burchmore of Polegate, Mr V Catt of Etchingham, Tina Davey of Robertsbridge, Mr G A Frost of Hastings, Colin Harmer of Mountfield, Chris Hawkins of Hastings, Nigel Henty of Durrington, Roger and Trish Jones of Mountfield, Jack Pleasant of Peasmarsh, Brion Purdy of Hastings, John Rackham of Brighton, Brian Scott of Hastings and my special thanks to Stephen Benz for his overall patience and advice.

I am also indebted to John Ash of Newick for details of Foredown Tower; to Lee Blake of the Sussex Paranormal Investigation Group; to Graham Buckley for his valued work in supplying a number of photographs; Jane Lewis of Chaseley Home; to Paul Foulkes-Halbard of Filching Manor for spending so much time with me; to Tony Richards for providing the detail of his experiences in Lewes; and also to Dr. John Surtees, the medical archivist, for the valued historical detail,

Special thanks are also due to Tom Perrott, chairman of the Ghost Club for the photographs, all his research work and for so kindly checking through personal records.

Front cover: Is this a ghost in the archway? When Mr Lovett-Darby visited Battle Abbey in 1974 he took a photograph of his daughter in the ruined Common Room. There was no one else in the area at that time but the print clearly shows a mystery figure in the doorway leading through to the lower rooms of the main building.

Back cover: The gatehouse of Michelham Priory. Photo: Tom Perrott